CARL MacDOUGALL was one of Scotland's m
literary writers. His work includes three prize
four collections of short stories and two wor
anthologies, including the bestselling *The Devil* c
held many posts as writer-in-residence both in Scotland and England, and presented
two major television series for the BBC, *Writing Scotland* and *Scots: The Language
of the People*. With Ron Clark, he co-wrote 'Cod Liver Oil and the Orange Juice'
– a parody of the song 'Virgin Mary Had a Little Baby' – which was adapted and
popularised by Hamish Imlach, and more recently by The Mary Wallopers.

He began his life in rural Fife, living with his mother and grandparents in a small
railwayman's cottage. His father away at war, young Carl had the freedom to roam,
exploring nature, observing the world with curiosity and innocence. It was an idyllic
but isolated existence. After the war's end, Carl's father returned, beginning the
process of slowly building a relationship with his son. One evening he failed to return
home from work on the railway. Carl was never explicitly told what happened. His
mother inconsolable, he carefully pieced together the misfortune that had occurred.

The family was forced to migrate to Springburn in the industrial north of
Glasgow, echoing the migration that Carl's Gaelic-speaking father had undertaken
in his own youth. The single-parent family was poor, the privations of post-war
Glasgow brutal. Tragedy visited again and again. Despite showing significant
promise, young Carl was failing at school. A target for the bullies because his
maternal grandfather was German, he escaped through his friendship with the feral
Francie. After the authorities intervened, Carl was separated from both his mother
and his friend. Carl had to come to terms with the calamities that had beset his
young life if he was to be reunited with those closest to him.

Carl died in April 2023. In his *Herald* obituary, Dave Manderson commented:
'His life force was so strong that he seemed indestructible, and it is difficult to
believe that his astonishing energy is gone. He may well have had more influence
on the Scottish writing scene than any other author. What has never been widely
known are the details of Carl's childhood and the challenges he faced during those
years' – as now revealed in *Already, Too Late*.

Praise for *Someone Always Robs the Poor*

'...the sheer accomplishment of the storytelling and the lively variety of writing
styles make it a compelling read.' DAILY MAIL

'A towering figure... has lost none of his distinctive style or ability to shock...
MacDougall creates a complex world over a dozen deftly crafted pages... [a]
masterful collection.' SCOTSMAN

'The towering voice of Scottish literature returns with this stunning collection...
told without melodrama, with MacDougall's cleanly-written prose... This is a

triumphant return to fiction after an absence of a decade for this award-winning writer.' SCOTTISH FIELD

'Brutal but brilliant.' HERALD

'Carl MacDougall's new collection is brimming with the qualities we've come to expect from this important Scottish writer: beautiful writing, real people, poignant and wounded like us, rich emotional wisdom, and a lovely wit.' ANNE LAMOTT, author of *Blue Shoe and Imperfect Birds*

Praise for *The Casanova Papers*

'Absorbing, intense and wonderfully written.' THE TIMES

'[A] beautifully realised requiem to love.' SCOTLAND ON SUNDAY

'An emotional history of peculiar power and intensity… an exceptional work, mediative and resonant.' TLS

Praise for *Stone Over Water*

'This novel… sets Carl MacDougall firmly among the pantheon of Kelman and Gray… sparkling and exhilarating… wise and, above all, entertaining.' SCOTLAND ON SUNDAY

Praise for *The Lights Below*

'A masterpiece… one of the great Scottish novels of this century.' GEORGE MACKAY BROWN

By the same author:

Someone Always Robs the Poor, Freight Books, 2017
Scots: the language of the people, Black & White, 2006
Writing Scotland: how Scotland's writers shaped the nation, Polygon, 2004
Painting the Forth Bridge: a search for Scottish identity, Aurum Press, 2001
The Casanova Papers, Secker & Warburg, 1996
The Lights Below, Secker & Warburg, 1993
The Devil and the Giro: Two Centuries of Scottish Stories (ed.), Canongate, 1989
Stone Over Water, Secker & Warburg, 1989
Elvis is Dead, The Mariscat Press, 1986

Already, Too Late

a boyhood memoir

CARL MacDOUGALL

Luath Press Limited

EDINBURGH

www.luath.co.uk

Publisher's Note: In writing *Already, Too Late*, Carl MacDougall set out to capture the sounds of his world, from Fife to Glasgow and beyond. The idiosyncrasies that characterised his memories of family, friends and relative strangers (including Katie, who frequently says the opposite of what she means) live on in this text; his story could not be told in any other way.

First published 2023

ISBN: 978-1-80425-055-6

This book is made of materials from well-managed,
FSC®-certified forests and other controlled sources.

MIX
Paper from
responsible sources
FSC® C011748

Printed and bound by
Ashford Colour Press, Gosport

Typeset in 11 point Sabon by
Main Point Books, Edinburgh

Very early in my life it was too late.
The Lover, Marguerite Duras

EUAN WOULD HAVE been 12 or 13 when we'd been spending our weekends preparing to tackle the West Highland Way.

A friend had given us use of a lovely, slightly leaky cottage through the woods and by the water at the foot of a hill. We found it easily enough, dumped our stuff and, as a treat, walked back to the village to have dinner in the hotel.

It didn't happen. The hotel was busy. I had a couple of work calls to make, so we bought sandwiches from the post office and I used the phone box.

It was dark by the time we got back to the car. There was no way we could get down the hill, so we gathered the sleeping bags, blankets and stuff and prepared to sleep in the car. This was high adventure. We had a long look at the stars and settled in for the night. I can't remember, I think the radio was on, but it was as romantic as possible, wind in the trees, owl hoots, the moon disappearing and suddenly reappearing like a magician's assistant.

Did you do this with your dad when you were wee? he asked.

I told him my dad died when I was six.

So I don't know how to do this stuff, I said. I never had a dad and don't know how to be a dad, so I'm kind of making this up as I go along.

He reached across, touched my hand and said, Well I think you're doing a pretty good job.

I didn't sleep. We left the car when the sun was rising, had breakfast and settled into the day. Euan found a kayak and paddled around, I sat on a bench by the door, thinking of an afternoon walk.

Around lunchtime he sat beside me, leaned in and said, Are you going to tell me?

I thought about it and shook my head. Not now, I said, but I will.

For
Michael, John and Joanna

PART ONE

Bankton Park, Kingskettle, Fife

...hearing the chink of silverware and the voices of your mother and father in the kitchen; then, at some moment you can't even remember, one of those voices is gone. And you never hear it again. When you go from today to tomorrow you're walking into an ambush.

The Other Miller, Tobias Wolff

ONE

Kettle Station

I JUMPED TWO puddles and ran up the brae.

My mother shouted, You be careful. And stay there. Don't you go wandering off someplace else where I'll no be able to see you.

The Ladies Waiting Room was damp. There was a fire in the grate and condensation on the windows. The LNER poster frames were clouded. Edinburgh Castle was almost completely obliterated and the big rectangle of the Scottish Highlands above the grate had curled at the edges. There was a faint smell of dust.

My mother took a newspaper from her bag, looked at the headline and sighed. Thank God, she said. At least we're early.

She had been cleaning all day, finished one job and looked around her.

This bloody place is never right, she said to no one. Now here's a wee job for you, see if you gave the top of that table a polish, it'd come up lovely.

She lifted the teapot from the range, gave it a shake and poured the tea.

My, but that's a rare wee job you're making there, she said.

And when the tea was finished she told me not to move: Not a stir. I want you here.

I wandered round the garden, looking for ladybirds or caterpillars under the cabbage leaves. The strawberries, rasps and currants were gone and tattie shaws were stacked on the compost. The smell of burning rubbish clung to the air.

Come you away in to hell out of there and look at that time. We'll never get anything done this day. Now, what I want is for you to get washed, arms, hands, face and more than a coo's lick mind, then get yourself changed into your good trousers and jumper; change your socks and you can wear your sandshoes. Then make sure you're back here when you've finished.

When I came downstairs, she looked at the clock. God Almighty, is that the time? Are you ready? Stand there and let me look at you. You'll have to do. Now, wait you here while I straighten myself out. And would you look at this place. It's like a bloody midden. Now, stand you there and tell me if a train's coming.

Are we going to the station?

Stand there and watch. When you see a train, give me a shout.

The railway dominated the back door, kitchen and garden. There was the tree and a beech hedge, a field and the railway line, wonderful at night, when smoke broke down the moon and a red and yellow glow hauled lit carriages and the shadow of a guard's van.

I knew there wouldn't be anything for another quarter of an hour, maybe twenty minutes, when the big London express came through. Then the wee train with two carriages and a single engine that came from Thornton Junction and went the other way to Ladybank, Cupar and eventually Dundee would saunter past.

So I watched the yellow flypaper that hung by the kitchen light, watched it twirl in the breeze and tried to count the flies.

Come you to hell out of there. We're late. We'll have to hurry.

No matter where we were or what we were doing, we walked by the station every day: We'll just take a wee look, she'd say. And this is what we'll do when your daddy comes back. We'll walk to the station and he'll come off the train.

Is he coming now? I asked in the waiting room.

No.

Then why are we here?

It's a surprise.

She'd been standing in front of the fire, her dress lifted slightly at the back to warm her legs. She put the newspaper back in her bag and we moved onto the platform.

And you be careful, she said. I don't want to see you near the edge of that damned platform.

I was sure we were going to Cupar, but didn't know why she wouldn't tell me, for any time we took the train she spoke about it all day, as if it was a treat, standing by the carriage window to follow the road to Ladybank we walked every week.

From Kettle station, the line stretched to infinity, making everywhere possible from this little place, stuck in the fields, bounded by trees, hedgerows and a string of road. It was early afternoon and autumn pockets of smoke hung over the houses.

The station was deserted and everything was still. A porter walked up from the hotel and stood at the end of the platform. He went into a store, took out a batch of packages and envelopes and left them on the bench. A light was on in the stationmaster's office.

Two women came up the hill. One stopped and looked in her handbag before answering her companion. Two men in army uniforms stood apart and stared across the fields. One lit a cigarette. A man who had just climbed the brae tipped his hat to the women and asked a soldier for a light.

A bell sounded and the stationmaster emerged, locking the office door.

Stand back, he shouted. Clear the platform, please.

Everyone moved and stared down the line. At first there was nothing, then the rumble and the hiss of steam made me slam my eyes shut and start counting. By the time I reached seven, the train was near. I opened my eyes and stood on the bench as the engine passed, surrounded by steam. Light bounced from the polished pipes, the driver leaned from the cab and waved his hat, the funnel belched grey and black smoke and the white steam vanished when the whistle sounded.

A woman waved and I followed her hand till it disappeared and caught sight of a girl standing by the door. She had blonde hair and wore a dark green coat. When she saw me she raised her hand and let it fall. I ran after the train, trying to find her.

I heard a scream as I ran along the platform, felt something grip my stomach and was turned into the air. The stationmaster held me in his arms. My mother was beside me.

Did you no hear me? she said. Did you no hear me shout?

He was excited, the stationmaster said. Wee boys get excited by trains. I suppose he'll want to be an engine driver?

Was that the surprise? I asked.

No. This is your surprise now, my mother said.

The local train with the wee black engine had drawn into the opposite platform. My mother tugged at my jersey, spat on a handkerchief and wiped my face.

Come on, she said. We'll see who's here.

The guard had the green flag raised when a carriage door opened.

He was sleeping, my granny told no one. If Babs hadnae been wakened then God only knows where we'd've ended. Don't let them shift this train till I'm off. Oh dear Jesus, what'll happen next.

A porter helped my grandparents and closed the door behind them. Aunt Barbara knelt on the platform and hugged me as the train slouched away.

I think you've grown, she said.

She'd been away two nights: Off somewhere nice, she said, and back with a surprise.

Where is he? my granny said. Is he here?

Here he is, Mother. Here, he's here.

My granny pulled me in towards her and smothered me into the fur collar of her coat. Then she ran her hands over my face: Marie; that wean's no right.

Barbara laughed and my mother shook her head.

He's fine, she said.

I turned and watched the red lamp at the back of the train fade along the line to Ladybank. My grandfather touched my head, picked me up and carried me down the brae. He smelled of polish and tobacco. This close, I could see he'd missed a tuft of hair on the curve of his jaw beside his ear lobe.

How are you, Carl? he whispered.

Fine.

I'd been warned. Don't tell anyone your grandad's German, my mother said.

Why not?

Because.

I only noticed his accent when he said my name. Sometimes, when he became angry, it was more obvious, but the way he pronounced Carl, with three A's, an H and no R – Caaahl – was different from everyone else.

Watch you and don't let that wean fall, my granny shouted. You can hardly carry yourself, never mind a wean as well.

This was the start of us living together and suddenly the house was smaller. There were five of us in the three-bedroomed cottage at Bankton Park in Kingskettle, Fife: my mother, my grandparents, Aunt Barbara and me.

Everything changed when my granny came. She was blind and found her way round the house by touch.

Something's happened here, she said. This is a damp hoose and it's never been lucky.

For Godsakes Mother, would you gie yoursel peace.

It's no right. There's something no right here. Do you know they're dropping bombs and he'll no move. I'm telling you as sure as God's in heaven I'm no going back to that Glasgow till they stop they bloody bombs. There's folk getting killed. They bombs'd kill you as soon as look at you.

My mother smiled and Barbara squeezed my arm.

Are you there? my granny asked.

He's here, Mother. He's got Babs's arm.

Then how does he no answer me? Marie, I think that wean's deaf.

TWO

Marie

SHE WOULD GET so absorbed she released what she was thinking by shaking her head, turning away or using her hands to shoo the thoughts before anyone could find them. And she would look at me as if I was a changeling left by the fairies and her own child, the one who was like her, had been taken. My earliest memories are of her naming my features, as if they confused and delighted her, as if she could scarcely believe her own brilliance.

Her hair was fine, soft and downy and her eyes were the palest blue I have ever seen, so light they sometimes appeared clear. Her body was misshapen. She was maybe five feet three or four and had small, angular legs, was stocky, rather than fat, plump or dumpy. But her hair had the wisp of a curl and she kept it short to avoid having to tie it behind the white waitress's caps she had to wear with a matching apron over her black dress.

They bloody hats makes me look like a cake, she said.

But at least they hid her hair, which was the colour of straw and often seemed darker at the ends than towards the scalp, where it lay, flat and straight across her head, suddenly bursting into a kink rather than a curl, as though it was the remnant of a six-month perm.

God Almighty, she'd say. What the hell do they expect me to do with this? And she'd brush her hair as though to revive it, lifting it from her scalp with her fingers.

God Almighty was a verbal tic, a time-filler, an exclamation and a way of entering speech.

None of her shoes fitted. Her feet were worn running in and out of kitchens. She had bunions and her shoes had a bulge below her big toe. When she died, I couldn't touch her shoes, couldn't look at them. There was so much of her in the light, court heel and stick-on rubber soles. One pair were dark blue but had been polished black because it was all she had.

I never knew they bloody things were blue when I bought them, she said, but they must've been, for I don't think the fairies changed the colour o' my shoes. Well, they're black now and to hell with it. God knows, it'll never be right.

This was a conclusion she often reached, that effort was worthless since failure was inevitable. There had been times when her future seemed assured and she told me she had more than she wanted, more than she thought she deserved. But she never got over the loss; and for the rest of her life she guarded against intrusion.

The trouble was time, she said. We didn't have time together, no what you'd call real time. You could say we were just getting settled, just getting used to each other, him to my ways and me to his when it happened.

She turned her head to the side and shooed the words away. God Almighty, no shocks, no more shocks. Warn me, tell me well in advance, but please God, no more shocks, no like that, though nothing could be as bad as that. Another shock would finish me.

She never trusted happiness, assumed it was temporary, an illusion, or both. She wanted it for other people and delighted in their success, but never embraced the possibility for herself.

It was taken, she said. The Lord giveth and the Lord taketh away, which doesnae leave much room for manoeuvre, never mind choice.

This, like most of her conversation, was a pronouncement, an absolute, a statement rather than a topic for argument or discussion.

She'd wander round the house singing, telling jokes and making herself laugh. And she made me laugh in more ways than anyone I have ever known. Even now, I often laugh when I think of her.

Away and raffle your doughnut, she said, and I am sure her interpretation was literal. Any other possibility would never have occurred to her. Most of her pronouncements were literal. Och, away and shite, manifest frustration or exasperation; and the worse thing she could say about a man was that he was a bugger, again, I am certain, with little or no understanding of what it meant.

When I was ten or eleven I asked about a bugger. She told me it was someone who took to do with bugs, fleas and the like. And she shuddered when she said it.

The closest she came to homosexuality was to call someone a Big Jessie or a Mammy's Boy. He'll no leave his mammy, she'd say, there's a bit o' the Jenny Wullocks aboot him. This meant he was hermaphrodite, or at the very least suggested behaviour that was neither one thing nor the other. She used it as a comic term, endearing but strong enough to retain distance.

These things were too realistic and realism was never funny. Work wasn't funny. Hotels were never funny, especially dining rooms and kitchens; though bedrooms were funny, especially when pretension was involved.

A favourite story was of the elderly man who booked into a country hotel with a young woman. As they left the dining room and made their way upstairs, my mother said to another waitress, Aye hen, you'll feel auld age creepin ower ye the night.

When the girl spluttered, the man told her she should do something about her cough. It could turn nasty and go into her chest. He knew about these things, being a doctor.

And do you do a lot of chest examinations? my mother asked.

Or the woman who arrived with three heavy suitcases. She never appeared for meals and the chambermaid was not allowed into the room. On the third morning the girl's sense of propriety overcame all objections. She found the woman dressed in a shroud and surrounded by whisky bottles.

I am drinking myself to death, she said.

Then you're making an awful bourach of it. You'd be better off going away and drowning yourself.

That chambermaid was from somewhere away far away in the north, she said, and had settled in Oban. Her language was Gaelic and she never quite got the hang of English.

Katie got my mother the job in the King's Arms Hotel on the Esplanade, where she was working when she met my father.

Put a plaster on my bag and make it for Oban, Katie told my mother when they were working in Fortingall. I wish I was back in Oban, for it's better here than there.

Katie was affronted by a French guest who told her, I want two sheet on bed.

Dirty rascal, she told my mother. What would he want to do that for?

And tell me that poem again, Marie, she asked.

And my mother would recite the whole of Thomas Campbell's 'Lord Ullin's Daughter' she'd learned in Teeny Ann's class at Mulbuie School:

'Come back! Come back!' he cried in grief,
'Across this stormy water;
And I'll forgive your Highland chief,
My daughter! – oh, my daughter!'

'Twas vain: the loud waves lash'd the shore,
Return or aid preventing;
The waters wild went o'er his child,
And he was left lamenting.

And what do you think happened? Katie asked. Did they die right enough?
They were drowned.
Droont, the boatman and everybody, except himself that Lord Ullin one;

he was all right, though I suppose he'd miss his daughter right enough. Och, yes, he'd surely feel sorry for the lassock that was dead; and there'd be times too when he wished he'd let her marry the Highland chief after all. Still, that'll teach him. See, if he'd anybody there that could've read the tea leafs, he'd've known the lassock was going to be droont.

Katie, who wore men's boots or Wellingtons and two or three dresses if it was cold, read the leaves on every cup. She read the visitors' cups without asking.

Och, here now, listen you to me, you're going to come into money, she told one set of visitors who'd called in for afternoon tea and had no idea what she was doing, but it'll never bring you any luck.

Your daughter's going to give you bad news, she told a woman. I think you can expect a wedding.

Now your man's going to be working away and if I was you I'd keep my eye on him. I'm not saying more than that but I can smell perfume from this cup and there's crossed swords and a separation that means a divorce, so you'd better be careful.

You're having an awful trouble with your bowels, she told another party, but it'll be over in a day or two when you've had a good dose of the salts. You could go to the chemist in Inverness. He's got good salts there right enough. And don't eat fish. You'll have an awful craving for a fish tea, but if I was you I'd avoid all fish and any kind of sea thing, or anything at all that's connected with water, which will mean anything that's boiled or poached, though you'd be all right with a cup of tea as well, but I'd steer clear of the coffee and the beer, especially stout for that and the coffee are black, as black as the lum of hell.

Is your salmon poached? a visitor asked Katie, who was helping out in the dining room.

Indeed it is not, she said. The chef buys it in Perth.

Marie, what's that poem about the charge for the light and the men that go half a leg, half a leg, half a leg onwards?

My mother repeated Katie stories word for word.

Language was a constant source of wonder, for she never owned the language she spoke. It was variable and changed according to her circumstances.

In January, 1919, two weeks after her fourteenth birthday, Marie Elsie Kaufmann began her working life as a domestic servant at 1 Randolph Place, Edinburgh. On her first day the housekeeper told her to turn her face to the wall if she passed a member of the family in any part of the house. When the housekeeper found an edition of Robert Burns's poems in my mother's room, she burned the book, telling her Burns was a common reprobate and the master would immediately dismiss anyone found with such a book in their possession. She was also told to speak properly and on no account to use slang or common language.

The first time I became aware of her transformation was on a journey to Oban. We were on our twice-yearly pilgrimage and shared the compartment with an elderly lady who was reading *The Glasgow Herald*.

After Stirling I stood in the corridor, the way my mother said my father used to, imagining wild Highlanders being chased through the heather, strings of red-coated soldiers behind them. I imagined them climbing the high bens, living in damp and narrow caves, fishing in the lochs and rivers, trapping deer and rabbits, occasionally stealing cattle and sheep to survive. I imagined whisky stills and wood smoke.

I remembered standing with my father as we approached Kilchurn Castle at the head of Loch Awe. That used to be ours, he said, but the Campbells took it from us.

I came into the compartment as we approached the loch, where the railway line used to skirt the brown and black water to watch the passing sleepers and stones, and was immediately aware of the change in my mother's voice. Her sentences were measured and her tone had altered. She spoke softly and pronounced every vowel. And I could tell from her expression she expected me to copy her inflections when I spoke in this lady's company.

Her natural voice, rhythms and inflections were Scots but she was trying to be English. This was the way she thought English people spoke.

But she never made the whole transformation. There was always the ghost of another voice, another language, lurking in the background. When she spoke what she assumed to be English she distorted the natural rhythms of her speech and obviously used the framework of another language, which pulled her voice in certain directions. There were things she wanted to say but could not articulate in English, or the language she spoke naturally articulated its own meanings, which were often beyond English. It removed her sense of humour and natural, quick wit, often making her seem lumpish and stupid, as though she had a limited vocabulary or was using words and phrases whose meanings she did not understand. It was the perfect vehicle for someone in her position, a member of the servant class. It meant she could not converse with her betters or could only do so on their terms, making her appear intellectually inferior.

And she did it willingly. Often enjoying the process. She gave the impression of another person when she changed her voice. By adopting the voice of another class, she automatically accepted their comforts and values as her own. This emptied her life of its concerns, made her forget who she was as long as the pretence lasted.

I became used to the transformation and didn't imitate her language, nor did I copy the way she spoke or tried to speak. I simply raised my voice, spoke slowly and tried to pronounce every letter in every word.

It made me ashamed of her. The changes in her voice were so apparent I was sure everyone was aware of them. When she told me to Speak Properly, I knew what she meant and felt everyone would be aware of my background. It made me even more self-conscious, more certain of the fact that someone would tap my shoulder and tell me I had no right to be wherever I was.

My mother pretended her way out of Keppochhill Road. It was easy to escape the constant scrabble over money, the slope in the floor, the rattling windows and crowded house, the shouts in the night and the interminable stupidity of the conversations and concerns. Acceptance, even survival, meant putting a face on it; anyone who lost that pretence was scorned, the drunks and gamblers, the folk who ran away, drowned themselves or went to the dogs: the lowest of the low.

It was easy to pretend life was different, that somehow the concerns of other folk neither touched or affected you, that they were like people who had been crippled from birth, who could neither run nor dance, that no degree of fineness ever touched them and no matter what they were shown, they would never be different. Because she knew better, and had experienced finer living second hand, she was better. That and the fact that there were standards, a line below which one dared not drop. The lesson was obvious and all too familiar, standing in every close and on every street corner.

You did not get into debt, you tried to save something, no matter how little and you bought nothing if you had something that could do. Square cushions were squeezed into round covers, a hairgrip served as a bulldog clip and with every piece of clothing, including my Aunt Barbara's old blouses which I was assured would make a lovely shirt, I was told, There, that'll do. Nobody'll notice.

Though I am sure she went without to buy my clothes when I complained, she was capable of blowing six months' wages on some triviality, like a wig. Is it all right? she asked. Jesus Christ, it's no a hairy bunnet, is it? To hell with it, it'll have to do. It makes a difference. I feel a lot smarter. It'll do for my work.

Anything for herself had to be justified, though the excuse was often slender.

Consumerism frightened her. She stood outside Grandfare in Springburn and only went in when she saw a neighbour she considered beneath her coming out with two bags of shopping. She wandered round with her mouth open, pausing at every aisle to admire the riches on display.

Dear God, I've never seen as much stuff. Look at this. That'll cost a pretty penny.

And when she did bring home a quarter pound of tea, she opened the packet with a ritualistic zeal and Grandfare became a byword for excellence.

I bought this at Grandfare, she said, producing two or three slices of ham. It'll be good.

I despised this, never equating the obvious reality of my mother's life with her attitudes. She voted Tory, firmly believing we needed the man with the money.

Why? Do you think he's going to give some of it to us or make more for himself? I'd say, and she shooed the idea away.

This was when she'd brought home scraps from the dinner tables. Instead of the left-overs going to the swill, she packed the slices of cold, cooked steak, ham and chicken, petit fours and what she called good butter into her bra and brought them home. Occasionally she brought the remains of a bottle of wine.

This is claret, she'd say. It has to be drunk slowly and savoured. Claret should be served at room temperature, so you let it breathe before drinking it, that means you uncork it and stand the bottle on the table.

Maybe we should put it near the grate?

Don't you be so bloody cheeky. You'll be dining in these places yourself some day and you need to know these things, otherwise you'll get a showing up.

I told her about a street corner politician who'd shouted, Roast for King George, Toast for George King. We want roast, not toast.

I hope you're not listening to Communists, she said. They'd have no hotels at all, so what'd we do then?

I always knew what she wanted. I would be educated, and enter a profession. This would be a natural transition that would happen without effort, as if my position was temporary; something would happen and my life would begin, my true life, the one I was waiting to lead, my destiny. I had, of course, no idea what this might be, but I knew I'd do anything to take me away from what I saw around me.

Dearie me, the Kaufmanns of Keppochhill Road, she'd say. What are we like? We'll never get out the bit. Never.

She encouraged me to read. And from the first it fired my imagination rather than provided the education she thought I was getting, especially when I read my granny's favourite novel: *How The Sheik Won His Bride*.

The front cover had a drawing of a bearded, turbaned man with pyramids, camels and sand dunes in the background. The back cover was missing. Pages were stapled together, with the title in red and bold black lettering and every chapter was preceded by an illustration.

That bloody story's no true, my granny said.

And even before I started to read, she asked questions to which she knew the answer.

What was his name again?

'In far Arabia, Sheik Ali Bin Abu was restless. The messenger had not arrived.'

Is he in his tent? she asked.

'For four long days he had stood by his tent watching to see if the sands shifted, if a cloud of dust appeared on the horizon, telling him his trusty Salman, whose fine Arab steed was the envy of a thousand bazaars, was approaching. The mission, he knew, had been hard and dangerous, but if it was possible to succeed then Salman would win the day.'

What does the letter say?

So I escaped by dreaming of what my life would be, imagining nothing but escape. It's difficult to know when or how it began, but from a time soon after my father's funeral, when life became unbearable, I lived in two worlds. There was what was around me and what was in my head. I escaped into an imaginary world and the springboard was what I read. I lived in books and relived their stories. They came alive, lived in me. Imaginary strangers made me happy or empathised with my sadness and confusion. Even when I did not know what I was feeling or why, when life offered no clues beyond loneliness, they stayed with me, walked beside me and told me just to be still, or when their tragedies were more dramatic, worse than mine, I could sympathise, talk with them and tell them I understood their loss, their misery, bewilderment and even embarrassment. Reality was often closer to what I imagined than to what I had experienced.

And I am sure my mother felt something similar. When she was with her mother, father or sisters she was more like them, more of an adult, except when she was with Barbara. Their intimacy had an intensity I assumed all sisters shared, though Margaret was different. She worked away, spent her summers at Gleneagles and her winters in London and came home at the end of the season, usually with a friend, a woman she worked beside. Margaret and her friends became part of the set up. They came on family holidays.

Mattie Ashton was from Barrow-in-Furness. She and Margaret were chambermaids at the Great Eastern Hotel by Liverpool Street Station. She told me how wonderful London was, how you could get the tube to any part of the city, go round Billingsgate fish market or the Kent orchards, see the Tower of London or Buckingham Palace, and how she and I would ride down Oxford Street on top of a bus that was scarlet, red as a rose.

Every year she promised. She pressed me into her chest and told me we'd have a lovely time.

Don't haud your breath, my mother said.

Mattie Ashton had what I am sure she would have considered a proper turn of phrase. Her conversations were interspersed with phrases like, I think you are quite correct in making that assumption.

I agree entirely.

It is the most appalling disgrace.

And, In other circumstances I might beg to differ.

What might these circumstances be? my mother asked.

There was a sudden, unusual hush, filled with anticipation. My Aunt Margaret shot a protective look. She clearly felt defensive and was forever making excuses for poor Mattie, who was worried about her weight, wasn't sleeping properly and had experienced a big disappointment.

When my mother asked if she had been to Furness, Margaret changed the subject; and when my mother persisted, she said, I'm too busy to go away up there. I've got better things to do with my time.

And after a particularly arcane pronouncement, which left an awkward silence, she told us Mattie came from a good family had been very well educated.

How can you tell? my mother asked.

No, she told Margaret after another squabble, I don't dislike her, but I don't like her either.

What is it you don't like?

She's a miserable bitch. I would've thought she could've contributed something in the way of money for her keep. And if she couldn't do it, what about you? Are we supposed to feed her as well as put up with her airs and graces just because she's your friend? No wonder she's worried about her weight. She'll no stop eating.

How did you get your finger hurt, Marie? Mattie asked one night.

An accident.

My mother's right forefinger was permanently bent from the first knuckle. It was the only time anyone outside the family mentioned it.

It happened when I was wee. I wondered what would happen if I stuck my finger in the door, she told me.

And for whatever reason when it came up later, when I was older, she told me there was a row. I wanted the shouting to stop, she said, though she had often implied her childhood was warm and cosy, maybe the happiest time of her life, full of promise, hope and dreaming. But she was capable of editing her experience in ways that weren't always obvious, so that contradictions became synchronised. Details emerged gradually, simple and unadorned, as though there was nothing more to add, another definite statement.

He doesn't like you, she said when I complained about my grandad hitting me, I thought for no reason. I accepted it as easily as my granny's unconditional love and thought he was old and maybe ill.

He doesn't like you, she said, because he's never liked me. Never. I hardly remember him saying a kind word to me, though I did what I could, tried to please him till I saw it made no difference. He couldn't control me. I wouldn't give in to him. Even when he left his shaving strap out in the cold, so that it froze overnight and became harder and sorer when he leathered me, I never let him get the better of me. And he sees you as the same.

This was when she became herself, when we were together, when she'd dream aloud and tell me her secrets, the first time they'd danced in the Drill Hall, Oban, what my father said and what he wore, what she said, what life was like during the First World War, when she and Margaret were at Balvaird with their Auntie Kate, walking the long road from the farm to school at Mulbuie, where they put up a monument to Sir Hector Macdonald, Fighting Mac, who went to the same school as her and Margaret, how she wished she'd listened when they spoke Gaelic and how she was always top of the class, even though she had marks deducted for bad handwriting, top of the schools in the whole Black Isle and dreamed of university, an education, maybe even to become a doctor, how she had a poem printed in the *Ross-shire Journal*.

This was long before I met your father, she said.

Meeting my father was the most important event of her life. She would look through the box where she kept her papers and produce a document.

That's another thing about your father, she'd say.

According to his Certificate of Service, he was a merchant seaman who volunteered for the period of hostilities only, was five feet five and a half inches tall, had a 37-inch chest, black hair, hazel eyes, a sallow complexion and a small scar above his right ear. He was awarded three chevrons and a good conduct badge. He was qualified in first aid and served as an ordinary seaman from 1 August 1940 to 12 November 1945, changing ships 14 times, beginning and ending on HMS *Europa*. He served on the minesweepers, was torpedoed three times and twice was the ship's sole survivor.

And when we went for our walks through town, along the terraces of Glasgow's West End, through Kelvingrove or Springburn Parks, she would name his features the way she'd named mine.

His growth was so heavy he shaved twice a day. He had a high forehead and was losing his hair, with little more than a clump of dark forelock. His jaw was square. He had big ears and a dimpled chin. His hands seemed huge. When he came home from work he scrubbed them with floor cleaner, never managing to free the dirt. He was a handsome man who smelled of Johnson's Baby Powder, which he used to cool his face after shaving.

Can you imagine what it must have been like for him in the navy, my mother said, having to wear Johnson's Baby Powder every day?

He combed his hair by the bedroom mirror, singing the Bing Crosby songs he'd heard on radio, 'Galway Bay' and 'The Isle of Innisfree', or the songs he had known all his life, 'Teddy O'Neill', 'An t-Eilean Muileach' or 'Kishmul's Galley'.

He was born in Ballachulish, raised in Combie Street and Miller Road, Oban and learned to speak English when he went to school. He sang in the Oban Gaelic Choir, danced at the Drill Hall, went to work and never came back.

That was the end of every conversation. And through it all like blood through a bandage were the things she didn't think she believed.

You wished if you found money or tasted the first fruit of the year. You wished when a baby was born, on the first star of evening or when a new moon appeared; and if you spat on the money or turned it in your pocket when you saw the new moon, you'd be rich. You wished when you saw the first rowan berries, when bread came out the oven, when a frog jumped on a stone, if you saw a midget, a club foot or a humph. It was bad luck to speak going under a bridge, bad luck to cut your toenails on a Friday, to keep a lock of baby hair or bring laurel or lilac into the house. It was bad luck to put shoes on the table, if you saw the moon in daylight or if a cock crowed at night.

If coal fell from the fire, a stranger was coming, but it was lucky if you trod on shite; if your hand was itchy you'd get a surprise; if two people shared a mirror there'd be a row; it was unlucky to throw hair or nail parings in the fire or to change the sheets without turning the mattress; and rain was expected if cows gathered in the corner of a field or the cat washed behind its ears. The hoot of an owl or rap at the window with no one there meant a death in the family.

THREE

Charlie's Dance

HIS PICTURE WAS in a silver frame beside the clock and below the oval mirror. The blue jug they'd been given as a wedding present with flowers round the lip was at the other side of the clock. Every morning when she lit the fire, showing me how to twist the paper and lay the coal, she dusted and moved them, wiping the hearth and shaking the rug in front of the fire, fixing the cushions, mopping the floor and moving the furniture and ornaments: Just to brighten the place up a bit, she said.

Now the house was crowded, I learned to put things in their place; but the most immediate change came when Granny needed the lavatory.

Take me. Quick, she'd say as she raised her right arm in front of her and I'd guide her through the kitchen, out the door and round past the garden and coal sheds to the closet by the next door wall.

Wait. Don't you move.

Every morning and three or four times more each day I stood, in all weathers, looking down the garden, past the vegetable plots and compost heap, past the hedge and over the fields to the railway line, trying not to listen, waiting for the flush and crack of the snib.

Where are you? she'd shout before she opened the door.

And back in the kitchen she'd stand by the range, shouting on my mother to make a cup of tea, Afore I freeze to death in that bloody place and you've to carry me out of here feet first in a box.

Now there were breadcrumbs on the floor and down the sides of chairs, jam, sugar and tomato seeds stuck to the oilskin table cover and coal dust and splinters gathered on the hearth.

Some furniture, plates and crockery had arrived from Glasgow, a double bed and side tables, the clock with its heavy chime, four chairs and a chest of drawers. Willie Aitken, the village joiner, had made some of our furniture, a tallboy, sideboard and tea trolleys with a desk and chair for me, but everything was cleared. We moved the table to the back wall, making a passage to the kitchen and doors were always open. And spare furniture was moved to the sheds or bedrooms.

With so many changes, we gradually made everything new, the way they do in stories when the poor become rich and goodness survives.

Mum and Aunt Barbara slept in the big bedroom at the front of the house. My grandparents were now in what had been Barbara's room, but I still had the wee room over the kitchen at the back.

The air became heavy. There was pipe smoke, voices and the plod of the clock. My grandfather spent most of his time reading while my granny sat at the other side of the fireplace, often talking to herself. If a window was open, she'd tell us there was a draught, except in the warmest days of summer when she sat in the garden, shouting for folk to tell her where they were and what they were doing. Every washing day, she told my mother to hang the clothes properly.

The extra washing took two days. Mum and Barbara did the ironing on Wednesdays and the sheets were changed on Saturday mornings.

Every day, Barbara cycled to the flax mill in Cupar. A couple of afternoons a week, while my grandparents slept, for an hour or two life stepped back to what it used to be when Mum and I walked to Ladybank where she changed her library books and bought the paper. When Barbara cycled into the square she'd put me on the back of her bike and we'd freewheel from the station, sit on the dyke till my mother came running down the hill and the three of us would walk to Kettle, no one hurrying home.

Is that the paper in? my granny cried when she heard the door. Thank God, that'll keep him quiet for a while.

Oh, good, he'd say, feeling down the side of the chair for his glasses and unfolding the paper carefully. Mum and Aunt Barbara made the tea with the wireless on while Granny talked to them or no one.

After tea, I sat on the floor beneath the table, listening to them discuss themselves. My grandfather wore brown boots with highly polished toecaps and leather laces that wrapped round his ankles and tied in a double bow on the side of his foot. He wore dark blue or grey woollen socks and dark pinstriped trousers. His top trouser buttons were always undone and after a meal he undid all his fly buttons and sat with his belly cupped in his hands.

Granny's woollen slippers had a sponge sole, a little collar that folded over the top and brown glass buttons at the side. Two buttons were missing. The slippers had a dark checked pattern, like a dressing gown, and were worn at the toes. She rolled her stockings down to her ankles. Her legs were the colour of pastry with dark blue veins on her calves and a cluster between her ankle bones and heels. Her right foot was always crossed over the left and her floral cross-over apron strings were sometimes loose and hung over the side of the chair.

My mother sat in her stocking soles. Once, I ran my finger along her foot and was sent to bed. Barbara's shoes were brown leather with a frill patterned tongue above the lace.

I was not always aware of what they were saying, though they seemed to speak about things they already knew.

It was Archie's first leave and we didn't expect it. He had a few days' rest and recuperation at Portsmouth, or maybe it was Plymouth, I can't remember; but he made his way to Glasgow, God alone knows how, without a pass or anything in wartime. We had two days and he had to go back. I told him I thought I was due and he said, You're the one who'll know, Marie. It was the last thing he said before he went back.

Granny shifted before she spoke. She would wiggle herself round to face whoever was speaking and, underneath the table, rock her hands in time to her voice. Was that before the Blitz? she said.

Just before, would that be right?

I cannae mind, though God knows I'll never forget that bloody Blitz. You'd think the wean would want to stay where he was rather than come into a world like that, bloody bombs dropping everywhere.

It lit the sky, Grandad said. Even from where we were, you could see the fires in the sky and the smoke and smell hung around for days.

The ground shook. There was the screeching, the whistle of the bombs, then the ground shook. Everything jumped. If it was like that for us, what would it have been like for the poor souls who were getting it. Everything jumped, the cups in the saucers and the clock on the wall, they jumped and landed in time for the shock to shudder through you and then it was quiet till the next whistle.

Just think, said Barbara, we used to go to the shows and ride the chairoplanes and big wheel to get scared. But when it comes at you for real, when you know you could die or that somebody's dying, it's a different story.

I don't give a damn, you can say what you like, my mother said, but it was the Blitz that brought him on. After the Blitz he was never the same. He never was right.

I mind you saying that, said Granny.

It seemed to unsettle him. He tossed and he turned and he punched and he kicked. I knew he was coming, though everybody said it couldn't be right. You even asked me if I was sure I'd been married long enough.

Indeed I did not.

You did, Mother. When I said I thought he was due you asked how long I'd been married.

Don't be so damned daft. It was me who made you go to the doctor.

After you'd asked how long I was married. And all he said was, Don't be silly. The child can't be due. But I'd enough time to get to Oakbank and that was it. Eight weeks premature.

And Charlie jumped the gates, said Barbara.

Granny nodded, That's right, she said. The hospital was closed and they wouldnae let him in. He was home on leave, God love him, and I told him I'd a funny feeling, so he ran all the way from Keppochhill Road to Oakbank Hospital. And he was the first to see the wean.

Quarter to six, that's when he was born. My mother was adamant about this. And they wouldn't let him in, but he jumped the gates and ran round the grounds, chapping windows and crying my name. Where is he? he shouted. I held the baby up to the window and he did a wee dance.

She had wanted her parents to move to Fortingall where she and Barbara worked in the hotel. Her friend Peggy Morrison came down to see the baby. They travelled back together and Peggy looked after me while Barbara and my mother worked.

My grandfather refused to move. If we're going to get it, we'll get it no matter where we are, so we might as well be here as anywhere else.

What I want is no to get it, Granny said. And where do you think has the most bombs, Glasgow or Fortingall?

But they clung on and at the end of the season we moved to Kettle.

Peggy came to see my mother two or three times a year. She spent her mornings in the garden, reading or writing into a notebook. In the afternoons she and my mother worked in the garden or walked round the village, took the train to Cupar where we searched for food and when we got home they cooked together and talked the whole time above the radio noise.

It was Peggy who introduced me to rice as a main course, to cauliflower cheese, baked potatoes and meatless salads. She made my first tomato and nettle soups, served kippers with cream, curried rabbit and baked oatcakes to go with my granny's crowdie.

She listened to the radio, especially comedy programmes, and was full of tales of London, of sleeping in tube stations, of mutilated bodies and bomb sites, of lost relations and secrecy, of parks that now were gardens, of air raid shelters with pictures on the walls and people who stayed in the shelters because they had nowhere else to go. She told us of the children who had been evacuated to Killin and Aberfeldy and whispered stories of land girls to my mother.

Peggy made a story out of everything. Some of her tales went on for days, involving families and journeys, dragons and witches.

My mother's favourite book was *A Man Named Luke* by March Cost. She showed me the inscription, 'For Marie, with best wishes from the author,

1941', written in blue ink. Peggy wrote that book, she said. And a few others. She gave it to me when I was carrying you.

Damned stuff, my granny said. Who in the name of God is going to believe in that sort of thing?

You haven't read it.

The best book that ever was written was that other book I like, what's its name again?

How The Sheik Won His Bride.

Aye, that's it. Anyway, how in the name of God can I read a book when I cannae see a hand in front of my face?

They'd have a hand or two of whist or solo, singing while they played, with the wireless in the background. And just before the *Nine O'Clock News*, the kettle would go on for tea and toast and jam before bed.

I never wanted to sleep on my own, always wanted to be with them, fearful of the upstairs dark, the shudder and made up possibilities. Granny's warnings made me fearful of damp, cold places and I took every chance to stay up late. The stairs were cold when I started the climb and I shivered as I ran into the bedroom and warm bed. I always thought I might hear something I shouldn't have heard, but it never happened. They just carried on, blethering as before.

Poor Charlie. I wonder where he is this night. He could be lying dead and we wouldn't even know, him and Willie both, as well as George and that man of Eva's, what's his name again?

Matt.

My Aunt Eva was small, tidy and precise. Her hair was always curled and combed and she seldom wore make-up. Whenever I saw her she was with my Uncle Matt, a tall, dark-haired Canadian who ducked when he came in the door.

God, you folks are tiny, he said.

He smelled of tobacco and I liked him very much. He held me higher than I'd ever been, threw me into the air and caught me, and when he held me indoors I could touch the ceiling.

Margaret was away, working in munitions: I'm a fitter, she told me, making shells to blow the buggers up. Charlie and Willie were in the army, no one knew where.

Barbara had married a soldier from Warrington, George Hewitt, who was in Fife with the REME, training after Dunkirk. I was certain everyone thought my Aunt Barbara beautiful. I especially loved the smell of her breath. It was tinged with lipstick and cigarettes mingled with violets and scented soap. The smell of talcum filled the house and her clothes always seemed to be drying on the range or kitchen pulley.

She was as tidy as my mother was scattered and would never let cigarette ends pile in the ashtray.

My mother was the only one who minded Babs smoking, solely on health grounds, but my grandfather's pipe was a different matter. He'd stand at the back door and stare down the garden. This was the sign for supper and for me to go to bed. They'd sometimes let me sleep under the table. But I didn't get to stay up often, only if I persisted and everyone was tired. More usually, just before bed, I'd get a spoonful of Virol, then cod liver oil, a glass of orange juice and a cup of milk. I hated the cod liver oil and would only take it from my Aunt Barbara.

You don't want to end up like that wee man you saw in Cupar, my mother would say.

Apparently, I'd seen a midget outside the Cupar Woolworth's on Crossgate and asked my mother, Did that wee man no take his Virol?

He was incandescent. Get out, you cheeky wee bugger you.

Don't you dare use that language in front of a child, my mother said. And when she told my granny the story, she didn't laugh.

How wee was he? she asked.

He was a wee man, Mother. God Almighty, I didnae measure him.

What colour was his hair?

Black.

Are you sure?

He was going bald at the back, but whatever hair he had on his heid was as black as the Earl o' Hell's waistcoat.

Had he shaved?

I never asked.

You be careful of wee folk, my granny told me. Don't you go near them, especially wee men; wee women maybe all right, but they can sometimes be carnaptious, especially if they've midgeon or murgeons and skulk about the place. But wee men are the worst. When a wean's ta'en by the fairies, they put one of these wee folk in its place and if you get talking to them they'll take you too.

Mother, for the love o' God, don't give that wean any more to trouble him, do you no think he's bad enough?

It'll no be that if he goes out one day and never comes back.

FOUR

Germans

ON STATION ROAD beyond the hotel, a dozen men passed Barbara and me; dark men in navy blue clothes with coloured patches on their jackets and trousers.

They were singing. I turned to see them, and as I turned, the men smiled at Barbara. She blushed, lowered her eyes and faced the wall. They were carrying farm implements, spades, hoes and rakes, one or two wore brown trilby hats and a couple had berets. As we reached Bankton Park, the singing faded.

We turned into the Pauls' farm where a smell of baking hung in the yard. A cat was sleeping on a rain barrel and clabber from the fields lined the middle of the road.

Mrs Paul was a stocky woman with floral aprons and her hair in a bun. She lived with her three sons in a smallholding too small to be called a farm, and too much a part of the village to be a croft.

Barbara and Mrs Paul were talking. I got bored and started back towards Bankton Park. No one saw me go and as I turned the corner a man in a beret, dressed like the men we'd seen, started running down the road towards Jamieson's farm. Barbara screamed as he jumped a dyke and crossed the field towards the Eden.

An army Land Rover turned the corner, slapping me against the wall. Barbara grabbed my pullover, lifted me and dropped to her knees as she held me into her, screaming. Mrs Paul lifted Barbara by the arm and I rose with her.

We could all have been killed, Mrs Paul said. No one knew it was coming. We'd no idea what was there. It wasn't his fault.

He shouldn't have gone off like that, said Babs. He's always doing it.

As she turned away there was a sound I'd never heard before, a crack that stayed in the air.

Oh my God, said Barbara.

There's men who're living with that sound day and night and have done so for years, Mrs Paul said as she turned away.

We watched the soldiers drag the man across the field and into the Land Rover. His hands were tied behind his back and blood ran from his forehead. He was on the back seat between two uniformed soldiers. He turned towards us and the wagon passed. He was obviously shouting but we heard nothing above the roar of the engine. As the car turned the corner, I start to cry.

* * *

Every day I ran with the Pauls' dog Sandy, across one of the fields to the end of the strip or round the rim of cornfield. One day Sandy chased a rabbit into the next field where the black and white tip of his tail jumped above the corn, and I followed. No one said anything, so I became more adventurous; and with the harvest in, I took the dog down to the Eden, followed the river upstream to the bridge on the Ladybank road and walked back to the village, me throwing a stick, Sandy fetching and dropping it, waiting for me to catch up with him.

Mum and Mrs Paul were at the end of the road watching us cross the field.

On you come, Mum shouted, just as I thought I was invisible.

Well, Sandy, said Mrs Paul, what kind of a dog are you, taking Carl away out of his road.

Carl knew not to go there.

It was Sandy's fault. Sandy led him down there. He does it all the time. I don't know what we're going to do with him.

I stood in the kitchen till my legs ached, while Mum and Aunt Barbara related unknown dangers, potholes, mud, the river and folk. I promised I would never do it again and was told the matter would be forgotten.

Of course we're not supposed to know about it, Peggy had told my mother, but you know how word gets out.

And everyone spoke till there was nothing more to say. It could cover an awkward meeting, or a frozen moment. And it didn't take much; the suggestion was enough: Did you hear the Cultybraggan Germans are at Ladybank now?

Cultybraggan Camp, near Comrie, had around 4,000 German prisoners of war: And they're far from being ordinary Germans, Peggy said. They are the most faithful and dedicated, the most active, the worst of the Nazis.

Just before Christmas, 1943, they'd held a drumhead court martial and executed a prisoner they suspected of being at least a defeatist and at worst a collaborator. Eight men were charged and subsequently hanged. Some were sent to Inverness-shire. Others, it was said, had come to Ladybank.

Now I knew the memory was thriving and I was frightened of what would be said; I had broken a promise.

That bloody stuff's gone and upset that wean, my granny said. And what the hell are we doing wi Germans here anyway? I thought we were fighting them.

They're prisoners of war, Mother.

33

If they're prisoners they should be in the bloody jail. How in the name of God are prisoners allowed to roam the streets during a war when they cannae do it at any other time?

Oh Mother, gie us peace.

It's all very well for you, but what am I supposed to do if one of them came in here and I didnae know or couldnae see him? What would happen? I could be murdered in my bed. You'd get peace then.

Why were you crying? my mother asked. She set me on the edge of the kitchen table with warm milk and sugar.

I don't know.

Did the shots give you a fright?

It was the man.

Had you seen him before?

No.

She turned away, took the pan from the stove and ran it under the tap.

It was the look on his face, I said. He looked frightened, as if he didn't know what was going to happen to him.

Dear God boy, you're too soft-hearted. You'll need to toughen up.

I don't know why you're surprised, said Barbara. He cries at just about anything.

He might have reason enough to cry, Granny said. We never were a lucky family. You mark my words, as sure as God's in heaven, somebody's put a curse on us. Dear God, Marie. Could you no have given that wean another name, something like Willie or Charlie or even Archie like his father? We're supposed to be fighting bloody Germans and he's got a German name.

I called him after my father. The name's on his birthlines and that's what it'll be.

My mother had been clearing the garden. Everyone, except Granny, was working, lifting tatties, carrots and runner beans. We had good crops of tomatoes and apples and had started to store the fruit and vegetables in the shed. The tomatoes had been separated and laid in the pantry or piled into the jelly pan for chutney.

My mother switched on the wireless and started working at the table in her usual dreamy way, staring past the garden and the field beyond to the railway line that passed the house.

Come you here to me, my granny said. This was when she inspected me for cuts and bruises. She'd feel my face with her hands and peer at my skin, as though she was trying to see.

Marie, you should take that boy to the doctor. He's no right.

He's fine.

He is not. The wean's sick.

There's nothing wrong with him.

It'll no be that if he drops dead. It'll be too late then.

How in God's name can I afford to take him to the doctor when there's nothing wrong with him?

You could save up. What's a half a crown compared to your child's life? Would they folk next door no see him? That bairn's no well. He's too hot. Maybe somebody else's put a curse on us. You never know what they bad buggers o' folk would do. This is a strange place. We don't know anybody here and there's a war on.

The next door Bairds were doctors. Mrs Baird had been a nurse when she met her husband and went to Edinburgh University after they were married. They shared an Edinburgh practice and bought the house in Kettle at the start of the war. Mister Baird still worked in Edinburgh. Mrs Baird and I met him off the train most Friday nights.

Are you ready for your stroll? she'd ask.

And Mister Baird always had a stick of barley sugar. The best sweet you could give a child, he said.

I suppose my mother retreated to Mrs Baird when things were tight at home. There was a constant bickering between my grandparents, though Grandad accepted it all with a stoicism that bordered on indifference; and Barbara was something of a buffer. As the youngest she was proficient in managing my granny's moods and knew how to deflect approaching storms.

You should go, said Mrs Baird. We were in her garden. Mum had come round on the pretext of borrowing tools. Mrs Baird was sitting on a bench by her back door and my mother was tying a climbing plant to the wall.

There's nothing to keep you. Could you find a babysitter?

Peggy would look after him.

Then you should go. Everyone will be fine here. If they want you, I think it would be a good idea for you to go.

Maybe I'll mention it, my mother said. See how I get on.

Mrs Baird gave me a biscuit before we left. Don't you say a word about any of this, my mother said. Not a word. Do you hear?

I had no idea what was being discussed. But it was disturbing. I'd settled into the ways of Kettle. I knew everybody and could go for messages on my own. There were no sweets, but I could tell who was baking and my weekend treat was a jelly cone from Scott's grocery in Kettle Square. I was desperate to stay and took my chance on our way to the station.

What was Mummy asking you about?

I think she would have told you if she had wanted you to know, Mrs Baird said. What I can tell you is that it is very important you keep your promise and do not tell anyone about our conversation. I'm sure you can do that, can't you?

And as I was leaving with my barley sugar a policeman leant his bicycle against their wall.

Is this the German's house? he asked.

No.

Do you know if a German lives here?

No.

What's your name, son?

I didn't answer.

What's your first name?

Carl.

Is that a German name?

I don't know.

Are you a German?

No.

What's your mother's name?

I didn't answer.

Do you know anybody called Hoffman?

No.

And is this your house?

I undid the latch and ran down the path. By the time I got to the living room, my mother was at the front door. She and the policeman came into the sitting room.

Just a routine check, he said. There's a war on.

Do you think we don't know? Granny said. That's why we're here. They bloody bombs'd drop you in hell.

Is there anybody Hoffman here?

My grandfather stood. He was taller than the policeman.

God Almighty. He's bringing the polis to the house next, my granny said. What in God's name's going to happen to us now?

Shush, Mother.

How can I help you? my grandfather asked.

We're supposed to check on everybody's movements, especially those of a different nationality.

I have two sons, two daughters and three sons-in-law fighting for this country. Now why aren't you fighting, may I ask? Why did your police service exempt you?

This isn't personal, you understand.

No, I don't understand. I think you'll find I am employed in this country's service. Now, I'd be obliged if you would leave me and my family alone. We have enough to put up with without you pretending to be something you're not.

Am I right in assuming your services are occasionally called on in the matter of interpretation?

If they are it is a matter between me and those who employ me. I think I would rather speak with someone of a higher rank than yourself, someone who already knew the answers to the questions you were asking. Did you come here of your own accord?

I had heard a rumour and with recent events being what they were I wondered if perhaps the man who escaped had been trying to make contact with you.

If I had any knowledge of that I would have mentioned it to the appropriate authorities, my grandfather said, turning into the kitchen.

I'll show you out, my mother said.

Who is he? Grandad asked.

A bloody ignoramus.

I meant apart from that.

I don't know. I've never seen him before.

And I don't think we'll see him again. Still it just shows you, you can't be too careful. In this place, even the walls have eyes.

Right, my granny said. Toast and cocoa and bed for you.

I wondered where Grandad went. He'd leave in the morning and often didn't come back till that night and occasionally stayed till the following day.

What's the matter with you? my mother asked when she came in with the cocoa. I was looking out the window.

Nothing. I'm too warm.

Marie, what did I tell you? That wean's no right.

He's fine. There's nothing up with him. Leave him alone.

He's too warm. Feel him. He's roasting.

I fell asleep by the fire with my head on my grandmother's knee. My mother wakened me and when I was at the door, I asked, When are we going to Fortingall?

My mother sighed. We'll see, she said.

Who's going to Fortingall? my granny asked. Is that you going and leaving us here?

We'll see, Mother. Nothing's decided. It isn't till next season.

I wakened again sweating, pulled the covers back and lay in the dark, listening to the clatter of the trains and the raised voices in the kitchen.

FIVE

Hospital

FOR DAYS I had a beat at the side of my head. I was warm, had difficulty staying awake and often wakened covered in sweat. At times it was difficult to walk. I had scarcely any appetite and longed to leave food on the plate.

Eat that up, someone would say. God knows where your next meal's coming from.

At first it was a minute or two of nausea, then it grew, never for any length of time and usually coming on at night, which meant I could pretend I was tired.

During the winter Grandad was away, back in Glasgow, for weeks at a time. The house was quieter. I missed his sudden, noisy sneezes. If he was in the sitting room the noise could be heard at the bottom of the garden. They arrived without warning, a sharp and sudden, Ach!

Barbara would look at me and laugh. My mother would put her hands to her breast.

I can't help it, he said.

Aye you can help it if you like, Granny yelled. You just do it to frighten folk. Would that no sicken your happiness, a noise like that. At least you can hear they bloody bombs coming.

Wheesht, Jo.

It's you that should wheesht wi' that bloody nose of yours. What a racket.

When he was gone, she missed him. Every day she asked, When's he coming back? And she always checked the post.

You know where he is, Mother. And you know why he's there.

George had a week's leave. He and Barbara walked me round the village and he came into Ladybank to meet her. They slept in my bed in the back room and I moved in with my mother.

And just after New Year, my mother's favourite brother, my Uncle Willie, turned up in the afternoon, swaggering down Bankton Park with a kitbag on his back.

Were yous trying to run away from me? he said as he opened the door.

Wheesht, Willie.

I turned up at Keppochhill Road and the place was deserted. The old boy's having the time of his life with the place to himself, living like a king; he couldnae get me up here quick enough. Is there any chance of a cup of tea or do I have to go roon the doors singing?

There's your bloody tea. Take it before it gets cold from the draught frae your mooth, my mother said.

Marie, come you here and I'll gie ye beardie.

Away tae hell.

My mother and Willie made each other laugh. At times it was difficult to tell if the banter was serious. It was a constant stream of complaints and insults.

God help you, son, growing up in this hoose with these women. Look at what's happened to me.

Honest to God, Willie, for the size of you you never shut up.

Is that you getting on to me about my height again? You'll gie me a complex. But I'll tell you something you don't know. I was six feet four last week but I got fed up with it.

Bloody six feet under's what you'll be. How long have you stopped smoking?

Since my last cigarette.

Is your chest bad?

It's fine. Now, listen, young man, if you smoke you'll end up the same size as me. I started smoking when I was 18 months old and look at me now, a fine specimen of manikinitis. Though I did go 47 rounds in a bare-knuckle contest with Samson MacTaggart, the man who ate the boiled ham raw. You couldnae gie him a steak pie because he left his teeth marks on the ashet.

Just before he left, Willie noticed my secret.

Marie, is that wean of yours no a bit deaf?

I've been saying that for weeks, Granny said.

If he is deaf, it's wi listening to the two of you blethering on.

I was in bed when he left. It was dark and the room was cold. I felt his beard on my cheek and his breath smelled of milk as he kissed me. I put my arms round his neck and he sobbed.

What would I no give for a boy like you, he said, stroking my hair and tucking me in. Pull these clothes up round you and get yourself warm.

I watched his shadow disappear and heard the fall of his step on the stairs, but expected him there when I wakened.

We'd taken Sandy down to the Eden and on the way back called in at Mister Scott's grocery for a jelly cone. I ate it sitting on the bench in Kettle Square while Willie gathered his breath.

Who's that daft bugger dressed as a polis? Look at the belly on him. Is that what's guarding us? Christ Almighty, he couldnae run if his arse was on fire.

I told him about the time he came round to see Grandad.

Did he, by Christ, said Willie.

He crossed the road and waited. When the policeman came out the Co-operative he tried to speak, but the man gathered his bike and left.

Not long after Willie had gone, the policeman showed up at the door.

God Almighty, my mother said. It's Crippen.

I am investigating the whereabouts of Charles Hoffman.

There's no one of that name here.

I am given to understand he should have reported to a police station and has not done so.

There's no Charles Hoffman here.

He's registered as being here.

Charles Kaufmann lives here.

And is Charles Hoffman here at present?

My mother pushed me into the kitchen and closed the door. You wait there, she said, and don't touch anything. I stood in the dark, shivering before moving to the wall of heat by the stove, though I still felt a draught at my back.

A train crossed the window in a lengthy strip of light. I stared at my reflection long after it was past, imagining the dusty smell of the carriages and the click of the ticket collector's punch.

It'll never be over, my mother said. He's an officious little bugger with nothing to do and he'll keep coming back till he finds something.

Somebody's put a curse on us.

My father had to register when the war started; it's got nothing to do with curses.

How do you know what it has to do with?

Because I've lived with it all my life, Mother. I've had it from the day and hour I was born, and so have all of us. You know that. Has nobody ever asked you, Is that a German name? Dear God, it's as plain as the nose on your face. It stopped when I got married, but I never thought it would follow me here. And the only thing we can do is to stand up for ourselves because nobody else'll do it for us.

You wouldnae have a wee drop whisky, Marie? Just for a toddy to help me sleep.

What happened to the stuff Willie brought?

I don't know where you've put it.

Well, you're just getting the one, mind. And if my father finds out I'm taking none of the blame.

Dear God in heaven, am I supposed to write to Glasgow or wherever the hell he is, just for a drink?

She smelled the whisky in the cup and rinsed out the bottle, boiled the water from the bottle and added it gradually. She held the cup in both hands like a bowl and carried the drink to the fire where she sat, staring at the flames, nursing the whisky and talking to herself, sometimes in Gaelic, as though someone else was there, or interrupting herself with a song.

Come you here and sing to me, she said.

There was a fair bit of music around the house. Barbara would sing whatever was on the radio and my mother was always singing low, sad songs, always slightly off-key. She sang songs of death and exile. I never understood what she was singing, why the people were always sad and longing for something they'd never get, or, worse still, what they used to have but lost. I had picked up some of the words, but didn't know how my granny knew I could sing them.

He doesnae sing, my mother said. And he's going to bed. Now mind, that's it, so there's no point you asking for more, because there is no more. That's the last of it, thank God. Poor Willie; I suppose he thought he was doing you a favour.

Wheesht. I'll be fine. Leave me in peace.

Tell no one what's happened here in this house this night, my mother said in the kitchen.

I don't know what's happened.

Don't say anything, not a word about the policeman being here.

It's him, my granny said. Gone to make some money and he shouldnae be working because he's German. Your husband's German, the polis said. Well, Jesus Christ Almighty, I tellt him, I never knew that. That's news to me.

Mother. Wheesht.

So what's to happen now? Telegrams and more expense because he thought he was being smart.

If anyone had gone it should have been me.

And what was I supposed to do, stuck here with him. Get that boy ready for bed.

Two days later my grandad was back. The policeman came every day, asking when he could expect to see Mister Hoffman.

Grandad arrived in the late afternoon in his black coat and Homburg hat with a small brown suitcase and a newspaper tucked below his arm. I was sitting on the step outside the house and watched him come the way Willie came.

Well, he said. Here we are, back again.

And I suppose you'll know we've had the polis at this door.

I remembered what Willie had said and started laughing.

It's no laughing matter, Granny said.

I was thinking of my Uncle Willie.

God Almighty, what next?

I'll deal with it, Grandad said. When he comes back, I'll deal with it.

I was in the garden about half an hour later when I heard the squeak of his bike and was at the kitchen door when he came into the sitting room, bicycle clips round his ankles and the pump in his hand. He was searching for his notebook when my grandfather spoke with no trace of his usual accent.

You have no right harassing me and my family and I consider your inquiries an intrusion on our privacy. I do not know why you are here, but I will be writing to my Member of Parliament and to your superiors.

You failed to report to the police station as you had been requested to do.

I was only asked to report to the police station after your last visit.

We have already had an escaped prisoner in this area. I understand you haven't been here. Where were you?

Where I have been is known to your superiors and is none of your business. I have said all I am going to say and have no intention of discussing this with you. Good afternoon.

I don't think you need to take it any further, the policeman said at the door.

In that case I don't expect to see you here again.

With my grandad home, we settled back to a steady, rhythmic existence dictated by the clock. It had been like a holiday we never knew we'd taken, but now he was back his presence was everywhere and the smell of his pipe filled the house.

That bloody auld pipe would gie ye the jaundice, my granny said.

The geese arrived in long, loose V's. I loved to watch them and often heard them call in the night. I had taken to climbing the tree at the bottom of the garden to see if I could bring them closer.

I ran down the road, through the Jamieson farm and was following the geese down towards the Eden when I found the dog. It was lying on the path, too weak to lift its head. I thought it was dead and was about to turn away when the ribcage moved. It was black with dull brown eyes, little more than loose bones and filth. When I bent to stroke it, the dog turned and tried to lick my hand.

I knelt in the dirt, not knowing what to do other than stroke the tangled and matted coat. Its mouth was opened and the clumsy breath smelled awful, as though it might stop at any moment. I had to go home. I'd get a row for being this far away, but couldn't leave the dog. There was something wrong; I knew it couldn't live, but didn't want it to die alone.

There would be no point in fetching someone. By the time we got back, the dog would be dead. And I knew my mother would tell me it was hard enough feeding me, never mind a bloody dog and Granny would trip over it. My only hope was to turn up with it. Mum wouldn't turn the dog away if I pleaded for its life.

So I lifted the loose ear and told the dog it had to come with me, that when we got home, if my mother didn't let me take it, Mrs Paul would look after it and that it could play with Sandy and I'd take it and Sandy for runs when it was better.

I stood, turned and counted ten steps. When I turned back the dog was on its feet. I leaned forward, my hands clapping against my knees and the dog shuffled towards me. I took a couple of steps back and the dog stopped; a couple more steps and the dog came too.

I've no idea how long it took us to reach Bankton Park, but I left the dog in the clabber and ran into the house.

No, my grandad said. There will be no dog in this house.

It's not your house, my mother said.

Are you seriously telling me you're going to bring a dying dog into the house? You'll have to stand up to him. You'll have to let him know he can't have everything his own way.

I think it's you who needs to learn that. He's a child. He doesn't understand. And he doesn't get everything his own way, as well you know. Let's have a look at this beast and see what we'll do.

When she lifted the dog, it whimpered. She carried it into the shed and laid it on a pile of sacks.

What the hell do you feed to a hauf-deid dog? she asked no one.

The dog tried to turn its head when I stroked it, but lay on the sack. When Mum came in with bread and milk saps the dog ate slowly at first, picking the food up with its tongue. My mother brought another plate and the dog ate without moving, lying on its side to lick the bowl.

You know it might not live, she said before bed.

And what will you do with it then? Grandad asked.

Do with what? said Granny.

Somebody thought they saw a dog, but it wasn't here, my mother said.

How in God's name could a dog come here? Just think of a dog running between your feet. That one round the corner is bad enough.

That night I added the dog to my prayer list. And when I turned out the light and lay waiting for the trains, I imagined how it would be when I was older, running with two dogs across the fields to the Eden.

I think we should let the men put it out its misery, Mum said in the morning.

The dog was facing the door when I went in with the saps. I thought it was dead. It registered nothing at first, but ate the food and drank the fresh water. I lay stroking the dog, telling it what a fine time we'd have, when it stirred. By the time my mother came in with the scrapings of the porridge pot it was half way up, peching as it tried to raise its hind legs.

What the hell's going on here? she said. Help it up.

I set the dog on the ground and steadied it while it toppled twice on its way to the door, then sniffed around the back of the coal shed.

My God, said Mum. Would you believe that? You go in and get yourself some milk or something. I've a washing to put out.

That night the dog stood and licked the bowl clean. And when I stroked the crown of its head, the tail wavered.

We'll need to think of a name, Mum said. Though maybe not yet, for it's got a long way to go.

Barbara was frightened of the dog. You don't know where it's been, she said standing at the shed door and refusing to go in. You don't know what diseases it's carrying and it could do with a wash.

What an awful trauchle you've brought to this hoose, Mum told the dog, kneeling beside it and stroking the fur. I think we should try to wash it, but God alone knows how. Do you think it would stand in a bath? We'll maybe need to use Derbac soap.

* * *

The earth was spongy, thick with clay after rain. I loved standing in the garden listening to the evaporation, which sounded like a light rain, a sort of drabble, so fine it soaks you gently.

I'd half-closed the door and was standing on the path when I heard the geese and ran down the garden, climbed the tree and slipped, banging my head on a post. I felt sick and dizzy when I stood and lay back among the rhubarb, with the smell of earth and compost. If I was unconscious it couldn't have been for long, for I wakened with the dog licking my face. And for the first time in a long time I felt the murmur in my ear.

I tried to act as if I was well, tried to keep my skin cool and walk with my back straight. Next morning my hearing had gone.

By the time a murmur returned to my left ear I had been exposed. My mother thought it was wax and tried to poke inside my ear with the corner of a towel. When she touched my right ear I screamed.

Mrs Baird asked how long I had been like this and no one knew. I lay on her sofa while she phoned her husband. I think he has a mastoid, she said.

I remember liking the sound of the word and asked her to say it again.

It's very serious, she said. He has to get to hospital immediately. The very least we can expect is a hearing loss, but, if it isn't treated, it could destroy the bone in the skull.

I remember little or nothing of the next few days and the story has been repeated so often I can no longer distinguish between what I remember and what I've been told.

I was taken by ambulance to the Ear, Nose and Throat Hospital in St Vincent Street, Glasgow and operated on immediately. My mother was told my right ear would probably be permanently deaf, that I should learn to lip-read and use sign language.

I think I'll wait to see how deaf he is, she said.

The thing is, we may not know, the doctor said. He may have been unconsciously lip-reading already.

I could not move or lie on my side while my head was bandaged and slept sitting up.

I used to put my finger in my left ear to imagine what life would be like if I was deaf. I asked a nurse for cotton wool and she told me not to be silly. I watched the way folk moved their lips and pretended I could not make out what they were saying.

My mother ran down the ward holding one of Mister Scott's jelly cones in front like a baton. When she talked to the medical staff, she cocked her head and nodded. I left a week after they removed the bandages, sat on the bed till my mother came running down the ward with a suitcase in one hand, holding onto her hat with the other.

Where can he change? she asked a nurse.

She was speaking to a doctor when I came out from behind the screens.

A fair proportion has been restored, he said. But there's no saying how long it will last. He could go deaf again, almost at any time, and if that happens there's not much we can do. In all likelihood he'll simply compensate and learn to live with it.

My head was bandaged and wrapped in a scarf. People stared as we walked up Elmbank Street to Sauchiehall Street and Charing Cross. I drank red lemonade and had a cake in the tearoom counter at the back of Ross's Dairy, then we took the tram to Keppochhill Road.

The house smelled of Dettol. She had made up a bed and lit the fire in my grandparents' bedroom. I had a bowl of soup and was put to bed.

I fell asleep and wakened with my mother standing by the window with the edge of the curtain in her hand. I could feel there was something she wanted to say, but was waiting for the right moment. And there were questions I was afraid to ask, when would the bandages come off and when would I be able to hear again. I was afraid to ask about the dog.

Do you need anything? she asked.

And before I could answer, I heard a clatter on the stairs and the tug of the bell.

Where is he? said Willie. Now that he's deaf, he'll be wanting me to sing.

I was allowed up and sat by the fire toasting bread through the grill while Willie blethered on.

This is good soup; but I have to say, if you like soup, and many people do, the Hameilldaeme Inn serve a very fine portion of elephant soup. Very nice, and the tastiest bit comes from just below the tail.

Willie!

What?

Bloody fine well and you know what.

I'm telling the wean about soup. Surely you want your child educated; but I'll tell you what, do you think you'd like a wee game of draughts?

My grandfather had tried to teach me and gave up saying I was too young. Willie's methods were different.

Now this here is the same as this here except it's different. And when you take one of them you place it over here in a wee stack and you put your thumb to your nose and waggle your fingers at your opponent.

Willie!

This is a version called Chinese draughts, which your mother has obviously never heard of, but that signal tells your opponent he or she is now free to move. Your grandad knows this version very well and next time you play with him, be sure to play Chinese draughts.

Right, that's it. Bed.

I'll tell you what we'll do, said Willie. You'll need to have a shave before you go to bed. Don't tell me your mother doesnae let you shave; I don't think she shaves herself, so she might not understand that men like you and me need to have a wee dig at the grave before sleep.

I was in bed looking at the comic he'd brought when I heard them in the lobby.

That's a wee message for my mother, he said.

Dear God, Willie, take it yourself.

Give it to her, Marie. You know she likes it.

And you know what she's like when she gets it. What'll the old man say?

What did he ever say? I'm going in now. And I'll tell him.

He sat on the bed, watching me pretend to read: That letter there's an S, S for snake, and it's like a big curly snake itself. And this one here's a C, C for Carl and C for cuddle, for Carl likes a cuddle and that wee bit there is where you get the cuddle and when you go in you get a cuddle like this and you make the letter O, which is what you say when you get a cuddle.

I loved his smell of soap and lavender hair oil. I knew this was how I wanted to be, that the sight of my Uncle Willie with his hair slicked back, his red, clean-shaven face, bright eyes, polished shoes and trench coat made my heart leap.

I had no idea where he stayed. I knew he had left the army, discharged early with a bad chest, he said, and was back working as a waiter. And there were whispered snatches when they thought I wasn't listening. Whenever he appeared, my mother asked: Any sign?

And he'd shake his head sharply. I'll tell you later, he said.

Sign of what?

They're looking for evidence that the Pope is, in fact, a Catholic. Rumour has it he's learning to play the flute and this is seen in certain quarters as a very bad sign indeed. Now, how many oranges do you think you'd find in a Sacred Hearted home?

He put out the bedroom light and with the lobby light on sat up beside me on the bed, with my mother listening at the door.

So, tell me about the dog, he said.

I told him as much as I could: But I don't think it'll live, I said. It's very ill.

You did a brave and a wonderful thing, trying to rescue a poor, sick dog, he said. It was very kind and generous of you, and your mother too, for she could just as easily have let it be, but she didn't; she knew it was important and she did her best to help. There are things we love, sometimes we love them a lot, and they're only with us for a wee while, but that doesn't mean we shouldn't love them or should love them any less. We can carry on loving them after they've gone. We can live with the love in our hearts and memories, and maybe even imagine what things could have been like, but it's not good to do that too often. But I know you well enough to know you'd've liked to've taken the dog we'll call Nemo for a run to the Eden and come back along the Ladybank road flinging sticks, the way you do with Sandy. And even though that's not to be, next time you and Sandy go along that road, I'm sure you'll see the ghost of a happy wee Nemo dog running there beside you. Now, what I want you to do is get off to sleep and I'll see you very soon.

He coughed and blew his nose in the lobby and was gone in the morning when Mum wakened me with tea and toast and told me she'd slept in.

Willie stayed here late last night, she said. God alone knows what time he got home. I hope he didn't have to walk in that rain.

47

We made sandwiches and tea for the train. Standing at the station, waiting for the platform information to go on the board, my mother looked into her bag.

Wait here, she said.

A man on a bench was coughing. When someone passed he stuck out his hand and muttered, God bless, inspecting his hand when they'd passed, in case he had missed anything.

My mother gave him a bottle from her bag.

Not a word about this, she said to me. Don't you dare breathe a word about this, not to anyone.

God bless you, the man shouted. God bless yous and I wish yous now a lucky, lucky life with happiness and as much good fortune as you've given me this day.

The train was crowded. As we left Queen Street Station my mother told me in a very loud voice this was the Edinburgh train, the train my daddy would get when he came home.

SIX

Trains

I RAN PAST the janitor in his brown linen coat, out the gates and along Rumdewan, past the warehouses and Kettle Holm, under the bridge and past the station, down Bankton Park and into the house where my tricycle was waiting by the door, with crossed flags in the brakes, a Lion Rampant and a Union Jack.

My mother shouted from the kitchen, Not today. There's no use going.

So I put the cat in the shoebox and hauled him round the house.

Patch was a black farm cat with green eyes, a white smudge below his chin, thick fur and a tail that wavered when he walked. He lost an ear in a fight.

Granny said, This hoose has mice. As sure as God's alive in heaven, there's mice in this hoose.

When I got back from hospital, my mother told me, We'll get a kitten for your daddy coming home. He likes cats.

I though they gave you hay fever.

We'll see, she said.

A week later Patch was sleeping in a box by the range.

Don't you waken him, she said. You can stroke him, but do it gently. Your daddy always strokes his cats below the chin and tickles them between the ears.

Next day Willie Barr, Tom Seath, George Aitken, Tom Lamb and Ann Wilkie came round after school. My mother gave them currant cake and a cup of milk. That's a Jamieson kitten, Ann Wilkie said. They stared at the box, bent, touched the fur and said, Hello, to the cat.

Miss Barclay says pets can be a burden.

And we nodded. Miss Barclay's opinions were important.

You're lucky, Willie Barr said as he left. My mother hates cats. They give her hay fever.

Have you got a cat here? my granny asked.

No.

Are you sure?

What have I just said?

I'm damn sure there's a cat in here.

Well, there's a cat that sometimes looks in, but it never stays.

You know I cannae have anything t'dae with cats in a strange hoose. I'll trip over them and break my neck, unless, of course, you're trying to get rid of me. Maybe we've outstayed our welcome.

I started school part time when the war ended and knew the war was over when I saw my grandfather pack the cases. The pile of cardboard boxes grew daily. And, without warning, a van backed down Bankton Park.

I ran round marvelling at the spaces, wondering how they would be filled.

Well, my grandfather said. And everyone stood.

Granny started crying. She shook her arms from side to side, let out a wail and started speaking to no one in Gaelic.

Come on, Mother, Barbara said. We'll miss the train.

Grandad took my hand and we walked to the station in silence. Granny, Mum and Barbara followed behind, whispering.

The station lights were lit, a ghostly yellow. We stood on the platform, Barbara holding on to me, rocking me gently while Granny sobbed. My mother and grandfather stared towards Ladybank. Small groups stared down the line. Few were talking.

Just think, my mother said suddenly, her voice so loud folk turned to see who was speaking. Just think how lucky we are. We've survived the war. Every one of us have come through alive. We've lost no one. They're all alive, thank God. We've a lot to be thankful for; I don't know how many families can say that. We've been spared. Archie and Willie, Charlie, Eva, Matt and George are alive. Margaret's alive and we're all here.

The train pulled into the station and my mother kept talking while Barbara searched for an empty carriage and Grandad helped my granny into the nearest compartment. Mum held me up to the window and we kissed them all.

We can start again, she said. Now that all that war is past, we can start again, make a new beginning, start afresh.

Barbara settled my granny while Grandad put his suitcase on the overhead rack.

We've a lot to look forward to, my mother said, as Barbara lowered the window and they touched hands, Barbara and her holding each other as the train moved away.

We're very, very lucky, Mum said, tears running down her face, Barbara waving a white handkerchief as we watched the red light on the guard's van fade.

We walked home in silence, my mother sobbing.

I suppose you'll want toast and cocoa, she said.

That night I watched the sky, knowing my father, wherever he was, could see the same stars, wondering if he was looking, if these were the stars they'd see in Glasgow and Oban and when a train lit the sky waiting to see if it stopped at Kettle station. I jumped into bed when I heard Mum's step on the stair.

Two days later after a heavy bout of rain, I was standing in the porch with the tricycle. It's no use, she said. We've missed the train. It's been and gone. There'll've been no one on it, so we'll have to wait till tomorrow.

I watched a soldier walk down Bankton Park. He seemed in no hurry, sauntering through the rain, looking round him. Stopping at the turn-off to the Paul farm, he took off his forage cap and lifted his face to the sky, turning round, letting his face get wet.

He seemed soaked through when he reached the door. He smiled and put out his hand.

Carl?

I nodded.

Give your mum a shout, there's a good lad.

She screamed. Charlie. Oh my God, Charlie.

And they hugged each other and danced in the mud.

With his braces hanging down, his shirt opened at the neck, sleeves rolled up and warming his feet by the fire, on his third or fourth cup of tea, he told us he came to see Babs. And where's Eva? he asked. And Willie? Any word of Bab's man? And what about your Archie?

He stayed two nights, long enough for a letter to reach Keppochhill Road to tell them he was on his way.

He was always sleeping when I left for school, but was waiting when I got out. He chased me up the road, played football outside the house, took me for walks down to the Eden and read me stories after tea. On the morning he left, we cleared the dead mice from the back door. And as the train pulled out he told me to remember to feed the cat.

Patch came running to the rattle of a saucer, expecting food before anyone was fed. He followed me wherever I went, lay across my books and played with my hair.

I suppose, as cats go, he's all right, my mother said, defenceless when mice and shrews, voles and birds were brought to the door. I made a graveyard beside the compost at the bottom of the garden and marked the graves with kindling crosses.

It was my job to light the sitting room fire every morning, to lay and twist the paper, place the sticks and coal. Patch would sit in the middle of the pile, unravelling the fire because he thought he'd find the string that hauled his twist of paper round the house, the one he kept by his box, carried in and dropped at your feet when he wanted to play. He could open doors and slept at the bottom of my bed. He followed me down the garden when I got a row or didn't get my own way and said I was going to find my daddy, to live somewhere else, Glasgow or Oban, he followed me down the garden and sat in front of me, purring.

His favourite game was to be hauled around in a shoebox. He would get off, wait for the box, jump in, get hauled round again, always from the front room to the kitchen, round and back, forever in a perpetual railway.

She sometimes said, We'll take a look. We might as well go down to the station and see.

We went to Glasgow for New Year. They all were home, except my father and Uncle Matt, a house full of people I didn't know.

My Uncle Willie was working in the Grosvenor. He was always breathless when he climbed the stairs.

How's that chest of yours, Willie?

What kind of question is that to ask a man? God, Marie, you're getting very forward. If I was to ask you how your chest was, you'd have something to say about it.

She went down to meet him after work and I was usually asleep by the time she got back.

Eva was going to England to meet up with Matt and she promised to come to Kettle. Barbara said she'd come through on holiday.

I'll never see that place again, my granny said.

Jesus Christ, Willie said, you cannae even see this place.

* * *

Cattul, Miss Barclay said. Cattul is a Celtic word which means the Battle of the Stream. Now sit up straight and pay attention. Is everybody listening? Good. How do you think the word Cattul became Kettle? Can anyone guess?

Outside a gull rose, circled and landed in more or less the same position.

Please, miss.

Yes, Ann.

Please, miss. They sound the same.

That's right. They do sound the same, but there's a story. Does anyone want to hear the story?

I waited for the gull to rise, but it turned its head and sniffed the air.

Miss Barclay had a thick, blue book, her finger marking the page. She had placed the Bible tract she used as a bookmark, a bouquet of flowers with

For God So Loved the World written in gold, at the top of her desk beside Jonathan's photograph.

Is everyone paying attention? Good. Now, who can tell me where Falkland is?

Please, miss. It's down the road.

That's right. Now who can tell me what's there?

Please, miss. My granny lives there.

And what else is in Falkland, apart from Alice Ferguson's granny's house? Does no one know? I can't believe no one knows what's in Falkland.

Please, miss. There's Falkland Palace.

And who died there? Come along, someone else. We heard last week, didn't we. King James v of Scotland died there; and what did he say? What prophecy did he foretell on his deathbed? That's right, one or two of us remember. He said, It cam wi' a lass and it'll gang wi' a lass. And who was he referring to? That's right, his infant daughter, Mary, Queen of Scots, who was born in Linlithgow Palace.

The gull had gone.

The book hit the desk. The next person I see staring out the window will not hear this story. They will be made to stand. Now, I don't want to do this, but if it happens you have been warned and have only yourself to blame. So, eyes front everybody. Sit up straight and pay attention.

The first three primary classes were taught together. We sat in rows, youngest at the front. Folk were fidgeting, which meant I could only hear snatches of Miss Barclay's voice and could barely see her lips move.

I know it's almost three o'clock, but as we are made to mention every week, even though it's Friday, school does not finish until the bell goes. Now, where were we?

Please, miss. Mary, Queen of Scots.

And where was she imprisoned?

Loch Leven.

Correct. You will remember from last week, we told you how Falkland was the hunting lodge for the Stewart kings, how they came from Edinburgh with their lion rampant flag and the real lion in a cage to show they were monarchs. They came to Falkland to hunt in the forest that surrounded the palace, hunted stags and wild boar which were roasted on the huge spits above the fire in the Great Hall, where they drank claret, which was the most popular drink in Scotland, imported from France, of course. This was where minstrels played during the meal, where jesters entertained the court and where ladies and gentlemen played Real Tennis in the ancient courts which have been preserved in the palace grounds. This was where the great scholars and poets came. Sir

David Lyndsay's play was performed in Cupar and he and other poets argued with each other in verse and where the royal parrot Papyngo was a greatly celebrated bird. Now, who can tell me what happened to the forest?

Please, miss—

That's right, it was cut down to build the Great Michael, the finest craft of its kind in Europe, by which we may take it, they meant the finest in the world, for while Scotland was a kingdom which traded with Holland and the Low Countries which was the centre of European culture, the rest of the world was uncivilised, populated by? That's right. Heathens.

Chalk dust danced around her. When she moved, dust followed, landing on her hair and spectacles, shifting when she breathed.

This book is called *Historical Antiquities of Fife* and we know what Antiquities means because we told you last week and we also said that a great Scottish novelist, Sir Walter Scott, wrote a book called, *The Antiquary*, which is about someone who is interested in Antiquities. Good. Everybody listening?

She held the book in front of her face and started reading:

One of the Kings, hunting in the myres of Kettle, came upon a spring of pure water bubbling up. The King alighted from his horse, and admiring the drink of the spring, his fancy struck with the resemblance which it had to a boiling pot, and indulging himself in an innocent pun on the name Cattul, dubbed it the King's Kettle.

The janitor walked past the window with the bell.

Now, there are, I think, three words in that passage, with which you may be unfamiliar. They are myres, alighted and pun. I won't ask, because I am sure they will be unknown to you. We will discuss them next week, when we will tell another story of the role Fife played in the history of Scotland. Ready, class. Altogether now.

We stood, closed our eyes and placed our hands below our chins.

Fingers straight, please. No clasping of fingers. Altogether, after me: Thank you for the world so sweet. Thank you for the food we eat. Thank you for the birds that sing. Thank you, Lord, for everything. Now I will pray on your behalf: Again, Lord God, we thank you for another week at school, for guiding us safely through our lessons, for our teacher Miss Barclay, for our headmaster, our staff and all the happy pupils here at Kettle School. We thank you for bringing our soldiers, seamen and airmen safely home to their loved ones and destroying the Heathen. We thank you for our King and Queen and the two Princesses, for their Government and especially for Mister Churchill, for the Church of Scotland, our ministers, elders and congregations, for our

Sunday Schools and our happy homes. This prayer we ask in Christ's name and for His sake we ask it. Amen.

And, the bell rang.

Right now, class. Primary Ones to the left, Primary Twos to the right and the bigger ones at the back in straight lines all of us marching: left, right, left, right, marching together in orderly fashion.

* * *

Facing the house was a small bower, built into a pointed arch with latticed sides and roof, a small seat, clematis and wisteria. Behind the bower was a field of oats.

I'd stand by the ditch and stare into the field, lost in the colour and the change of colour, the way the wind shaded the ears as it shaded the sea. In summer the oat field was brindled with poppies. There was a hefty stone dyke and a string of barbed wire at the top of the embankment. A ditch defined the end of the field, which was edged with dog roses, creamy white and pink and gold.

There were sometimes specks I could blow away. The leaves were dusted from the road, which was more of a track with grass in the middle and a sheuch at the side where rainwater gathered and ran to the stank in the Jamieson's farm at the bottom of the road.

After rain, when the air was veiled and chill, these leaves became seven-masted boats sailing down to where the corn dhows would race and overtake them, tumbling the rapids.

The Jamieson farm was bigger than the Paul place, with a field at the bottom, a tractor and a trailer. A car sometimes came and went, stirring the dust, and men walked up the road at night, some time around the back of five. They coughed, I thought, because their throats were dry from the fields and the dust on the road. They spoke in whispers.

Apart from a car or the wheeze of a train, the noise from the farm and a voice on the radio, sometimes a dog barked or a cock crowed, a horse's whinny or the moan of a cow crossed the fields.

I strained to hear the noises of the trains and could tell the difference between a small local service, a heavy express and a goods train.

When the field was empty I stood on the dyke and stared past the Jamieson farm, watching. You could see them more easily from the edge of the garden or the kitchen window, but here you could see further. You could run to the station in time to see the train pass, or better still, stand below the tunnel, eyes closed and feel the rumble.

Hurry, my mother said dragging my tricycle through the door. Hurry, we'll be late.

It was cold and raining. First the kitbag, then a man in a white sailor's hat and a dark sailor's suit. He stood at the end of the platform while the train creaked past. My mother screamed and ran towards him. I stood still. I did not know this man.

Let me see you; for God's sake, boyan, let me look at you. And he threw me in the air. My mother screamed, but he caught me as I fell and laughed.

In the house, he dumped his bag at the door. Where's the kitchen? he asked, ducking his head as he came through the door.

A *piseag*, he said. What's its name?

He laughed and lifted the cat. For God's sake, Marie, make us a cup of tea, he said, stroking the cat below the chin. Patch raised his head, rolled back and closed his eyes.

SEVEN

Rest and Be Thankful

THE BUS SMELLED of diesel. The small lights along the ceiling burned orange in the daylight and luggage creaked round every corner.

The man in front smoked Sweet Afton. He'd changed seats with my dad and though we were midway down the bus, a streel of hot air drifted through the chromium circle of mesh and plate behind the driver and smoke mingled with the stench of unwashed bodies.

I held the tickets tightly, counting the daffodils and primroses by the side of the road.

My face was pale and broken by trickling lanes of condensation on the window. My hands and forehead were damp. The heater looked forbidding, like the mouth of an angel in *A Handbook of the Stars*. The woman in front had a greasy line along her collar. Her hair was black. I closed my eyes, hoping to sleep.

We stopped at the head of the Rest and Be Thankful.

Fifteen minutes, the conductor said.

By now I was dizzy and my throat felt dry. I stood by the door, where the wind smelled of peat and water. My cheeks were tepid. There was a rush in my stomach. I closed my eyes as small lights jigged behind my eyelids. I could not swallow and just when I was about to faint, when the pain in my head and the surge in my stomach were too much to bear, my belly heaved as if to turn inside out. I opened my eyes and saw the roadside, my father's hand on his head. I slammed my eyes to the retching, the relief and splash on my black leather shoes, drying almost immediately to an insipid, creamy white. A sudden ache capped the top of my head. Dizziness came in waves, with a flash of black against my eyelids every time, black that became red as I braced myself for another rush that tasted of bacon fat and acid.

Someone asked, Is the wee boy sick?

I retched again and leaned my head on the side of the bus, smelling the tyres and the Johnson's powder from my father's face. I felt clammy and dizzy with sweat in my hair. The back of my tongue and my throat felt swollen as though breath would come with another retch, which would contract my stomach and stretch the pain beyond my head. There was only the taste of the fat and grease, mingled with the acid that sharpened my teeth. I crunched them together to feel the gnaw, trying to take air into my stomach. I longed for something sweet, for another taste I knew would make me dizzier.

I raised my head and thought I would faint, cuddling into my father's stomach. Is that better or worse? he asked, wiping my mouth. He kissed my brow. You'll be right as rain in a minute.

Across the road was a bow tent. Canvas sacks and tarpaulins covered branches or sapling trunks, bent and held to the ground with stones. A man, with white moustache and flowing hair, a Glengarry bonnet, kilt jacket with silver buttons and trews, a worn set of pipes on his shoulder, marched the length of the bus and back on the other side of the road, playing while his wife lilted the tune.

She took water from a riffle in the burn, let it run over a black can with a wire handle, put the can on the fire and, while her man was playing, took the bonnet from his head and went round the passengers. There's tea in a minute, she said.

My father put sixpence in the cap. Does he know 'The Glendaruel Highlanders'? he asked.

Ha-da-ree-dum-drah, Hi-the-ree-a-dum-a-drah, she sang, and the piper took up the tune, turning downhill towards Ben Vane.

She took money from the cap and put it in her apron, came back along the line and faced my father, smiling. The piping stopped. Five minutes, the conductor shouted.

The woman's hands were filthy, her nails cracked and torn; dirt ran through her skin. She unclenched her fist and held the sixpence in front of my father.

Take it, she said. You have a lovely child, but he's been smitten and so have you. He'll know nothing but misery, sadness and loss. I can see it in him. His children will be grown before it lifts, if ever it lifts.

He doesn't travel well on buses, my father said. He's just been sick.

She touched my hair, ran her hands across my head, then placed them on the crown. He'll be fine, she said. If he has a sip of tea, he'll sleep.

Her eyes were warm, like my father's, brown and limpid; when she smiled, her face was as lined as her hands. Her hair had been stretched to the back of her neck and gathered in a bun. She wore a crossover apron, a black skirt and jumper. She smelled of woodsmoke and grease.

Across the road, she took a packet of tea from her apron pocket and poured a puckle of leaves in the boiling water, took the can from the fire and washed a cup in the burn. She poured the black tea into the cup. There, she said. Drink as much as you can. You'll be fine enough.

I slept all the way to Oban. When I got to my grandparents' house in Miller Road, they put me to bed and I slept till morning.

* * *

Being in Oban was being home. My father seemed to know everyone and they all knew him. There was always somewhere to go and someone to see and we wandered the town, from Miller Road to Ganavan, up Glencruitten Drive and down to the harbour, where the fishing boats were moored and women in heavy clothes, carrying cardboard boxes, their dogs on a string, came sideways down the island ferry gangways, while men leaned on the railings and stared at the town.

Well, Haddie, you're back. And this is your boy, they'd say. He got the nickname watching shinty.

They confused me by asking when we were coming home and how long we'd be in Oban this time.

We'd better not stay, my father said. The tinkers at the Rest told us we were cursed, me and him together.

Och, that's that then. You'd better away now.

And we left by train. Uncle Ronald worked on the railway and got us privilege tickets. He saw us to the station and stood with my dad, talking till the train moved away.

Good, he said. That's it fixed. Ronald'll see to it. We'll soon be home.

Do you mean here or Kettle?

First the one and then the other.

He laughed as he gave me a couple of comics and opened the paper.

More trouble, he said. Still, this is better than the bus, wouldn't you say?

Later, when we went by train for every journey, he'd stand in the corridor from Connell Ferry, humming to himself and smiling. I'd hold the wooden rail that ran along the window, trying to see what he saw. Joey'll be at the window, he'd say when we came into the hill of the edge of Glen Cruiten. She knows we're coming. Look out and see if you can see her waving.

And he'd hold me out the window waving a handkerchief trying to find Aunt Joey's window. When the train wound into Oban Station there was usually someone waiting.

You are how? my grandfather asked.

EIGHT
Ivanhoe

THE HOUSE WAS crowded.

Granny was through from Glasgow, asking folk where they were and what they were doing. She sat on the bench by the kitchen door with her face turned to the sun: Marie, she'd ask, are you sure that war's over?

God Almighty, Mother, how many times have I got to tell you.

Then why are there planes? There never were planes afore the war.

Of course there were planes, it's just you could never hear them in the city.

If I heard everything else, how could in the name of Christ I no hear an airyplane?

People stayed a night or two and moved on. I liked it when the men came back with a couple of bottles of beer, sat with their stocking feet against the fire and sang.

And if someone was through from Glasgow I could stay up later than usual, for when my father came home a new regime was established.

Half seven at the latest and lights out at eight, he said. Your mum and I need some time together. We need to catch up.

Tea was ready for half past six. He was home around ten past, washed and changed and stood at the kitchen sink scrubbing the little rivulets of oil and grease from his fingers, looking into the garden and the railway line beyond. When a train passed, he looked at the clock and often made predictions.

She won't be in Kirkcaldy for seven, not at that rate.

It's never too early to think about the future, Miss Barclay said. I would like you to bring your father's occupations to school. Find out as much as you can, come to class and tell us.

I'm a railwayman, my father said. Right now I'm working in the engine repair shop, helping to fix things. That's a bit complicated, so tell her I do the most important job there is, I help maintain the permanent way, the tracks and the sleepers, the bolts and the gravel filling between the sleepers. I help maintain the signals and the signal box. It is my responsibility to see the train has a smooth, efficient track to run along and if we do our job properly no one ever thinks of us or what we do.

My, my, Miss Barclay said. That's remarkable, a background job.

It is anything but background, my father said. She only thinks it's background because she hasn't seen it or maybe even thought about it. It sounds as if she got on a train and thought nothing more about it, except how long it would be before she reached wherever she was going.

This was after tea, when he asked about school. We ate together and I had to clear my plate.

Eat it up, every last drop. And you're in your own bed tonight. I don't want you coming in beside us, wakening everybody up, including the cat.

He got a fright. I think it was the wind.

He needs his rest and so do we. And there's no use crying. It hasn't happened yet.

I'd heard them talk. I was all they ever argued about. His voice became insistent, rising above my mother to end the discussion.

I don't want you hitting him. He's never been hit and I don't want you to start now.

Maybe if he had been walloped he wouldn't be so soft. He needs to toughen up. He's been spoiled, crying over everything.

When he said I'd been spoiled, I was sure he meant I was damaged and could never be restored, that I could never be what he wanted me to be.

And more than anything, I wanted to please him. The trip to Oban had shown me things I could never have known, that maybe even my mother didn't know. He was different in Oban, lighter. His stride changed. His steps seemed longer. The slow pace of Kettle had gone and there were times I had to run to keep up with him. He was more relaxed, laughed more easily, sang all the time, seemed gentler, more content.

It was in his voice. When he spoke Gaelic, his voice softened. He and my Uncle Michael almost spoke in whispers and when there were three or four of them together, their voices seldom rose above the women's voices, which often seemed shrill.

Did you like Oban? he asked on the train going back.

I nodded and snuggled into his brown suit.

Aye, and we'll soon be back there, your mum, you and me, the three of us; back home.

* * *

The snows were so thick the sledge my father had made in the railway workshops, which I'd got at Christmas, was used on my birthday. Every day the radio said snow in the north and floods in the south. Flocks of sheep were lost in the drifts. Easter Day was freezing.

Fruit and vegetables came into season then disappeared; my mother sold most of her strawberry crop, and there seemed to be continual appeals for clothes, crockery and used paper. In Kettle School we were taught to knit and sew, shown how to darn a hole in the heel of a sock and mend a torn garment.

I was aware that a sense of peace arrived with my father. The restlessness, sudden shouts and warnings had gone, there were no more struggles with furniture and movement, no visits from strangers. Patch settled in front of the fire or on my daddy's lap and, apart from the wireless, the only fresh, often unpredictable sound was my father singing.

He was away in the morning before I got up and came home tired, often falling asleep in front of the fire, suddenly waking and going out to stand in the garden or maybe walk round the village on his own.

What's up? she'd ask. Is it back?

If he answered it was a shrug or a shiver.

This was when I was unsure of his moods. I never doubted he loved me or my mother, never doubted he wanted to be with us or that we would move to Oban, but sometimes when he wakened suddenly he seemed lost in the dream and looked as if he did not recognise me.

Is my daddy all right? I asked when he wasn't there.

Shush, my mother said.

She was standing at the sink, dreamy and staring into the garden. She waved her arm into the air and soap bubbles scattered around her.

Shush. Whatever made you say that?

I don't know.

You must know where it came from.

I sometimes think he doesn't know who I am.

Of course he knows who you are. He carried your picture. All through the war he had our pictures, yours and mine with him all the time. They never left his side.

She wiped her hands on a dishtowel and moved the kettle onto the hotplate, took me over to the table, sat by the corner and stood me in front of her.

Your daddy saw terrible things in the war, she said. They all did, every one of them, some more than others. And the sea's bad enough, but when you're on minesweepers, picking up weapons often in a storm, mines that were left in the sea to blow you up, it's more dangerous than you can imagine. Then he was torpedoed. The boats he was on were hit by enemy torpedoes.

Were they German?

Of course, but the Germans we were fighting were the enemy.

Were there different Germans?

The ones who were here, like your grandad, they weren't the enemy. The enemies were Hitler's people, Nazis. Your daddy was torpedoed three times and twice was the only survivor. I don't know how because he never says, but it sometimes affects him, I know that and I also know we are very lucky to have him back home with us, safe and sound. We're lucky, very lucky indeed.

He could have died.

And he must have lived with that every day, him and the others, so it's not surprising he has these awful turns. If it's bad for us, think what it must be like for him. But he's still your daddy and he's still the same man everybody loves. Now, since we're like this, nice and cosy, let me ask you a question.

She paused, looked at me and smiled, then drew me in to her. I loved it when we were like this, alone and secretive, the way it was before.

How would you feel about a wee brother or sister?

I don't know.

I think a wee girl would be nice. Your daddy's none too certain, though things'll change when we get to Oban.

It was said so casually as if it was insignificant, dropped into a conversation before a glass of milk with toast and jam and never referred to again.

Did I show you this? she said, as if they were treasures.

We went on a tour of the houseplants, the gaudy red geraniums on the table by the window, the pilea with leaves like wee saucers, the bulbs at the back of the cupboard and the carrot that grew in water.

Plants arrived when her family left. While they were here she grew strawberries, peas, beans and tatties. There were raspberries, redcurrants, London Pride and heather by the back door. The geraniums and presumably the carrot had been moved inside by the time we found my father at the end of the train.

* * *

Days stretched between school and tea. I remember my days suddenly being filled and rather than being on my own, left to wander round the garden, my head elsewhere, after school we took the Pauls' dog Sandy down to the Eden bank, or we wandered through the fields and across the village, looking at each other's houses, watching the cars and lorries pass along the top road or waiting to see who came off the train.

They sometimes asked whatever happened to the dog Willie called Nemo. I said he couldn't stay because of my granny.

Your mother will have taken him to the vet in Cupar.

She never said.

She might have thought it would upset you.

And we stood in the field unsure of how to proceed.

You could maybe ask, someone said.

And I knew I never would. Nemo was gone when I came home from hospital. It was better to keep Willie's dream than to find my mother searching for a suitable explanation.

Our school classrooms opened onto a hall, which was also the gym and dining hall. We stayed indoors when it rained and I loved the sudden burst of energy that came with the janitor's bell, running home, jumping over puddles and crashing into the house, breathless.

I didn't expect my father to be home. He was sleeping by the fire when I ran through the room. He wakened suddenly, shouted and lashed out. His hand connected with the back of my head and I fell against the table leg. He was white and trembling.

She ran to him, put her arms round him and held him.

I screamed louder.

He put his arm round her.

Shush, she said.

He sat back on the chair and she came to me, lifted and held me, wiping my face with her apron. He was staring at the fire. He turned and smiled, touched my face and kissed me.

I'm sorry, he said. I didn't mean to hit you.

So I set about toughening up. I didn't know how, but thought it had to do with endurance, like the heroes in stories. When I read how they had struggled across deserts, climbed mountains, fought rebels and trudged through ice and snow, I was sure I could be braver.

I sat in the coal shed watching rain run down the brick wall, listening to the drum against the roof, shivering. I took off my pullover to feel colder; and when my head hurt and my teeth rattled, when I could no longer feel my legs when I nipped the skin, I ran into the kitchen. Next day I had a cold.

Miss Barclay was off and Miss Beveridge replaced her. She asked if I had a cold. I nodded. Hot milk and treacle and an early bed, she said.

When's he going back? I asked.

He isn't going back. He's home now.

I want him to go back.

I was standing on the stone kitchen floor hopping from one leg to another.

Why do you think it would be a good idea for your daddy to go back to war and risk getting killed rather than stay here with us? See if you can tell me.

I don't know.

Maybe you could think about it and let me know what you come up with.

Something was wrong and I was part of it. It was there when I wakened and was waiting at the end of the road. It walked me to school and spoiled my sleep. Things had changed. My mother was happier. I became convinced I was in the way. Their life would be better if I wasn't around.

I knew I had nowhere else to go, but I longed for other places. There were gangsters in Chicago and artists in Paris, earthquakes in San Francisco and fires in London.

I made a list of the places I'd been, Fortingall, Glasgow, Kingskettle and Oban, and asked my Uncle Charlie.

Holland, Belgium, Germany, France, England, Wales, he said.

Willie's list was more or less the same, Except Wales, he said. They wouldnae let me intae Wales. I was too big for them.

Aunt Margaret had been to the Canary Islands and England, my mother and Eva had been to England and Barbara said, Nowhere.

My father smiled: Never thought about it, but not as many as Matt, he said. He's been more places than anyone, except maybe your grandad.

Matt said there were buildings in New York that went up to the sky, sometimes so tall they blocked out the light. He sat with the encyclopaedia and showed me photographs, told me about the Niagara Falls, which were near where he lived. He told me about Mounties and the Rocky Mountains, cowboys and horses, Red Indian totem poles, wigwams and reservations.

My granny sang in Gaelic and when I asked to learn the songs, she told me not to bother, that I'd be better off learning songs that were useful. Then she would cry and talk about the First World War when my grandfather was interned and she was working in the Royal Infirmary.

A man came in and his brains were hanging out, she told me. He'd been through the Somme, got wounded and shipped back to have his leg amputated. They used to let the limpers out for a walk and he was crossing the road when he slipped and fell in front of a lorry. He was still alive, still breathing and screaming with a hole in his head.

And when Carrie died she couldn't breathe. She'd cough up lumps of blood and needed washed down and there was nothing to her so she had no energy and died.

Parts of me didn't connect. I did not know enough and no one would tell me. I needed more information and when I asked, I was told to be quiet. When I asked about the past they changed the subject. When I asked about Germany my grandfather told me he was tired. Uncle Matt told me about Canada but nothing about his family.

I couldn't connect the place talked about with the relations we didn't see, folk who were away, uncles and aunts, older cousins who were never mentioned or discussed in whispers. I'd heard about family feuds, bits of the same thing that were disconnected and thought I understood what it was before knowing the word.

I was in the way. If they told me anything, it was a mistake; so I knew I wasn't wanted, but was stuck. I'd need to wait till I was older before I could do something about it and maybe by then things would change.

Your mum tells me you're good at school, my daddy said. That's great if you are. You should stick in. We had to work the minute we were able, as soon as we could write our name and count our pay. But, if you're able and God spares us, we'll make sure it's different for you.

We'd walk round the village. Long days of rain brightened in the evening and my father needed to be out. After tea, we'd go together and he'd talk about Oban, where we'd stay and what we'd do, shinty matches and football at Mossfield. He'd ask what I'd learned at school, what I'd done and he'd try bits of Gaelic on me, sometimes singing.

And every night while the wireless mumbled, I lay in front of the fire, hot down one side, cold down the other, with the *Adventure Annual for Boys* or the *Boys' Book of Heroes*, reading again my favourite stories, David Livingstone and Christopher Columbus, Scott of the Antarctic.

My favourite book had been *Minsey Winsey Mouse: His First Christmas*. I knew the story by heart and could identify some of the words on the page before I went to school. After a week, Miss Barclay told me to play with plasticine because I could read.

Not everyone has been as fortunate as you, she said. Not everyone has had your advantages. So you can amuse yourself while the others learn.

Why don't you let him read? my mother asked.

Thank you for your advice, but I believe what goes on in my class is a matter for me alone.

This was when we met in Cupar. My mother, father and I had been at the putting green. We were walking up to the train when we met Miss Barclay.

I want a word with her, my mother said.

You're surely not stopping him reading? my father asked.

Excuse me, she said. I have a previous appointment.

On the Monday, Miss Barclay gave me a copy of *Ivanhoe* by Sir Walter Scott.

There you are, Carl, she said. You can read while the others are learning.

I told my mother and that night after tea I heard her and my father whispering in the kitchen.

Don't worry, she said. I'll have a word with the bitch.

Next morning I was slightly ashamed to see her waving as she walked across the playground. The class went quiet when she knocked the door.

I was on my way to see the principal teacher, Miss Barclay, but thought it best to have a word with you first, if you can spare a moment, that is?

Very quickly then.

I am right in thinking you gave a child in your class *Ivanhoe* to read?

Silence.

That is correct, isn't it?

Silence.

He isn't lying is he? Please answer me Miss Barclay, and I would also be obliged if you would look at me while I am speaking to you. I do understand you are far more capable of assessing what goes on in your classroom than the likes of me, and given that is the case, how would you assess the competence of a teacher who asked a six-year-old child to read a novel that was surely meant for adults?

How dare you speak to me this way.

I am sorry you don't feel able to discuss this, but I will refer the matter to the principal teacher and hopefully he will have something to say.

Three days later I was given a letter Miss Barclay told me was addressed to my mother. She read the page and handed it to my father. He read it, threw it in the fire and laughed.

Silly bitch, Mum said.

You can take your own books to school for reading time, said Dad.

Heroes aren't always found in books, Miss Barclay said. Her brother Michael was a hero. He'd been killed in the First World War, along with her fiancé, Jonathan Strachan. She carried their pictures in a heart-shaped gold locket that hung round her neck.

Jonathan's photograph was in a leather frame on her desk. He had blond wavy hair and sharp eyes, a straight nose and what could have been a weak chin.

He was a Christian and a patriot, a hero who died for his country. And children this is very important, she said, we must never forget that heroes are often ordinary men, and women too, people who do extraordinary things, things they would never normally do; people who are called to make sacrifices they would never consider making and do so willingly, without flinching or cowardly denial, because they are asked. Perhaps the bravest heroes of all are those whose names are found on war memorials, those who make the supreme sacrifice so that we may live in freedom, and because of their sacrifice, we too are called to make sacrifices and do so willingly, led by their example. They did not cry or fear the pain.

Michael fell at the Somme. She told us of the battle and the charges, drew maps, read Rupert Brooke, told the story of the Flanders Poppy and the Angel of Mons. Earl Haig was a hero, she said. Jonathan was gassed and wounded at Passchendaele. He died two years later.

I told her Granny's story about the one legged man and she sighed.

Really, she said.

NINE

The Bait Gatherers

LOOKING OUT A railway carriage, the wind in my face, being dragged up Glen Ogle, with handfuls of white smoke and steam behind us; or being held close while I threw a penny then two ha'pennies into the Forth; playing snap with my father while we drank tea, my hands and face blue from picking brambles, his hand covering mine when I shouted.

This was after we'd sat on Ganavan beach, when my mother poured tea from a flask and milk from a sauce bottle with a screw of paper on the top and both sides of the tea and sugar container my father took to work were filled with sugar. We had red and yellow plastic beakers filled with tea: Watch, my mother said, it's hot. Well-fired rolls with butter and tomato, custard cream biscuits and home-made currant cake were spread on a tea towel with sand on the edges.

I was wearing woollen swimming trunks and my father dried my back, having thrown me into the sea. We were swimming, his hand beneath my chin, then he held me and turned me round in the air, so I dived from his arms into the sea.

Another time, we went to Dundee. Wallace Paul took our tickets at the barrier at the top of the stairs. We had lunch in Draffen's department store, where my mother bought me a pair of grey top hose with blue bands on top, then we searched for crockery. We got some plain tea plates then ran downhill to catch the train for Perth, where my father and I walked around while my mother looked for more crockery and my father met a man who worked on the railway. They talked outside Cairncross the Jewellers in St John Street. I looked at the necklaces, rings and brooches made from Tay and other freshwater pearls.

You can sometimes see them from the train, he told me. They fish the river in flat-bottomed boats between here and Dundee, looking for mussels on the riverbed, picking them up with hazel twigs. Did you see men hanging over the side of the boats when we passed?

I wanted to please him in his brown suit and trilby, so I nodded, though I could not remember what I saw on the river.

They hang over the side with a long funnel with glass at the end that lets them see to the bottom of the river. And they've to be careful, for the Tay can be muddy and they might raise the silt.

Then there was Edinburgh. The carriage from Thornton Junction was crowded. Look at that, Marie, he said. All these posters are for places where the train doesn't go. Loch Ness, the Cuilins, Glencoe.

Walking up the Waverley Steps, to Princes Street, the Gardens, Mound and Castle. I could not imagine anyone living there.

You'll need to see the Castle. And then go down to Holyrood House. We'll come back when there's more time.

It was raining, late afternoon, the streets were shiny and the pavements sparkled. I imagined all of Edinburgh was lit like Princes Street, that anyone could walk in off the street and take what they wanted from the warm and friendly shops.

We sat in a tearoom. I drank milk and ate a scone with butter and jam. People pushed umbrellas before them as they ran along Princes Street and tramcars passed with misty windows. My father read the paper while my mother talked with a woman at an adjacent table.

It was difficult, she said, trailing him around the shops. He's very good, but loses attention. He gets bored quickly, especially when it's wet.

Weather makes such a difference.

We're going to take him to the National Gallery.

At least it's dry.

Some paintings were too big, with awkward subjects, people dressed in robes and costumes, standing in a way I could not understand. Neither could I see them properly.

I closed my eyes as we passed, especially when the baby Jesus was being fed from an exposed breast. I had walked into a room where a woman was feeding a baby. She screamed when she saw me and covered her chest. The baby cried. My mother shooed me out of the room; so I knew I should not look at breasts and saw them only going into a gallery, or turning to leave at the end.

In the chilly atmosphere and wet clothes, suspended between my parents' hands, I stared at *The Murder of David Rizzio* where my mother told me the story of jealousy at court. On a green leather seat, I stretched my legs, extended my toes, and looked at *The Bait Gatherers* by William MacTaggart; two boys and a girl gathering mussels in wicker baskets. My father smiled. I'll need to tell the bodach he's in a painting, he said.

The boy looks like Carl.

Do you fancy a Glengarry bonnet like that?

In the next gallery I shouted, Oban.

Tell the child to be quiet please, said the attendant. Everyone else was smiling, including my father. Alone on a wall was a dark rectangle.

Who would believe it? he said. The painting was of the sea front at Oban, with the High Free Kirk to the right of centre. We'll need to tell the bodach right enough. First it's him and then it's his kirk. He'll be all over Edinburgh next.

Has he been to Edinburgh?

Damn the fear of it.

We stayed in Glasgow. Again there was a search for crockery, warnings of gales and snow, paper shortage and a gift of bananas. My father and grandmother spoke Gaelic while my grandfather read the paper, then we played draughts.

If you do what your Uncle Willie told you there'll be trouble, my mother said.

That night after tea I went next door and asked Alec Irvine if he'd like to come in. We played draughts in front of the fire while Daddy, Uncle Charlie and Uncle Willie got ready to go out. I slept in the big feather bed in the small bedroom, reading *The Magic and Wonder Book for Boys and Girls*.

Smiling dolphins towed a raft of sailors out to sea, away from the island where palm trees swayed. An octopus gave the ship's biscuits to a penguin in a sailor's hat and the penguin helped the octopus throw the biscuits into the open mouths of the fish, who were dancing in a ring around a buoy.

Or we were away on a hill cottage in the Borders between Scotland and England, where Black Bob lived with Andrew Glenn, who worked as a shepherd on a large sheep farm. Season after season, year upon year, Bob kept watch, tending flocks on the wide hillside. He was a champion sheepdog, far above other dogs, a famous dog trial winner. Time after time he had saved his flocks from dangers, foxes, killer dogs, storms, fires, floods and blizzards. Bob and his master were the pride of the district, the talk of shepherds and country folk, and Bob was a great favourite with the children.

Then a man in a baggy red and yellow suit and matching bunnet hit the words on a screen with a long thin pointer in time to the tune. Chorus girls beside him raised their hands from their knees to their mouths, encouraging us to sing. The reflections from the stage lit my parents' faces.

We took four tramcars to get to the first house at six thirty. In the queue outside, a man with a twitch, dressed in a heavy overcoat and wellington boots held a framed, hand-coloured picture of himself as a boxer, tied round his neck with string. He thanked and blessed everyone who passed; the litany of fighters he had beaten obliterated by the singer who delivered his voice from the side of his mouth, his cap limp with a few coppers. By the door, women sold sheets of tablet and toffee boilings.

The doorman wore a faded maroon uniform. He had a cigarette cupped in his left hand: Stalls straight ahead, circle to the right and balcony up the stairs at the side, please. And have your money ready.

The theatre smelled warm and damp. In the foyer we collected the tickets and found our seats while the band played the opening chorus.

Then we stayed with Aunt Flora in her small whitewashed cottage at Balaclava Way. Her husband ran a ferry called the Plover from Ballachulish to Kinlochleven, the Electric City of the Highlands. Uncle Michael worked at Ganavan and Katie was at the putting green. On the way from the putting green to Ganavan, we passed the small cottage shaped like a threepenny bit where Mary Ann and Ellen lived, my father's cousins who were very old; I imagine they passed their days playing the piano to each other.

I ran round the beach or played endless games of putting. My father, still trying to teach me to swim, threw me into the water again; and just before sleep, I remembered my mother's scream as I went into the air, the sudden power of my father's arms as he caught me while my mother shouted my name. On the road back to Balaclava, we stopped at Mary Ann and Ellen's where I sat on a huge sofa in a dark and heavily furnished room.

The smell of sea ran round the town. Charlie Boyd worked on the ss *Columba*, sailing to Tobermory, past Staffa and parking outside Iona before sailing back. Coming up the Sound of Lorne, he looked across me and said to my father, That's us back in Oban, Archie. You couldn't miss the smell. And they laughed.

At the end of the summer a woman in black appeared at my Aunt Joey's gate in Glencruitten Drive, asking for a cigarette. Next night there was knocking; when Katie went to the door, no one was there.

Then Margaret heard crying in the rhododendrons. I'll never forget it, she said. It was terrible, an awful sound; I could have nightmares thinking of it yet. It was like a wail followed by loud, long, heavy sobbing.

Uncle Michael cut the rhododendrons. I remember him doing it but did not know why. There was talk of bad luck, but that was usual.

Iain and Richard Campbell and I played up the glen and my grandfather told us to get out of the burn. Stay away from the water, he shouted. I liked Iain and Richard, even though they were Campbells. My granny was a MacDonald.

I knew nothing of the significance. My father was hardly back in Kettle a week. Do you know what I fancy, Marie? he said coming home from a walk.

What's that?

A pint.

He went in the bar of the Station Hotel and caught up with us before we'd turned the corner along Bankton Park. That was quick, my mother said. Did you get your pint?

I couldn't drink in the place, he said. There's nobody there but a bloody Campbell.

The summer was warm. Patch rolled on a sunny rug, the doors were open and wasps battered the windowpanes. They rested on the glass, brought a leg over their head, took off, circled and battered the glass again.

My mother came in from the kitchen. Where were you? she asked.

Nowhere.

You must have been somewhere.

I've forgotten.

Well then, let's see if you can remember. Just sit there, that's the place, on the chair by the fire; sit there till you remember. And we'll switch off the wireless to see if that'll help.

The wireless was in a mahogany case, with a yellow dial, a green cursor and a small red light.

Oslo. Prague. Vienna. Athlone.

Can I have my atlas, please?

What for?

I want to look up the places on the wireless and see if I can find where Uncle Matt has been.

I think you should sit there till you mind where you've been.

She knew I'd been down by the Eden on my own. Her punishment for this and every other offence was to sit in a chair for anything up to an hour. I'd come whistling across the field as Peggy Morrison was getting ready to leave. My mother was baking more strawberry scones. Peggy's four were wrapped in newspaper.

She told my mother about prisoners of war who'd been marched through a village. Men were in uniform and village women with children at their hand lined the pavements as they passed. The man in front was carrying a framed, coloured picture with the string round his neck and I imagined he was holding it the way the boxer outside the theatre had shown his younger self. Peggy said he walked like a bird, flat feet, head bobbing, and as the troop passed a woman from the crowd stepped in front of the leader and spat on the picture, then stood her ground. They split ranks and marched round her, while other women cheered. The men ran onto the bus and shut the door while the women on the street dispersed. The man with the picture sat at the back, polishing the glass with the woman's spittle.

Peggy's stories seemed so complete, more than snatches of gossip. Even the smaller, almost incidental snatches left a trail. Willie Strachan was killed in Belgium. His mother ran into the street screaming his name. She ran round the village looking for him. Where are you? she shouted. What have I done, Willie? What have I done?

Dear God, my mother said. Dear God bless us all. If that's the same woman Peggy mentioned before, she's lost a man or a son. God love her. Our man came back safe, but for some folk the war'll never be over. Flora for one.

My Aunt Flora had lost a son, a cousin I never knew, lost on HMS *Coventry*.

A handful of flour, teaspoons of other stuff, salt and bicarbonate of soda, all in the bowl with milk which she tucked under her arm and stirred while she sang:

> Ho ro mo neun don voyach
> Ho ree mon neun don voyach
> Mo callach, leauth voyach
> Sa fos me a hu.

She sang it with my granny and my daddy knew it too. I'd sung it in school. Miss Barclay played the piano and had told me to sing the English words: We don't know any Gaelic here, do we class?

> In Glasgow or Dunedin,
> Were maidens fair to see,
> There's never a Lowland maiden
> Could lure my eyes from thee.

I stood beside Miss Barclay, turning the page while the class sang. I had stopped answering questions and had only mentioned the song because she asked if anyone knew the Gaelic words. When I leaned across, her breath smelled like vapour on the surface of a small, still pond.

These strawberries are fair coming on, my mother said, greasing the baking tray. How's your memory?

I might have been down at the Eden.

Well, maybe you should sit there for a wee while longer to see if you can mind if it was the Eden. You've been told about playing down there on your own and told about going near water. Were you at the station watching trains?

No.

You sure?

I never went to the station.

Well, you'll maybe mind where you were by the time your daddy comes in.
And how's school?

Fine.

How are you and Miss Barclay getting on?

Fine.

When my dad came home he hung his cap and haversack at the back of
the door, took off his boots and overalls and in his stocking soles, shirt and
trousers came into the kitchen, to the same conversation.

Did you get these sharny boots off?

What's for tea?

By now he was over by the range, his arm round her waist, trying to peer
into the pots, always naming what he saw: There's potatoes and cabbage and
stew. Fine. Maybe there's a scone or a pudding as well. And there you are
reading. *Ciamar a tha thu, a Carl?* No answer was the loud reply. Reading
and reading and always reading. *Cha mhisd thu siud.*

Mum told my father I'd repeated Peggy's story. God love her, he said. But
at least our lad wasn't down by the Eden where he's not supposed to go. I
wonder, Marie, do you think he was on his way to see the trains?

The Eden estuary was a sanctuary for gulls and waders. Puffins from the
Isle of May clustered with the ducks and dippers who wandered upstream,
where the riverbed was a mass of mud, stones and shells. The bank was
crowded with nibbled leaves and surface debris that clung to twigs and plants
that seemed to open in the afternoon, undulating willow moss that trembled
below water, trivial plants with tiny flowers and elegant leaves sprouting from
soil on the stones in the middle or edge of the river.

Water shifted over the mud and stones the way a moire pattern ripples over
fabric. The only movement was the lazy fish and eels who looked lost.

By the path on the shelf of a bank between the mud and the harder earth
on the edge of the field, I hauled a clod and dug a small chamber where I
buried my treasures, things I found and wanted to keep, but my mother would
never allow in the house.

I found what could have been an otter skull, too small for a dog, the wrong
shape for a cat, in the wash of stones by the bridge. There was a line down the
centre where the skull was joined and huge cavities high on either side of the
head for the eyes and ears with a small nose and long teeth on the upper jaw.
Duck and bird skulls were smaller. The bone was thinner, the design simpler;
huge holes for the eyes and ears, slits for the beak and nostrils and a concave
cradle for the brain. They had been picked and washed as clean as the bones
of the unknown creatures I buried with my shining stones, plaited grass and
flowers.

On our walks to Ladybank my mother picked clover heads and ate them wrapped in sorrel, she called soorocks. She picked wild flower stalks, reeds, rushes and sedge, then plaited them in a posy tied with blades of grass and hung them upside down in the kitchen to dry. Or she'd weave the stems of grass together, gather wild flowers and put them in a small blue vase by the kitchen window.

My granny broke the vase. I was looking for something, she said.

My mother replaced the vase with a white stone marmalade jar.

That new vase is nicer than the one that was here before, my granny said.

Do you like the look of it?

It's a lovely shade. I can't see it right because the light's on it, but I think it's better. That other one never was right. It didnae belong here and never brought any luck.

I didn't know they were coming and heard them before I saw them.

Where is he, Marie? Where's that boy? He should be home by now. Something happened to him.

Oh shush, Mother, for God sake.

Is that him? Let me see him. Come you here to me and tell me what happened to that cat. Is it still here? Cats are never lucky. They run around the floor and people trip over them.

Don't you start on him. I told you we haven't seen Patch for a while.

The cat was sitting on my grandad's lap.

There's a bloody cat in here. I know there is and as if that's no bad enough, there's a rabbit here now. What the hell are you doing bringing a live rabbit into the house. It should be deid and in the pot.

For a while a fat grey rabbit with a hutch and straw was over by the potting shed. My mother called her Molly and I loved the way her nose wrinkled, how she dribbled down the carrots, swede and lettuce leaves I poked through the grass.

Then Aunt Barbara was incredulous. You didn't, Marie. For God's sake, don't tell me you put them together. How could you be so stupid?

Cats and rabbits sometimes get on.

My grandfather wouldn't let me into the sitting room, but took me down the garden to see the rhubarb and maybe find a strawberry or two.

Where's Molly?

Molly's fine. She's sleeping.

Later I was told she must have escaped. I saw blood on the carpet and watched while my mother tried to scrub it clean. The hutch door was left open or someone took her, somebody stole the rabbit, she said. I hope they'll take it in, for it'll never last this weather.

Who in the name of Christ would steal a bloody rabbit that does nothing but eat lettuce and trip folk up, my granny said.

My father was an early riser, out the door often before my mother was awake. He was neat, a tidy man who folded his trousers and hung them over the back of a chair, sometimes rolled his socks and put them in his shoes, hung up his shirt and rolled his ties, folded his handkerchiefs into the corner of his drawer. His shoes were always polished.

Every weekend he was first up, rattling my door when he took a cup of tea to my mother, telling me he was ready to go. And we'd walk round the village, usually to see the signalman, who was a Gaelic speaker, while I stood on the station platform looking down the straight line of track, the smell of wood and tobacco in the station master's office, the cheery fire and yellow gas light, the huge mugs with strong, sweet tea; the sense of discovery, messages from other stations, parcels, mail sacks.

Coming back from the station, my hand wrapped round one of his long, elegant fingers, he was singing 'Galway Bay'.

And I was reading by the fire when he crossed the room going into the kitchen when Delia Murphy came on the radio.

Ah, he said, his left arm in the air, extended from his side and pointing towards the wireless while he stood perfectly still.

From the kitchen, my mother shouted, Bed, Carl.

Shush, my father said. Shush, Marie. Let him listen.

Railwayman Killed

A railway employee, Archibald McDougall, Bankton Park, Kingskettle, while crossing the main Dundee–Edinburgh line about 100 yards east from Burntisland Station last night, was struck in the back by a south going passenger train due in Burntisland at 5.31pm and instantly killed. It is presumed that he was crossing the line from the railway workshops in order to get to the north platform for his train home.

The Scotsman,
Friday, 26 September 1947

TEN

Love, Marie, 1939

WHEN MY GRANDAD went to identify the body, the mortuary attendant handed him a wedding ring with the initials 'AMacD' engraved on the front and 'Love, Marie, 1939' on the back. The shaft of the ring was broken.

Her scream kept me awake for years and wakens me every time I hear it. She tried to say his name.

They'd slept in that morning and had a row.

When he left for work, she thought, Thank God he's gone.

* * *

When's Daddy coming back? I asked when I'd finished my tea.

Soon, she said. He's been held up. You know what these trains are like. Maybe that's him on his way now. Listen and tell me if you can hear him. It's either him or a wee mouse running up the wall.

Marie, you'll have that wean as bad as yoursel, filling his heid with nonsense.

My granny moved towards the fire to find her chair where no one else sat.

Suppose you get yourself washed, then get you up the stairs and cosied up in bed.

She poured the boiling water from the big brown kettle into the enamel basin, put the soap and flannel by the sink, let the cold water run into the basin, refilled the kettle and put it on the stove. I had washed my face and hands when she warmed my pyjamas and slippers on the kitchen range.

Every night we had the same ritual. I washed myself, put on my pyjama bottoms and slippers. Then with a towel round my neck she washed my hair, twice a week with Derbac soap, and then with the usual red Lifebuoy.

I dried my hair in front of the fire. My grandmother stacked the grate with cinders. I don't know how she did it, but she'd rake the ashes and store them at the back of the fire. She pulled the cinders down with the coal rake, toasted the bread with a toasting fork and knew by touching when the toast was ready. It was a bedtime treat, buttered toast and tea.

I was reading when my mother came upstairs. The Bairds had given me a children's encyclopaedia. Every new section had a footnote to remind us of the theme, Crafts, Games, Needlework, Puzzles; and the illustrations had titles, 'A Quaint Group of Figures of the Stone Age', 'Harvey Explains to King Charles How the Blood Circulates Through the Body', 'A Harvester on the Rolling Plains of Canterbury'. Other pieces showed how to make shadows on walls, construct submarines from peashooters or build a dolls' house for your sister.

Right, she said. What's going on in the world tonight?

Within minutes she'd put out the light.

Nothing yet, she said, though I hadn't asked. He can't be long now. He must have been held up; or maybe he's working late. You'll see him in the morning.

* * *

The policemen came at 25 to nine. My grandfather opened the door. They came into the house and took off their hats.

There's been an accident, the sergeant said.

And she screamed.

I ran downstairs. My grandfather stood by the living room door: Back you get, he said. Get back up to bed.

I turned to go when I heard my mother sob and tried to barge past him, pressing downwards, refusing to be lifted and crying.

The wails and keening terrified me. My grandmother's world was peopled by ghosts who initiated or communicated curses, blights, insults, consequences, revenge and insisted on obedience. There were laws and ordinances that could neither be broken nor abused; there were people and places that should be avoided; her very language was cursed. We were clearly experiencing some sort of consequence, someone had strayed and this was the result of their disobedience.

And I struggled to take my share of the blame. I had a part in this consequence or curse and had surely instigated the keening. I was continually being told to behave; and though I did not know how I had caused such grief, standing, shivering in the lobby, tears dripping from my chin, I knew it was my fault as surely as I knew my name. I needed to put it right, to make amends.

My grandfather positioned his body between me and the door. He seemed immense. The bulk of his stomach spread across the frame.

The shivering spread up my legs and through my arms. My teeth rattled and it was pointless trying to draw the snot back into my body. I watched it gather on the floor.

Go back upstairs, my grandfather said. Look at the mess you're making.

Someone'll have to wipe that up.

I didn't move. Another wail came from the sitting room. My grandfather turned towards the door and I tried to turn the handle. He gathered me into his arms and I kicked and screamed till he put me down.

Again, I tried to push past him. He grabbed my pyjama jacket and yanked me backwards. When I rushed towards him and slipped on the snot, he caught and lifted me, but put me down immediately, breathing heavily, his face turning red. He bent his head and his breathing got heavier. He'd start coughing soon, maybe even bringing up phlegm and that would be my chance. I waited while the cough rattled up his chest and when he started wheezing, I rushed to the door. His cough stopped and he straightened himself, swung me round and clouted me across the head with the back of his hand.

Get up these stairs, he said. Get back into bed and not another word from you.

He dragged me up the stairs one at a time, him on the step above each time, hauling me up. There were beads of sweat on his forehead. He was exhausted. I knew I had overpowered him and waited for his grip on my arm to slacken.

Please, Carl, he said. Go back to bed. Look at what you're doing to me.

I tried to rush past him down stairs, but he grabbed the back of my pyjama jacket and lifted me into the air, swung me upstairs with the buttons digging into my neck and shoved me into the bedroom. I stood by the window, enjoying the cold, hoping the shiver would intensify, thinking a train might pass or that something would happen to divert their attention, something big enough to make me rush downstairs and tell them. I imagined rushing into the room and shouting. It's all right. A spaceship's landed.

The wet garden shone in the pale yellow light. I stood feeling the weight bear me down, as though a pressure point had been established in my head making it too heavy for my body, and in the morning could not remember getting into bed.

ELEVEN

Sir Bedivere

IS THAT YOU up? Granny said when I appeared in the kitchen. She'd made porridge. I brought the milk in from the door.

You get the top of the milk, she said. Babs and your mother are sleeping, thank God, and so's your grandad. God alone knows what time he got back here last night.

Where was he?

Out. So the best thing you can do is get yourself washed and dressed and ready for school. There'll be some trauchle in this hoose the day.

The weather had been warm; the men at the farm said it was sure to get colder, maybe even as bad as last winter, if not worse; but since we'd started back at school the days had been warm and cool.

It was Friday and we had my two favourite subjects; every Friday afternoon we had drawing for an hour, then reading. We were allowed to read on our own.

By lunchtime no one had spoken.

There's been a terrible tragedy, Miss Barclay said before she took the register, and we all have to be nice to each other. We have to behave like proper ladies and gentlemen, for when tragedy touches one, it affects us all. We have recently come through a terrible time, a conflict where we had to band together, to show our strength, and just when we could be forgiven for thinking tragedy had finished with us some of us find we have to go through it all again. You know who I mean, and all I ask is that you think for yourselves; think how you would be, how would you react in this position.

We've no to speak to you, Rab Duncan said.

I stayed in the classroom at playtime and ate alone at lunchtime.

In the afternoon Miss Barclay gave me a book. It had a blue cover and a picture on the front. It was a version of King Arthur and the Knights of the Round Table, set in a heavy text with reproductions of Victorian paintings.

This is from my own library, she said, and I went home at lunchtime to bring it to you. I wanted you to read the story of Sir Bedivere, the knight to whom King Arthur entrusted Excalibur. Twice Sir Bedivere tried to fool his dying king, but Arthur knew what had happened and eventually Sir Bedivere was shamed into throwing Excalibur far into the water, where a hand caught the sword, waved it three times and disappeared.

I want you to remember Sir Bedivere, she said. I want you to remember his valour and his ability to do his duty. He became a great knight who saved our country from foreign invasion.

I loved the story, especially the bit at the end where Sir Bedivere carries Arthur to a barge with fine ladies in waiting. He rode off and in the morning met a hermit beside a new tomb. He asked whose tomb it was; the hermit said many fine ladies had brought the body and Bedivere knew it was King Arthur.

* * *

Throughout the weekend my mother scarcely moved. She stared into the fire. When she stood she seemed smaller, visibly shrunken, as though air had left her body.

The house was busy and I spent a lot of time in the garden or sitting by the kitchen range. I was sent to bed early and stared at the ceiling, trying to decipher voices from the rooms below.

On the Sunday night, after dinner I was at the table with a glass of milk and a jotter. I wanted to show my mother the drawing I had done of the hand coming from the lake to catch Excalibur. As I approached, she turned her face to the wall.

Talk to him, my granny said.

I can't.

Look at him.

I can't.

For Godsakes Marie, do something. Tell him. He has to know. You can't ignore the child.

I went back to the table and pretended I was drawing.

I can't sleep in Archie's bed, my mother said.

What?

He's there. Every night. He's in the bed. Cold as ice. Lying there beside me in the bed.

For the love of God, Marie, you'll need to pull yourself the gither.

He's here in the house. I can feel him near me. He hasn't left us. I knew he'd stay.

My grandfather knocked his pipe against the wall of the fire, tore strip of newspaper and tried to relight the dregs of his pipe. I was fascinated by this performance, especially the way his jaws expanded and collapsed.

Marie, he said. His accent was stronger when he said a Christian name. Marie. Listen to me. Now. Listen.

I'm listening.

Look at me, Marie.

What is it?

Open your eyes.

They're open.

This cannot go on. You've a few more days like this to go through and you can't let things collapse. You have to think of your son.

I can't.

You have to.

You don't understand.

What don't I understand?

He's here. All the time. He's in the kitchen, sometimes he's here and on the stairs. He's nearly always on the stairs and he's in the bedroom. I can't sleep there. I lie awake and feel him with me, in the bed beside me. He wants me to sleep. I know he does. But I can't sleep. And not just because he's there. I keep thinking if I stay awake I'll see him and maybe he'll talk to me.

Is it the same as Willie Strachan's mum?

My mother let out a yell and my grandfather raised his arms and waved me in towards him. He smelled of soap and tobacco.

Who was this? he said.

Peggy told us about him. He was killed in the war and his mother ran round looking for him.

No one spoke and as the silence became heavier I left my grandfather staring at the fire, the pipe in his hand, and stood by the window looking on to the road. There was the ditch, the bank and the fence to the bare field. I watched the balls of rain gather in lines and run down the glass.

A man I'd never seen passed the window. He came back up the road and stopped again outside the house. He knocked on the door. I turned into the kitchen to get washed and changed for bed, knowing I would be sent out anyway.

My granny had left the oven door open and I stood, my feet on the cold linoleum feeling hot and cold at the same time.

Just you carry on through there, she said. It's your house. You live here, and never you mind these daft buggers.

When I went into the sitting room, the conversation stopped. No one looked at me as I passed through and as soon as the door was closed I heard the voices gather again.

My grandfather came upstairs. I heard his heavy breath on the stairs and could feel him holding onto the handle at the other side of the door.

Well, he said. His face was pale. Small beads of sweat had gathered on his brow. He looked very old and sick. Clusters of white hair jutted from the side and back of his head and he wiped his dome with a handkerchief, looking at the sweat, before putting the hankie away. He was breathing heavily. His chest rattled and his body rose and fell with the strain as though a dog was growling inside his body.

Your mother's not well, he said. She's had an awful shock and you'll have to help her get over it. You'll have to look after her. You mustn't upset her. She's your responsibility. You'll have to become a man now.

What have I done?

What?

It's my fault, isn't it?

He shook his head and turned away.

No, he said. It's not your fault.

He put his hand on my head.

No. It's never your fault, Carl.

* * *

My granny said, Go out and play.

Unless she said my name I never knew if she was speaking to me or not.

When I got up the house was empty, except for her, sitting by the fire.

Are you there?

Here I'm here.

Good. Are you dressed?

Uh-hu.

Speak properly. Say, Yes.

Yes.

Have you washed?

Uh-hu.

And brushed your teeth?

Uh-hu.

And combed your hair?

Where is everybody?

They left last night. They got the train through and they'll be back tomorrow or maybe the day after. We won't know what the hell's going on till they get here. There's porridge in the pot and milk on the sill.

I stood by the door and stared down the garden. I was sure my mother would be back, but nothing was certain. Everyone was acting strangely. No one wanted to speak to me. I was always in the way and my mother barely looked at me.

I didn't know what I'd done. I knew my dad had left and was sure he'd gone to Oban. Lying in bed I worked it out: my daddy's gone to Oban and they've gone to get him back.

I ate my porridge at the living room table. Granny sat by the fire, talking to the flames. I could not make out what she was saying, blethering in her usual mixture of Gaelic and English.

Do you want me to go out and play?

You've to go to school.

Where has everyone gone?

Oban.

Is my daddy in Oban?

Eat your porridge, she said. It's nearly time for you to go. And come straight back.

I got to school early and hung around the playground. Most of the children ignored me. One or two girls spoke and I liked that. I preferred girls. They weren't so boisterous, but I found it difficult talking to them. We weren't interested in the same things.

Women were better conversationalists than men, who usually asked a single question, two at most, then said something silly, like, You'll find out soon enough. But the women I knew could talk for hours, had dozens of questions and even helped with the answers.

Miss Barclay told me I didn't need to do too much.

I'm pleased to see you in school today, she said, which I found strange.

I said nothing. I'd grown to like her and thought she liked me, but I occasionally felt sorry for her; she had a melancholy look about her, especially when she powdered her face and highlighted her cheekbones with two uneven circles of rouge.

I think we'll try and make this easy for you, she said.

Thank you, miss.

I wouldn't like you to get ideas above your station. I think you're the sort of child who could easily fall into the trap of vanity, so we'll have to make sure you come on at the same rate as everyone else. But for this week, we'll come and go a little. What's your favourite activity?

I didn't answer. Already I could feel the other children looking at me strangely, pretending to be busy.

I know you like reading and drawing too, so shall we say that for today, as a special treat, we will pretend it's Friday and have reading and drawing in the afternoon, not just for you but for the whole class. And never forget Sir

Bedivere. We are all called on to be brave, to hide our feelings when we think our behaviour would upset others, especially those close to us who may have been dreadfully hurt already.

I tried to stay out the way, imagined that if I said nothing I would become invisible. The story of Sir Bedivere made sense of what I could neither explain nor confirm, the feeling that something had been passed to me. Whatever happened was obviously my fault. Why else had my father gone and why wasn't my mother speaking to me. Nothing I could now say or do could put it right. I would have to thole it, put up with the shame and hope they'd forget, the way people forgot Sir Bedivere's shame when he saved the kingdom.

I left school as Sir Bedivere, waving my sword and guiding my charger past the Warehouses and Kettle Holm, under the bridge and past the station. Just by the Co-operative, John Paul stopped the tractor and I got a hurl down Bankton Park standing on the back. Sandy was at the gate and Mrs Paul came out to see me.

She took me into the kitchen and gave me a glass of milk, took a scone from a tray on top of the range, shooed the cat from the table and buttered the scone. I sat on a stool by the range and watched her ironing, drinking the milk and eating the warm currant scone. I loved the Pauls' kitchen. There was always a smell of baking.

Mrs Paul sang while she was ironing. She usually asked who was at school, what the lessons were, who was ill and were there any girls I thought were cleverer than me. Were there any girls I liked? There was a smell of hot metal and steam. Her sons' shirts and underwear were hanging from the pulley and clustered round the range.

Tom Seath was off school today, I said.

Oh my, she said. I hope he isn't ill.

That would normally have been the start of a long discussion on the nature of illness, going off alone and playing near running water.

Ann Wilkie was there?

Yes. I saw her this morning.

Last week Mrs Paul wondered if Ann and I would marry. I told her I could not imagine marrying someone who didn't live in the same house as me.

But if she's your wife she'd come and live with you.

That's why I thought of marrying my Aunt Eva or my Aunt Barbara because they already live there, so it'll be easier for them because they know everybody already.

That's a very sensible way of looking at things, she said. I wish all men were as sensible as that. Most of them say more than their prayers.

I didn't know what she meant, but didn't tell her.

I finished my scone. Mrs Paul put a loaf and two scones in a bag. That's for you and your granny, she said. Take Sandy round to the house then send him back.

Sandy barked when he reached the door. My mother or father usually gave him a bit of bread or a biscuit. I heard my granny shuffling towards the door.

Don't bring that dog in here, she said.

I tore a bit from my scone and gave it to Sandy. He ran back to the farm.

It was ten past three and my granny was standing at the back of the door. The clocks were stopped and a sheet hung over the mirror. The curtains were drawn

I took off my coat and shoes and buttered the scones in the kitchen. I put the bread in the bread bin, took my scone and sat by the fire.

When will they be back? I asked.

My granny sat with the plate on her lap.

It'll be a while now, she said. They'll only just be back from the grave.

TWELVE

Kettle Church

SUNDAY SCHOOL WAS in the Kettle Church hall. We sat on wooden seats in a room where the walls were covered with framed parchments of the Kettle Church Cradle Roll on which our names were written with the dates of our christenings.

Jesus changes everything, the man in the suit said. He changed the water into wine, raised Lazarus from the dead and He can change your life.

The woman beside him had short, curled hair. She held a framed picture: Holman Hunt's *The Light of the World*.

This is the door of your heart, she said. And Jesus is knocking; this morning he is knocking on the door of your heart asking you to let him in, asking to enter. As you can see, it's a strong, stout door with no handle and can only be opened from inside. Jesus cannot push his way through. You have to open the door and let him in. The brambles and undergrowth, the darkness represents the sin that surrounds your heart, which should be a garden with pretty flowers and light, but we are born in sin, so he is standing knocking, knocking on the door of your heart, asking you to let him in. Will you let him in? Let him in now, children. Let Jesus in. I know there is one person here who needs Jesus, one boy in this room who is living in torment and misunderstanding, who is going through the grief of bereavement and whose heart may harden because of the blow. I plead with him and I plead with you all, do not harden your hearts to Jesus. Open the door. Let Him in.

He died for you, the man said. Died on the Cross. He shed his blood so you might be free. Ask Him; and ask from Him what your heart desires. Ask and it shall be given unto you. Seek and ye shall find. And when the soldiers stuck their spears in the side of our Saviour, the Bible tells us, blood and water gushed forth. Blood and water.

The man lifted a tumbler of water from the desk to the light. Blood floated through the water in a series of red and random movements, four to five strands of red rippled through the water like rushes, the trailing roots and undergrowth gliding with the flow of the stream.

Blood and water from our Saviour's side, the man said. Give him your heart. Let him comfort and aid you. And we sang:

> As the Saviour to help you,
> Comfort, strengthen and keep you:
> He is willing to aid you,
> He will carry you through.

That night I asked my mother how blood and water could be in a glass?

Her eyes were red and her lip trembled. My Aunt Barbara ran out of the room. My mother stared at the fire.

And that night I dreamed of blood and water and Jesus at the door of my heart.

A few days later my mother and Aunt Barbara were making the bed in the upstairs bedroom. I sat on the stairs trying not to listen but could not move. My mother was sobbing. She could not stop. No matter what she was doing, it gripped her and she could not prevent herself from crying.

It'll never stop, she said. Never. It'll never go away.

Marie, you'll need to pull yourself together. There's Carl to think of; now Archie's gone you'll need to be mother and father.

A wail made me run upstairs. My mother sat with her head in her hands staring at the floor, her shoulders shaking. Barbara was beside her, holding, trying to shield her. They looked up and saw me at the door.

My daddy's dead, isn't he?

My mother said, Go out to play.

* * *

Then I am alone on South Street, Kingskettle. The time on the Kettle Church clock is a quarter past six and I am walking from Station Road, past the church into Bankton Park, where I'll run along the lane past the Pauls' Farm and down to the house.

As I pass the church there's a light in the corner. At first it is dim, like the light from a torch, but then it grows brighter, brighter than the sun. My father is standing to the left of the church, just in the bit between the wall and the doorway, the bit where the men gather on a Sunday morning before and after the service. He is smiling in his dark blue demob suit, white shirt, maroon tie and studded collar. His shoes are shining and his eyes are bright. His hair is receding, but the light lifts it slightly, as though heat was rising from beneath him.

I turn to run to him, call his name and his smile widens. He stretches his arms to hold me then changes slightly before he goes. He is gone and I stare at the space where he was and as I turn, Jesus has taken my father's place, first of all as *The Light of the World*, then as the crucified saviour, his arms outstretched, hands and feet bleeding, the wound on his side dripping blood and water onto stone. He is smiling. His hair is waved and his eyes are soft. He has nice teeth and his beard glistens in the light that comes from above.

I do not want to go, but cannot stop as he beckons me forward, to run to him as I ran to my father. I am close enough to see the creamy folds in his robes, his red cloak trembling in the breeze.

He opens his mouth as if to speak, but no words come. He is as silent as my father. With every muscle tense and iron, I turn and run, away from the pull. I am losing my strength, running through a swamp, away from Jesus who pulls me towards him. And just as I am about to be caught, as his arms almost enfold me forever, I am wakened, screaming and sweating, sobbing and holding onto my mother in my room where the bedside lamp is lit.

There, she says. There, there, there. It's a dream, Carl. Just a dream.

And that is how he came to me, every night, in his demob suit and trench coat.

Or I am wearing sandshoes, socks and short trousers, a dark blue jersey with a turned down collar fringed by a line of dark green wool. I am running round the village.

The wind is in my face and my arms are stretched out at my sides. I am an aeroplane, then a horse, then I am running.

And as I run, I take in the village, sometimes rising like a figure in a Chagall canvas, a floating part of the landscape, flying over the village while wandering its streets, running and flying home from school.

And my father is waiting in the church corner. He sees me flying and jumps into the air beside me.

* * *

The moon and the image of the moon in the mirror lit the room.

Shuddering as the floorboards creaked, my feet touched linoleum and I wondered if I should have dressed in bed, moving to where I'd left my clothes by the empty fire. Trying to stop the rattle in my teeth, watching my body darken as I pulled on the clothes, rubbing my arms for warmth, I pulled up my socks and tied my sandshoes in a double knot for safety.

I could not be disturbed.

Crossing to the window, I wiped the condensation from the glass, blinking as the moonlight hit me, screwing my eyes to avoid the light, then opening to find the garden and the tree at the bottom of the garden, the fence and the hedge and the field beyond. I pressed my finger to the pane, watching the print stay on the glass, bigger than the window or the world, shifting the view as light shone through the fingerprint.

The sky was clear. The moon made everything black; stars hauled ships across the world. I could see the garden clearly; the path with lavender and pinks on the edge by the grass where I sometimes played, the little line of roses with a flowerbed in front, the stretch of strawberry plants and potatoes, cabbage, carrots and kale I'd planted or helped my parents plant, the red and black currant bushes, the raspberries and pear trees, the apples and the lettuce rows, tomatoes in the greenhouse and heather by the fence. I knew I would never see them this way again. The garden was grey and shades of grey, darkest blue and almost yellow where the light hit moisture on the tip of a leaf or the bark of a tree, the colour of milk, darkening into heavy cream. Thick moonlight. Everywhere.

Floorboards moved when I crossed the room. With the door wide enough to prise me through, past the room where my mother and aunt were sleeping, down the stairs and into the kitchen, past the tablet of heat in front of the stove, the plod of the clock and the pantry with last night's pudding still on the shelf, the sour milk for cheese and the jam my mother made from berries.

The inside door was varnished pine with an iron lock and bolt. The key was cold as I turned the handle and passed the grating where I scraped my boots, the tubs of geranium, red and white.

The garden glistened. I ran down the path; my sandshoes wet and top hose damp when I reached the fence where the rotting posts and strips of wire mingled with the hawthorn bush on the edge of the field.

I found the nest where we'd seen the eggs. Here, my daddy said. Look in here, and he parted the branches. There were two small eggs, blue and spreckled, dotted brown, like the cover of a book I'd got at Christmas.

I looked at the house and into my room, trying to find my print on the window. The curtains in what had been my parents' room, where my mother slept, were drawn. I could see the pattern, floribunda roses and ivy leaves.

I breathed in the air and nothing happened; the only sound was my body working, taking the air in and out. The smell of nightstock, grass and roses mingled with the damp smell of night.

Creamy and blue, cold with no wind, the night on my hair like stars in the sky, nearer than ever they had been, brighter than they would be again.

In my trousers and jumper, sandshoes and socks, with my body cold, tingling from the wet, I lay on my back by the edge of the path, near the rhubarb and the compost heap; I lay on my back and stared at the sky, weighed and black to the point of creaking. The moon in the corner smouldered through wisps that passed on their way from the sea. I made shapes and faces, recognising their names and constellations from the *Star Spotters' Annual*: Ursa Major, Ursa Minor, Orion's Belt, The Plough.

And the geese cried just before I opened my eyes and saw their lines blinking through the stars, the flap of their wings like the vent from rising heat. I stood to be nearer, to see them leave, when I felt it, felt it then I heard it, or thought I heard it, for I felt it first and then I heard it, coming from nowhere like the sound of God.

The lights and a line of light, a string of starlights crossing the land to the clatter of mice rampaging home, past owls in the hedgerows and crows in the field, the voles below corn. When I stood, I felt the rattle, trembling as the train approached till I could not tell the rumble of the train from the rattle of the cold, the shiver and the noise, the smoke and light that was suddenly on me, a mile away and clear as day, the red and yellow fire, smoke and steam that filled the sky and closed down the moon. I slammed my eyes shut and felt it pass through me, felt it leave till there was cold and damp and the cat at my legs, rubbing and arching its back.

I felt the fur, saw the cat lift his forepaw, turn, curl its tail and run up the path, stopping to see if I was coming, then turning to the sound of the disappearing train. I followed Patch, up the path and into the house.

The cat climbed onto a chair by the fire. I took off my shoes and socks and walked across the flagging on the kitchen floor, up the stairs and into my room, where I stood by the window. The smoke and the steam and the clouds were gone. The night was clear. I could see the stars and feel their light, the garden, the cat and the ghost of a train. I could see my fingerprint smudged on the window.

Back in bed, I closed my eyes, opening them quickly and the room was alight.

I must have slept, but could not remember. Next morning, the damp shoes and stockings told where I'd been, that the night was real; and whatever had wakened me must have been the light.

PART TWO

538 Keppochhill Road, Glasgow N1

From breakfast on through all the day
At home among my friends I stay;
But every night I go abroad
Afar into the land of Nod.

                    The Land of Nod, Robert Louis Stevenson

THIRTEEN

Stragglers

SOMETIMES A STAR fled across the sky, flared, dipped and fell.

I wondered where it landed, if the blue light had melted where it wasn't night. Did it land in South America, by the Orinoco or Amazon basin; did it melt in Greenland or fall to the sea? Would a star land here? Would it come sparkling down in the garden, fill me with light and take me away? Would I know when it landed? Would it come from nowhere or the other side of the world and land in our garden during the day? If I looked would I find it, and when I found it what would happen?

Would the fall be as random and surprising as memory, which could assail without warning: my daddy running towards me with his hands cupped, shouting, What's this here?

A field mouse blinked.

Harvest, and the men stacking sheaves. The women brought tea and scones, sandwiches, pies and tarts. I helped my mother pack and as we were leaving, he shouted.

There, there, there, he said. Take it. Go on. Gently, Carl. Stroke it gently.

The mouse lay in my hand. Its whiskers tickled. I was sure I could feel its heart tremble.

All winter, spring and summer I looked for mice in the field.

Then the slow shift into autumn: fields glowed red with stubble burning and geese called as they left. There was always a straggler, one who had detached from the rest, who seemed anxious to stay.

I slept in the upstairs room where dust swirled in the morning. I'd run to the lavatory by the coal shed and longed for the light, when ice on the windows made us stay indoors. The house was dark, the garden bare.

I imagined we would stay here forever; and for years after we left, in places where I felt a stranger, new folk at school and someone else's cat, I always dreamed I'd fall asleep and waken in the bed by the sloping roof at the back of the house, where I'd stand by the window when my parents were asleep, teeth rattling with the winter chill, a blanket round my shoulders, staring at the stars across the field, counting the number pressed into one pane, afraid to blink in case the weaker signals disappeared.

* * *

I loved magpies and the silly way they landed. They need glasses, my mother said, when one headed for a post, missed and hit the wire, took off and tried again.

Crossing the field with Sandy I heard the squawk of a magpie in a tree. When I stopped there was a fainter sound, like a second bird in the same tree. Then there was the chattering, a kind of mumbling where the voices alternated till it sounded like four or five magpies in the tree. Sandy barked and the magpie flew away.

It's a school of magpies, my mother said when I told the story.

I laughed, imagining.

How many were there? my granny asked.

I think only one.

How many did you see?

Just the one.

Ane's a joy, twa's grief; three's a waddin, fower's daith, she said, turning away.

* * *

Willie's handkerchiefs were sprecked with flecks of crimson.

When he coughed his face turned red, then white, then it glistened yellow as he tried to catch his breath before another spasm. The first time I saw it, I cried. His hand clawed the air, as though he could shovel handfuls into his mouth. Each new intake was relished as it moved through his body, as though he was testing his breathing to see if it would stay. When he was sure the air was firm he keeled back in the seat, staring at the light.

That ceiling could do with a coat of paint, he'd say.

He was a small man, with wavy hair, natty ties and starched collars. He looked like his mother, had seen Benny Lynch beat Small Montana and the Moscow Dynamos field 12 men at Ibrox. But my favourite story was the man who said everything twice, everything twice.

No matter what it was, he said everything twice, everything twice, which took him a long time to say anything, anything; no matter what, what; longer than usual, because he said everything twice, everything twice. Sometimes he even said things three times, said things three times, he said things three times, but he usually just said everything twice, everything twice.

Now, this man who said everything twice, everything twice, worked as a waiter, which made things difficult if there was more than one customer wanting breakfast, which meant he had to take the orders for at least two breakfasts, though the man taking the orders said everything twice, everything twice and when he was dealing with one customer, it sounded as if he was dealing with two.

I'd like some ham and eggs, please.
Ham and eggs.
Yes, ham and eggs.
Ham and eggs.
Just the one plate please.
Of ham and eggs.
Ham and eggs.
And I'd like a plate of porridge.
A plate of porridge.
With ham and eggs for me.
Ham and eggs.
And a plate of porridge.
A plate of porridge.
With ham and eggs.
And some tea and toast.
Tea and toast.
Though I'd prefer coffee.
Coffee.
Wait a minute, it was ham and eggs.
Ham and eggs.
And a plate of porridge.
Ham and eggs.
No a plate of porridge.
A plate of porridge.
With the ham and eggs.
Ham and eggs.
Could we have another waiter, please.

Another waiter? What's wrong with me, wrong with me, said Peter Price, the man who said everything twice, everything twice. Maybe his name was Tommy Twice and not Peter Price, but he was the man who said everything, everything twice. I asked him once; I said what's your name and he said, Peter Peter Price Price, so he must have been the man who said everything twice, everything twice.

His bed was in the Glasgow front room, high into the recess and well above the floor, where he lay with his back to the wall, facing the door. The windows steamed when the fire was lit.

The front room fireplace was maybe five feet tall, a heavily decorated cast iron grate with green tiles down either side of an oval lintel. A glass and golden clock stood at the centre of the mantleshelf, the workings on display. It had a delicate chime, like the tinkle in a music box, a round, enamelled face with floral decorations, heavy pink roses round the keyholes, small forget-me-nots elsewhere and the numbers in frail Roman numerals. The hands were thin, like black wire, and there was a ball mechanism at the base which did a half turn to the left, then back to the right, left and right forever. The key was heavily filigreed, kept in a glass pocket at the back of the clock.

There were plaster ornaments on either side of the mantelpiece, a girl to the left, a boy to the right. She held the skirts of her green dress to the side as if about to curtsey. Her golden hair was tied with a dark green ribbon. She had blue eyes and a rosebud mouth. Brown curls crumpled from below his battered hat. He wore a blue open-necked shirt and brown dungarees. They had bare feet. He carried a fishing rod.

My Uncle Willie lay beneath a cream coloured quilted bedspread dotted with pink and maroon rosebuds, his head on a pair of starched pillows. I stood on tiptoe, but he always told me to climb up beside him.

He was too warm or too cold. Pale and sweaty, he struggled to free himself from the blankets where he had been enthusiastically tucked in. His hair was often stuck to his forehead. He reached for a table by the bedside and always asked for a cup of water. Let the tap run, he said. I like it cold.

I filled the cup above the brim, then slow-marched the 18 or 20 steps across the kitchen, down the lobby and into the front room and round the corner to Willie's bed, watching the water tremble, afraid it would spill.

* * *

She slept in the room on a chair by the fire, washed and changed him three, four times a day, fed him and sat by the bed, holding his hands while he moved in and out of consciousness.

She was continually tired, especially when the doctor came in his three-piece suit and university tie, always with a small, brown case. They spoke in whispers behind the door, sometimes in the lobby. When he'd gone, my mother would sag, then force herself to rise.

During the day, we knew he'd be fine. Every night we'd sit in the room, watching for change when he seemed the same.

With her back to the bed, my mother said, George, would you see.

He took the hand-mirror from the mantlepiece and held it to Willie's mouth. The mirror was clear. He shook his head.

And while my grandmother, mother and aunt were crying and my grandfather stared out the window. George sat me on his knee.

You'll miss your Uncle Willie, he said.

Two days later, the room was cleared and the bed was stripped. There had been a funeral.

* * *

There were times when Granny pretended vision.

There's a nice shade of green in the coat that woman's wearing, she'd say, staring at a near-empty street.

Where, Granny? What woman?

Oh, she's gone now.

On other days, you knew she could see. It had to do with the way she peered from the side of her eyes, adjusting to the light. It had to do with the tone of her voice.

Don't you think I cannae see what you're up to, for I can see you well enough.

When someone was expected my granny would look out the front room window. Here he's now, she'd call. Here's Babs just off the tram. And sure enough, she would be at the door minutes later.

She wore a wraparound apron and slippers, her straight white hair cut just below her ears. Her eyes were yellow and white. She looked at me the way she looked at Rupert Bear cartoons, closely peering, with a faint expression of disbelief.

Sometimes, she wore dark glasses over the others, turning from the sink to bump into a chair, turning from the window in the front room to stand by the small table with the ornate brass lamp that had once been an oil lamp, searching for something to touch, lost on the edge of the room. Who's moved that table? she asked no one.

She worried about hospital. Taking her to the doctor and then the eye specialist was an expedition, planned days in advance.

How can I go? How can I get down the stairs when I cannae see? God Almighty, you'll be wanting me to go out of here in a box next.

Mother, it's no my eyes that need done.

I can see fine.

And when she left for the operation weeks after Willie's death, she went quietly, like a child, holding my mother's hand, Barbara behind her. You watch yourself on these stairs, she said to Barbara, who was pregnant.

Your Aunt Barbara and Uncle George are expecting a baby, my mother said. It seemed a strange thing to say. I wasn't sure what she meant.

Granny was away a week. Every day someone went to see her. I went, her eyes bandaged, she sat up in bed. Hello, son, she said when I arrived. I knew it was you, *a graidh*. You shouldn't be here. You've to watch yourself on they tram cars. They shake you about. God knows what could happen to you. Are you eating right? You don't look well. Are you getting enough sleep?

Mother, your eyes are bandaged.

I know, and they're awfy itchy. I think it's the stuff they put on them. What have you brought to eat? The food in here's no right; turn your stomach.

Interesting name, Kaufmann, the surgeon said, looking at my granny's notes, looking at my mother, looking at me and back again to the notes. German, is she?

I'd've thought you could've guessed from my mother's accent that she might not be German, my mother said.

He returned to the notes, flipping the pages back and forward. Well, he said, her eyesight will never be good. We have removed one of the cataracts, but the other was inoperable and the one we removed could well return, and if that happens we may well have to repeat the operation. Her short sight in the eye we've done will never be right, but her long sight may well be fine. Difficult to tell, really. All depends.

I will never go through that again, she said. Never again, as long as I live. Do you know they stuck this needle in my arm and the next thing I know, I'm lying on a trolley with my eyes all bandaged. And the itch and pain. Dear God, I don't care if I never see. It was you that wanted it, well you can do it yourself next time, for I've had my fill. And they bloody glasses'll never be right. How in the name of God do I have to wear glasses when I cannae see?

She was always footering with them. Eventually, the ends were covered with sticking plaster, the corner hinges sewn with thread.

She stood by the window, her eyes bandaged. The doctor brought the glasses a week after she came home and the bandages were removed. Here, she said when my grandfather was sleeping. The house was still. Here, she said. Here you come, over here.

I knelt in front of her and she ran her hands over my face and hair, smiling as she traced my features, finding my hair then working her way down my eyes, nose and mouth like rain.

Carl, she said.

* * *

I had no idea what was happening. There were days off school and weekends in Glasgow, time spent on railway benches or watching rainwater slide down carriage windows.

One time when we arrived in Glasgow, Aunt Barbara wasn't there; two or three days later when I came home she was feeding a baby in the front room. There was a sudden burst of activity and silence as I was shepherded out the room.

Don't go in, my mother said. Wait till she's finished. You can see him when he's fed.

This is Michael, Aunt Barbara said.

He was parcelled in a white shawl, big eyes crinkled against the light. When he was turned towards me, he turned into the shadow, his snubbed features and fine, black hair were all I could see. I reached into the shawl and took his hand, examining the fingernails as he unclenched his fist, wrapping it suddenly around my finger.

Get you away from that wean, my granny said. Go on, off you go. Don't touch it. Away out and play. And Barbara, don't you let him near that child. God only knows what he would do if he got the chance.

* * *

Patch left when my father died.

Some bugger's away wi'im, my mother said.

Marie. Someone's listening.

Och, well, I'm telling you somebody's away with that cat. They'll need a mouser and they'll have lifted him.

Then she told me the Jamiesons needed a cat for the farm. There were too many mice. He'll be fine, she said. He'll have a whole farm to roam in.

Who'll feed him?

Mrs Jamieson'll look after him.

But where will he sleep?

I'm sure they'll find a nice place for him. He'll be all right. We spoke about this. You said it yourself. He wouldn't like Glasgow and you know we wouldn't leave him unless we knew he'd be safe.

Are we going to Glasgow?

No.

Then where are we going?

Nowhere.

Then why are we packing?

We're just sorting things out.

So I ran round the village, turning left down Bankton Park, past the Station Hotel, round by Kettle Square running round to say goodbye, holding pictures.

The cottage with its low roof, small rooms and whitewashed ceilings, up and down stairs, a big back garden and colour at the front. From the hawthorn hedge at the back, a field of cows and the railway line to the sea where every night the train that killed my father passed our kitchen window just before five o'clock.

With sun in the garden, the back of the house was lit. The patch at the front, marigolds, cornflowers, snapdragons, phlox and daisies, sometimes caught the sun by day, when the upstairs rooms were cool and shaded and the scent of stock filled the kitchen and the red and yellow nasturtiums seemed gilded with a colour deeper than their own.

While people were packing, I circled the place, then slept in the house for the very last time. Without a sound, the ghost of one world lay down on another and I was stranded like a heron, unfolding its wings as it lifted to fly.

It was raining. The station smelled of wet stone.

All the way to Thornton Junction, I watched rain gather on the window, then roll down the glass with the world in its eye. Out of Thornton, beyond Kirkcaldy to where we were going, we ate tomato sandwiches and drank milky tea. The taste of white pepper on a tomato sandwich made with plain white bread, butter and salt. Four sandwiches in a waxed paper bread wrapper and a flask of tea.

The smell of the train, the rattle of the ashtrays, smoke and steam in the dusty carriage with pictures of the seaside above the seats, looking for pictures of places where the train didn't go, and a mirror in the middle, between the luggage racks, maroon and grey patterned seats.

Crossing the Forth Bridge, where my daddy held me up to see, sticking my head out the window to throw some money into the water. Make a wish, he said. Make a wish and if the money hits the water your wish will come true.

FOURTEEN

538

WE STOOD ON the pavement, my hand round her finger. A heavy, cloudy vapour mingled with cooking smells and dust came from the coal ree and potato shed behind us.

Look, my mother said.

Granny was waving from the front room window. Mum picked up the suitcase. We'd best go up, she said.

The house was crowded; our furniture piled along the lobby and by the front room door. Everyone was tired. My mother told me to change in the front room. I put on the sandshoes, jersey, socks and trousers I usually wore in Kettle. When I went into the kitchen she was crying.

Granny was in her chair by the fire. Mum sat by my grandad's chair holding her mother's hand. My granny nudged my mother, who turned towards me.

Go out and play, she said.

I crossed to the sink and drank a cup of water, looking out the kitchen window to the four lopsided metal washing poles on the backcourt, across the washhouse and middens to the park where a group of boys were standing by the wall on the edge of Keppoch Hill. I recognised Robert Smith. His granny and Auntie Annie lived next door.

My mother sobbed.

I'm just going, I said.

There was a stillness on the stairs that carried expectancy, as though it would be suddenly broken by a shout or the sound of boots on stone. Toby followed me out. He was a grey mouser who got fish heads on a Friday. His hair was sleek, his eyes were amber and he smelled of ashes. He rubbed himself against the black sandshoes that were a size and a half too big with lavatory paper stuffed in the toes, the shoes I'd grow into.

The walls were green and the top was whitewashed with a black line separating the colours. I could see the boys through the staircase window and leaned against the convex wall that ran from the floor to just below the window ledge, trying to catch what was going on: they were picking sides.

I walked along the road, not yet used to climbing the washhouse or the midden walls, turned at Vere Street, climbed the wee hill and followed the wall along the top to where the boys were standing, suddenly afraid of the stammer I'd developed. I stopped by the dyke and drew in my breath, aware of sweat on my back. My hands were clammy.

What do you want?

A red-haired boy at the edge of the crowd came forward. His left eye turned outwards and his hair was rough and wiry. Teeth were missing and he took his hands from his pockets.

Ask him his name, said Robert Smith.

What's your name?

Carl.

There were a few sniggers.

That's a lassie's name.

Ask where he comes from.

Where do you come from?

I used to live in Kettle, but I live here now.

They laughed.

Where?

Kettle. The proper name is Kingskettle. It's a place in Fife.

They laughed louder.

Carl's a German name, sure it is, said Robert Smith.

Are you a German? asked the red-haired boy, suddenly colder.

No.

His granda's the old German that stays up my granny's close, said Robert Smith. My da got killed by the Germans.

So did mine, said the red-haired boy. Do you speak German?

No.

He pushed me against the wall.

You a fucken German?

I'd never heard the word before. The force and the shock of the force hit me like a mouthful of spit. I shook my head.

You've either got a lassie's name or a German name, so if you're no a fucken German how come you've got a fucken German name?

He grabbed my collar and pulled my face towards him. His breath smelled of stale bread and tea. When he spat in my face I heard Robert Smith laughing. I thought I was going to cry.

You starting school?

I nodded.

What class?

Don't know.

Better no be mine.

What'll you dae if it is?

A boy at the back with a spring of dark hair came forward. He shoved me away and stood in front of the red-haired boy.

See if any o they clowns annoy you, tell me, he said. Okay? We're going in for our tea, then we're playin fitba. You can be on my side.

I had never played football before.

They walked to the steps at the other end of the wall. I went back the way I'd came. When I turned, they were staring. I was pleased I hadn't stuttered and held back the tears running towards the close where Robert Smith was waiting.

You better no play with them or I'll get Willie Simpson to batter you, he said.

On the stair, I held on tight and caught my breath. The Sunday school teacher had said I was a baby. She had been talking about Lazarus. I tried to concentrate, but knew there were tears on the rim of my eyes. And Miss Barclay told the class she found me crying in the sheds.

Your daddy's dead, isn't he? Willie Barr had asked.

I told him I didn't know.

My daddy read it in the paper, he said.

There is a baby in this class, she said. And we all know who it is.

I opened my eyes. A big man in a jacket, boiler suit and cap was in front of me. I'd heard him whistling on the stairs. He had steel capped boots and his face was black. He smiled.

It's all right, son, he said. This is your close. You live here. Up you come to your granny's door.

The bell was louder than I'd heard before. The man tugged tightly and the noise seemed to echo down the stairs. Loose wire, he said, smiling when the door was opened.

I found this wee boy on the stairs, he said.

My mother was flustered. Thanks, she said.

There were strangers in the kitchen. They sniffed when I came in. Two women blew their noses and Granny wiped her eyes with her apron.

Who hit you? she asked. Were they throwing stones? They're bad, weekit buggers o boys.

Oh, dear God in heaven, said an old woman with dark brown hair. He's his father's double.

Except his hair is fair and curly. Archie had dark hair.

But it was curly.

God bless us all; he has the look of him, just the way he stands.

And he has his father's chin.

Were you crying? my mother asked, when the women had gone.

I didn't answer.

Why were you crying?

Nothing.

It must have been something. Was that these boys?

No.

No one cries for nothing. I'll see them. I'll have a word with their mothers.

You want to get that boy a helmet in case any of they boys fling stones, my granny said. God Almighty. He was never in at Kettle, now he doesn't want to go out.

He's a stranger, my grandfather said. He's just arrived. But, he'll have to learn to stand up for himself. You can't fight his battles.

It's all right for you, sitting there, said Granny. You don't have to face them.

After tea, I watched my first football match, leaning on the kitchen sink, wondering if I could run with a ball at my feet, header it or tackle someone to take the ball from them. Then I sat by the fire, in front of the range, watching the flames through the spars, making shapes and faces with the coal. Toby was purring. The clock struck seven and my mother poured a kettle of boiling water into a basin in the zinc black sink and filled the basin from the swan-necked brass tap.

That should do you, she said, and when you're washed you can read for a wee while, special treat. You're in your granny's bed tonight. There's folk coming.

And later, when she'd drawn the curtains and I'd washed at the sink, with clean pyjamas and a hot water bottle, I wondered if Patch would do what the cat in *True Animal Stories* had done, followed his family, arriving at the doorstep on Christmas Day.

He'll be fine, my mother said. Don't forget, he went away on his own, though I think somebody took him. It would've been cruel to bring him here. He's a country cat with country ways. He has his own wee bit, he'll get on fine and Toby's here.

I stared from the window, trying to ignore the sobs in the room next door. Across the backcourt, the hump of city hill and a straggle of lights from the Back Lawn to the school. I knew some lights would stay on all night and loved the idea, staying up late to read, lying in the dark, imagining what went on in other houses.

With Toby at my feet and the room lit by the city, I thought it was raining but couldn't distinguish rain from the noise around me. Toby stuck his wet nose in my eye, someone was in the lavatory and I went to sleep.

* * *

There were 11 families: the Chisholms, their lodger wee Annie, Alec Cameron and his new wife in the close; Delacourt, Hewitt and Keaney on the first floor; then Kaufmann, Dewar and Miller; with Alec's mother, his father and brother Harry Cameron, Gentles and Esplin on the top floor, more than 30 people. Every house had a lavatory, just by the door. In other closes families shared, one for each landing on the turn of the stair.

As well as the lavatory, we had two rooms and a kitchen. The bedroom where my grandparents slept was next to the kitchen where I slept with my mother. At the end of the L-shaped lobby was the front room facing Keppochhill Road. This was where my granny watched the Cosy Corner empty at nine o'clock on Friday and Saturday nights. Her sight had been partially restored, some times seemed easier than others; if she lifted her head and peered from the side she could give a running commentary on who was drunk, who'd been lifted and when they might be seen again.

There was a railway yard, a coal ree and potato shed opposite the close at Coldstream Place; there was Brownlee's City Sawmills and the whisky bonds on Craighall Road, where a horn sounded three times a day, at eight o'clock, one o'clock and six, except on Sundays.

In the railway yard, engines and wagons loaded and shunted; the clang of their buffers was like no sound I had ever heard. Single horses shied on their way to Huggies slaughter house on Pinkston Road and there was the ponderous haul of engines, shining green or blue and black, from the NB Loco works in Springburn, dragged by a pair of steam-driven locos with moulded rubber wheels that occasionally seemed to stop for breath on their way to the docks.

Within three closes, 530, 538 and 546 were the post office, Delacourt's Dairy and Mrs Fraser, the newsagent, whose sister Ada was said to be blind, but vanity prevented her from wearing glasses. Their counter was fenced with wire and there was a wire grill inside the door, which had two metal signs, Wild Woodbine and Player's Please, at my eye level. Condor, Ogden's, Gold Flake and Craven A for Smoking Pleasure covered the wooden partition round the drawer that was their desk, till and office. The counter was covered with daily and evening papers, women's journals, cowboy magazines, detective stories, comics. The shelf behind the counter held tobacco, sweets and stationery, Beecham's pills and powders, Askit, Elastoplast, cigarettes and bandages. The floor space was smaller than half a lobby, covered with a linoleum that had memorised a brown and green pattern, broken by nails and wooden floorboards, lit by a gas mantle behind the counter and a single-bulbed electric light by the door.

Delacourt's Dairy door had a plain glass top with filigree edging. The counter was crowded. Jean and Mrs Delacourt added up the messages by writing with brown oval pencils onto the white marble top, which was wiped a hundred times a day with the same grey cloth. The sawdust was replaced twice a day. The shop was big and mostly white, with tiles around the counter, bordered in dark green and crimson with a contented cow grazing in a buttercup field beneath an oak tree in the middle, all lit by three white balls around strong lightbulbs with wisps of flypaper in summer.

The counter was L-shaped, with jars of biscuits facing the door, the bacon, hams and butter were on the counter by the slicer, or on the marble shelves beside the sausages, cold meats and eggs.

Even in summer the window was bright, with rosy hams, cream and yellow cheeses, butter, eggs and Scotch tomatoes. The window was whitewashed if days were hot, with oblong peep holes for folk to peer through; or the produce was written backwards inside the window, always with the letters mingled since Toe Jamieson altered Butter to But, Ham to am, Snowballs to no and removed completely the last two words of Good Dairy Produce.

Behind the counter were packets of Lipton's Tea and bottles of Camp Coffee, jars of marmalade, jam and sugar, Bovril and Marmite, packets of flour and Atora shredded suet. A glass dome on the counter was battered with flies. When the dome was lifted with one hand, the other waved above the cakes until something was selected and snatched, the lid slammed quickly, then they'd check to see if anything was trapped. Jimmy was fat, but Mrs Delacourt was wee and pretty; Jean took after her mother.

Two bare shelves ran down either side of the post office walls. There were leaflets and a sign pinned to the wall: Please ask for the pen. Thank you. There was a wire-fronted counter at the far end of the shop, a bare wooden floor and a couple of bald lights on a plum-coloured flex. Mrs Anderson stood behind the counter.

I swear to Christ, my mother said, that woman never goes to the lavatory.

Jackson piled their vegetables in front of the shop, carrots and onions, turnips, potatoes and leeks.

Bugsy Brown and the Jamieson's have never bought a vegetable for soup in their lives, my mother said. Bugsy makes the soup by boiling his waistcoat and the Jamiesons steal the stuff.

Wee Bugsy Brown lived in the next close and broke boxes and pallets then went round the doors selling sticks.

God love him, my granny said.

He keeps his money in the soap so's his wife'll never find it, my mother said and that man Jackson's the most miserable bugger that ever drew breath. I don't go in if he's there. Not that his wife's much better. He tried to charge me thruppence for a stalk of rhubarb. Good for the bowels, he said. Cheeky bugger. He could peel an orange in his pocket.

Inside was as dark as the post office. There was barley and broth mixture, custard, rice and sago on the shelves, with apples, pears, bananas and oranges in wooden crates and boxes underneath, beside the cabbages and syboes, cauliflower, turnip and new potatoes. There were two piles by the door: Cheap Fruit and Bashed Fruit in tomato baskets with signs that were written long ago. The shop smelled of earth.

* * *

Every night it snowed. The hills and the wall, the backcourt and the ropes across the backcourt, the washing lines, midden and the washhouse were white. Coal in the coal ree, tatties in the tattie shed, the engines and goods trains, policeman's box and street lamps, tram stop signs and junction boxes were white, everything connected by lines of white bunting that ran along Keppochhill Road where the tram wires, electric cables and phone lines used to be.

I'd stick my head out the window, press my finger in the line of snow and scoop up a mouthful that tasted of air. I dressed in front of the range, hopping round the kitchen from one foot to the other, waiting to get warm, watching steam from the kettle change on my skin, wishing school was over before I left the house.

We shivered in the playground, marching as quickly and orderly as possible, waiting for the announcement, which always came by half past nine. Burst pipes meant we had the day to ourselves.

The Kettle sledge was the best in the street, and when the Catholic school came out Francie and I went in search of the long runs, sometimes starting at the pitches, going down the school brae and turning at the Back Lawn, or charging from St Theresa's downhill to Saracen Street.

How come you never came oot't play fitba? he asked.

It was Saturday and I'd been sent out to play.

Don't let them bother you. Any trouble, let me know. Come on, we'll go down to the canal and see what's happening.

That's a bad weekit bugger of a boy, my granny said. A stone's never out of his hand and he's aye shivering, standing as if his body's frozen without a pick on him. God love him.

I wore all my clothes; shoes, socks and jumpers, a blue gaberdine trench coat, a scarf and gloves. Francie wore what he always wore, trousers and jumper, socks and sandshoes. I gave him my coat when we were away from the window.

Alec Irvine and Willie Simpson followed us.

Beat it, said Francie.

We're only going up here.
Where?
Up here.
What for?
Nothing.
Where's your sledge?
We're no going sledging.
Beat it, said Francie
And when we were alone, he'd ask, Who were they guys again?
Trappers.
Lookin for bears.
Elk and moose.
Right. We've got to get to the tradin post at the tap o this hill and then we've tae guide the sledge past they eskimos or indians, some bastards that are chasing us.
Fuck em.
Yeah, fuck em.
Okay, Zeke. You got the money for the provisions?
I'm no Zeke. I'm Hank. Who're you?
Bob.
Okay, Bob. We'll need to be mighty careful o they bears going up this hill.
We'll take turns of pulling the sledge and keeping look out.
Sure thing. I got the provision money here, Bob, so we'll get us some fancy food.
What you got in mind, Hank?
Chicken.
Ham.
Fish and chips.
Roast beef.
Chocolate.
Caramels.
Fudge and macaroon bars.
Toffee.
My turn to keep look out. You haul the sledge.
Yup. There's eskimos ower by that igloo but.
Sometimes it was six or seven o'clock when one of us pulled the other into the street. We'd meet up after tea and stand in the close with the men.

FIFTEEN

The Men

THEY STOOD OUTSIDE the Co-operative, on the corner of Vere Street and stared past the New Hooses down towards the Mosshouse. The men stood or squatted on the corner after tea; kids came down with their fathers and now they stamped their feet on the corner by the Vere Street hill.

We'd've been beaten, said Billy Carson. Hitler'd've won if it wasnae for the Americans.

He said he'd been a cowboy in Perthshire, working on a farm during the war. Doing what a cowboy does, he said, taking the beasts from one field to another.

The Americans never fought to defeat Fascism. All they wanted was to protect their trade routes.

My mother said Andy Walker was a Communist who spoke at political meetings and had even been arrested. He'd been everywhere, places whose names were beyond adventure.

We sailed into Fiji on a Wednesday afternoon, he said. The folk came out in canoes and gave us fruit. They traded with us; not trade as we know it here, but a system as old as time, barter. We exchanged gifts. Then they put on a feast for us, everyone singing and falling asleep under the stars, waking with the cold and going back to the ship in the early morning light, the sort of thing that makes you glad to be alive, helps you forget yourself for an hour or two, maybe even allows you to become someone else, at least for a wee while. But the thing I loved best was the sun coming up on the Indian Ocean. It was dark and then it was light, not quite as sudden as that, but within five minutes everything changed, everything.

It seems to me the system that's presently in place in the Soviet Union is just about right, he said.

Here we go.

The trouble with you is that you have no imagination and cannot envisage a world that's different to the one you know. Try it and see how you get on. Think of what you don't like here and imagine how it could be bettered.

Things are changing. The war put an end to the old order.

But the changes are temporary. The system's still intact. Look at what's happening across the world. Revolutionary movements have begun in the most unlikely places. The old order brought us to the verge of collapse, so the solution cannot be found within the old system. It is incapable of adapting and cannot change. It reproduces the old problems: perpetual exploitation, misery for the many, wealth for a few.

And if my granny had balls she'd've been my grandad, Conor Flynn said, smiling. And for a moment it broke the atmosphere.

This is where the Soviet Union under the leadership of Comrade Joseph Stalin is succeeding, and this is why it is succeeding. They've done away with the old problems, they've replaced the old order and are facing the future with new ideas. This is why revolutionary movements in Palestine, India and China, places we thought would be the way they were forever, are changing because of the success of the Soviet Union, and, this is the important part, despite the propaganda war being raged by the capitalist press, workers are waking up to the fact that another system exists, that it doesn't have to be this way; there's another way of living.

If it's so bloody good why don't you go there?

Because this is the society I want to change. The Chinese or Indians are not running to the Soviet Union, asking them to solve their problems; they have taken matters into their own hands and are changing the societies they inhabit. And that's the future, the way forward, not just for us, but especially for the youngsters.

God Almighty, the laddie's no long at the school.

Political awareness can never be taught too early. The present system depends on keeping workers in the dark.

The weather was sharper than expected. Going home, I saw Toby cross the road with something in his mouth. When I got in the close wee Annie smiled: He's brought you a present, she said.

Toby flexed himself round my legs. The rat he'd left at the foot of the stairs was still breathing. The close smelled of gas and was lit by the pale blue and yellow flame from a broken mantle.

Annie scooped up the rat. When she lifted the shovel, the rat sprung and sunk its teeth into the wooden handle. It stayed there, an inch below Annie's thumb, its teeth imbedded in the wood.

Bloody rottans, she said. Worse than men and men are dirty buggers.

She caught the rat by the tail and bludgeoned it against the wall, the thud still rising when Toby and I reached our door.

* * *

Davie Sanderson was a small man with a mouth so narrow he appeared to have no lips. His children looked like him.

God love them; they're no beauties.

Marie, shush.

Davie told us he wanted to emigrate, to get on in the world.

Andy Walker said, The way out of Keppochhill Road is education. If you're too stupid to be educated, then you'll have to find a way of exploiting others, get them to make the money for you. It doesn't take brains to do that.

Did you ever think of emigration?

Sometimes I think about nothing else, said Connor Flynn. I'd go in a minute, but the wife is loath to leave her mother.

It's the wife who's nagging me to go, said a wee man I didn't know. Ever since her sister went to Australia, that's all we get: South Africa, Canada, Australia, New Zealand. Christ, you'd think it was like going to Rothesay to hear her.

Why don't you go?

It's a big decision. If you've people there, family, that'd be different. To go on your own's a big undertaking.

Do you know, you've to pay for everything over there. I heard – was it Jeannie Anderson's cousin that went to Canada or someplace like that, maybe it was Australia – anyway, she had a wean and they'd to pay for everything, even the clouts they used, she'd to pay for them and her food and even for the nursing. Everything. And if you'd no money they didn't even let you in t'the hospital in the first place. You could have your wean in the street for all they care.

That's the Labour government that's changed all that. We don't have to depend on charity now.

We sat on the stairs, the men smoking. Somebody's cousin had married an American and sent home photographs of her family outside a sprawling white home beneath a tree covered in dollar bills. Someone's brother went to America and disappeared. Last heard of in Pittsburg, he said.

Pittsburgh, Pennsylvania, said Andy Walker. A steel town. That's where Carnegie went.

Tell me this, said Junior Johnstone. Are Laurel and Hardy real?

Of course they're real.

How do you know? Have you ever seen them? Apart from in the pictures, and that's not real.

How could they be on the pictures if they're no real? It's a film. There must be something real to photograph.

They could photograph anything and you'd be none the wiser. You wouldnae know if it was real or no. I lie in bed at night and wonder how the pictures work. It could be that Charlie Chaplin, Laurel and Hardy, Buster

Keaton, Charlie Chase, any of them, they might no be real. They could be ghosts or illusions, anything.

But you hear them talking. They walk about, they drive cars and everything.

Ah, but how do you know that's real? The cars are no like cars we've got here. If it was Keppochhill Road, say, or the Glasgow Green, some place like that, then we'd know they were real. But it's America, and we don't know what America's like, so they places might no exist at all. It could be anywhere. It could be the moon for all we'd know. Hear what I'm saying? It could be an imagined place. It could even be someplace near, like Edinburgh for all we'd know. It could be a dream they're giving us, making us believe we can put up with this catastrophe here, go there later and all will be well.

I know what America's like, said Andy Walker. I've been there.

And you've never had a good word to say about the place. You hated it. Every time you mention America it's no like Laurel and Hardy or Robert Taylor or anything like that. You talk about America as if it's Govan or Finnieston, or maybe even worse, someplace that's no very much at all.

A wee guy in the work thinks America's nearer than they say. When you look at it on an atlas, it doesnae seem too far away, does it?

It takes days to get there.

That goes for nothing. It'd take days to get to Rothesay if you went to China first. And you'd still be none the wiser.

Maybe Americans wonder what we're like. Maybe they think there's no such place as Scotland, or that we wear the kilt, speak Gaelic and play the pipes. Maybe they think we're all in the army, cause that's the only kind of Scotsmen they ever see.

Ask the weans what they know about America and it's cowboys, what they see on the pictures, nothing else. Isn't that right, son?

The men and their talk made me think of my father. I often wondered if he'd be waiting with the men when I left the house. First I imagined he'd be in Glasgow; then I thought I'd come in from school and there he'd be, waiting for my mother to get ready, raising his eyes when she asked if anyone had seen whatever she was looking for, saying, It's wherever you left it, telling us we'd a house in Oban.

There'll be more of you, my mother said in Kettle. I'd like a wee girl. Would you like a sister? I'm sure you'd like a sister, wouldn't you?

I am gone to prepare a place for you, the minister said, telling us how good it is to go somewhere new, when someone has prepared a place for us, a ready meal and a warm bed. Some people actually describe these things as Heaven, he said. You hear them, every day on the street, that would be heaven, they say, usually meaning something they haven't got. But that isn't Heaven.

Heaven is where we'll be with God and where we'll see our loved ones again.

Was he in America? No one told me he had gone; no one answered when I asked, so he might be coming back. I tried not cry because I knew he'd return, the way he came back from the war, standing behind steam on a station platform. I imagined he'd come back limping.

I'd read a novel, *The American Adventure*, where Slim and Buddy lived near the woods. Slim's dad was killed when a mineshaft collapsed. Buddy's dad had a row with the boss, said he did not want to be a miner and set off to find work as a trapper, selling bear skins. He was away all winter and while he was gone the boys trapped beaver and when they went down to see their traps they found a dead body floating in the creek. Then Old Grammer Lincoln got crotchety and just when they thought he'd gone forever, when you were caught up with the dead body and the beaver lodges and Old Grammer Lincoln saying Lordy-sakes, Buddy's dad limped over the hill. His foot had been caught in a bear trap but he had wonderful adventures, working as an extra in Buffalo Bill's Wild West Show with Sitting Bull and Annie Oakley.

My mother sat by the fire.

Mother, she asked my granny.

Shush, Marie.

I want to know. Is it true? Did my father only identify Archie with his signet ring?

You know fine what happened.

Is it true?

Your father went down to Burntisland. They wouldn't let him see the body and showed him the ring.

His wedding ring?

That's right.

And what was that song he sang?

SIXTEEN

Compositions

EVERY DAY THE headmaster, John McDougall, told us, You will march from school in orderly lines. You will walk along the pavements as though you were still marching in school. You will honour the school as you honour God and your families and you will not bring shame or disgrace to their names by behaving like hooligans.

On my second day, we were marching from the playground into class. Alex Irvine, who was at my back, clicked my heels and tripped me. I stumbled and caught the headmaster's legs before falling.

He adjusted his tartan tie, looked down on me and looked away. Back to your class, he said. You're a disgrace to the Clan MacDougall.

Miss McClure smiled and we all smiled back.

Your stories should first of all be interesting, she said. If you find them interesting then others will find them interesting too. And don't show off. Write about what you know. Never forget the subject; always keep it in your mind's eye, don't stray: write about your family, don't be afraid to tell us what they're like and I am sure they will live for you in a new and exciting way.

Now your last compositions were very striking, some were good and one was exceptional. Carl, will you come to the front? I want you to read your composition in a loud, clear voice. Head up, back straight; now, on you go.

I got free school dinners every day, meat, two veg, steamed pudding and custard. I sometimes watched the boys play football or walked round the back of the school by the ash-covered pitches above the Back Lawn on the road to St Theresa's, watching the way water gathered, in little rivulets from a hidden source.

I was running back to school when the ragman came out of Benson's Bar, at the top of Pinkston Road. The cart wasn't heavy: rags and plastic windmills, goldfish and balloons. His cheeks inflated when he blew his bugle and his voice seemed sweet when he shouted: Delft for rags; any kind of old rags.

The pony had been standing on the brae and had difficulty stopping itself from being hauled backwards. He stood astride the shafts of his cart, cracked his whip and shouted, Hup. The horse did not move. He swore and cracked the whip again, this time bringing it down on the horse's head. The pony threw its head, lost its footing, the cart rolled back and the ragman fell on to the road.

While the pony scratched the road, red and yellow sparks rising from its hooves, steam from its nostrils, blinking and shaking its head in the rain, crying, the ragman whipped the horse till dark patches spread across the fur, till blood and rain dripped on to the road.

The pony bucked, and in a flurry of sparks from its hooves and the metal rimmed wheels, hauled itself to the top of the brae where it trembled in the rain, the ragman wet and exhausted.

I want you to write about your family, Miss McClure said. Write about the ordinary things around you. I want you to write about your mothers and fathers, your brothers and sisters. I want you to write about yourselves and what you know of your family's past.

Please, miss, I asked at the end of day. Can I, can I, can I?

Take your time, Carl. Take a deep breath and think about what you're going to say and then you're more likely to say it clearly, without a stutter.

Please miss, can I write about something else?

What would you like to write about?

I don't know.

I think I'd like to see what you have to say about your family. I'm sure it would be interesting. Any aspect of family life that appeals to you would do; the idea is to take your time, not too long, of course, then hand it in.

I sometimes ran from the boys' playground, up Scone Street, along the Back Lawn and galloped down towards the Long Stairs like the Pony Express, making sure the mail got through, arrows whirring past, long hair flying. But I knew my granny would be watching, so I walked along Keppochhill Road, past the Auld Hoose, the Slavin dairy and Capaldi's cafe, past Carlo's fish and chip shop, the chemist and Austin's Bar, past the Long Stairs and along three closes to Jessie Jackson's and the post office.

I dropped my schoolbag by the door and made my way past the furniture in the lobby. My grandfather was reading and grunted when I told him I was going to the library. In the lobby, Granny gave me a penny and told me there was soup for tea.

Possilpark Library children's section was to the right of the door in Allander Street. The woman examined my hands, then looked at the book I returned: *A Star Spotters' Guide to the Heavens*.

This book was issued a week ago. You can't have read it all in that time.

No, miss. I haven't, I haven't, I haven't.

Hurry up.

I haven't read it all.

Then why do you want another book?

I've written down, written down.

Spit it out.

There's things I need in another book.

Five minutes then. No more.

The fiction panels were along the wall at the back and down the side, three shelves high with books displayed along the top. I picked three books with the word family in the title.

One book only. One at a time, she said.

I chose *The Swiss Family Robinson*.

* * *

Marie. You should get that boy a helmet.

Aye, so I will.

Look at that: there's they bad weekit buggers of boys flinging stanes and one of them could wallop him on the heid and what would you do if he's lying there wi his brains hanging out like that poor cratur who got hit by a bus?

In the Springburn Co-operative I stood behind my mother.

Do you have a helmet that would fit this boy, please?

I'm not going to wear it.

Shush.

We have leather helmets, madam. Strong and very hard wearing.

How much?

I think that one is seven shillings and sixpence.

Then it'll do somebody else.

It's an exceptional garment. Hand stitched and with a fleece lining. There are aviator's earpieces.

I don't want something that'll make him deaf.

This one's made of what I think is a Rexine type of material.

Do you want me to put a chair covering on his head?

Marie, you'll need to get that boy a helmet. It's a cold and a bitter day and that boy of yours is out there, walking about without a scarf to his neck or a coat on his back. God Almighty, what'll happen next.

Some havoc with my name attached was ready to spring. Innocent occasions were fraught with danger and God was useless. We never were a lucky family; someone had cursed us. Some malign authority had concocted a recipe for disaster stretching to my generation and beyond.

And keep you away from that canal. If I find you've been down at that canal or anywhere near it, up Jack's Mountain or the Stinky Ocean, I tell you I'll have something to say about it. There's no sides on that canal. Drunk men wander in and drown so what would happen to a child, for I wouldnae put it past some bad weekit bugger of a boy to push you in, and then God only knows what would happen. What would we do then with you in the canal? You'd probably drown, for nobody'd hear you, not a soul. You'd be screaming and screaming and screaming. God Almighty, think of the torment.

Johan, my grandfather said. Jo, for the love of God, woman, would you give us peace.

It'll no be that if anything happens to him.

I was told to walk along the wall, well away from the edge of the pavement and to stay clear of anyone who coughed or spat in the street. Horses were erratic, you couldn't trust a horse, never knew what it was going to do. She'd seen a man kicked by a horse and for years after he was never right in the head, poor soul. I had to watch tramlines and could not cross the road, nor go anywhere alone. I couldn't ride a bicycle or eat food prepared in another home. I had to keep away from fire and water, gas and electricity, unmarried men and big girls who'd been here before. Games were worst of all. Football pitches were littered with ruptured spleens and broken limbs, concussion was usual and if you got that it sent you daft. Rope games meant you could trip, running was dangerous because of broken glass. Something could happen. I had to be careful.

Did you never think about a helmet? I'm sure next time you're in Springburn you could go into the Co-operative and pick up a nice helmet for a shilling or two.

They don't have helmets.

Are you telling me shops don't sell helmets?

They're waiting on more coming in.

He can't play football without a helmet. That ball's hard and would batter his brains out. And look at these bad weekit buggers o boys, they're never without a stone or a lump of brick in their hand.

* * *

I wrote something about a family who'd been shipwrecked on an island near Oban. The damaged ship forced them to remain on the island, despite the presence of pirates. They lived in a tree house, till one of the boys sails off with the pirates.

Was this what you wanted to write about? asked Miss McClure.

Yes, miss.

I hoped you might write something about your own family. Why didn't you do that?

Please miss I, please miss I, please miss I.

Take your time. Stop talking, take a deep breath and hold the air inside you. Now, let it out and tell me.

Please miss I don't know what to say about my family.

I'd like you to try.

I wrote about a family who lost their father just before Christmas. He'd gone to work and never came back.

Miss McClure read the story and smiled. I would like to know what happens afterwards, she said. Who are his friends?

I enjoyed it when she called on me to read what I'd written to the class, loved the attention and didn't stammer; which made it difficult when I spoke to the other kids. I felt I couldn't speak to anyone in case I stuttered. When I stammered they made a fool of me or turned and walked away. Girls would start a conversation just to hear me stammer. And when I stumbled they'd laugh till I moved away. Then they followed, repeating questions I couldn't answer:

Are you a German?

Where's Kettle?

Is Carl a girl's name?

How do we know your dad's dead?

Miss McClure gave me a story to read.

It's by a girl, she said, but I think you'll enjoy it. I used to teach her and she was a bit older than you when she wrote this; I know she went to university, but I don't know if she survived the war.

There was no name on the story. It had been torn from a school jotter and was written in blue ink with the title at the top of the page.

A girl comes home from school excited about the Romans, who had camped near Glasgow and built a wall, more of a ditch and a dyke really. This meant they had been where she was, that although they wouldn't have lived in the same street, they could have walked where she walked, that the places where she and her friends liked to go could have been places the Romans visited.

She had tried to imagine how a Roman girl would feel. Their lives were so different, but the Roman girl would have been angry and lonely, afraid and tired. She'd have been bored and excited by school. She would have hated housework, but knew it had to be done.

The Roman girl would have few toys, no dolls or prams, but she had her friends and they'd talk about their lives and families, their brothers and their brothers' friends, who were serving in different countries, one in Spain and the other in Germany. The girls hated the climate, hated the rain, the wind and the cold and they couldn't understand why people wanted to live here or give their lives to defend it. They missed home and wanted to learn how to cook using the ingredients they had at home, like lemons, to swim in the warm sea and eat grapes they couldn't get here. They hated sewing and loved to sing together. Their friends were the most important things in the Roman girls' lives and they spent time together in each others' houses, doing their hair and telling each other stories.

Miss McClure asked if I liked it and pointed out one or two things I had missed or hadn't considered important, such as the way the writer had used paragraphs and how she had never lost the sense of imagination, that from the beginning, it was clear that she was imagining this, that she hadn't dreamed it or read about it in a book. The fact that she imagined it made it believable and kept it in the present.

I'd like you to write about your friends, she said.

I think I'm going to be, going, I think I am going to be busy, miss.

And what are you going to be busy doing?

Helping my mother.

I'm sure your mother would give you some time off to do your school work, especially if she knew it was something you liked doing.

I had long conversations with pretend friends, devised scenarios where people would be proud of me, where I would be welcomed into the community as a hero. When I was asked who I'd been with, who my friends were and what we had done, I made up boys' names. When my mother said she didn't know them, I gave fictional addresses.

It didn't take me long to realise she knew a few folk in the area, but not many. She left the house just after six to clean a lawyer's office in the Lion Chambers in Hope Street and finished in time to serve breakfasts in the Central Hotel. She did morning coffees till mid-day when she went to the railway headquarters at 302 Buchanan Street where she served lunches till half past two. She was in when I came home from school, but often went out at night to do a function, and was usually not home till after midnight. She was the only wage earner.

Your mother's tired, my grandfather told me. It's important you don't do anything to annoy or upset her. You should do what you're told and try to make life easy for her. She's changed.

My father isn't here, I wrote. I said I missed his voice, missed his singing and the way he walked. I missed the scrape of his beard and couldn't smell Johnson's Baby Powder. I thought he'd left because of me. I had to guess what happened, because I wasn't told. I didn't know what it meant.

I wondered where we would be and what we would be doing. I didn't want to do what other boys did with their fathers. When he came back it would be different.

Then I wrote of the difference between Keppochhill Road, Kettle and Oban. And gave Miss McClure the composition.

* * *

I told Francie I'd stayed awake and seen the sunset. That's no the sunset, he said. It's Dixon's Blazes.

How do you know?

One of my Das used to work there.

How many Das have you had.

Two, I think. Maybe three.

And what's Dixon's Blazes?

I think it's a big foundry, like Alan Ure's. That red sky comes from their fires. Last night, when my Uncle Tommy was drunk, he got us out of bed and made us stand in front of the fire like soldiers. Some day, he said, yous weans'll stand at the Border and fight the English. Not at all, said my Uncle Danny, They'll die for Ireland, every one.

Francie knew things I didn't know. We found a used sanitary towel on the ash tracks by the pitches, poked it with sticks and stared.

What is it? I asked.

It has to do with shagging, he said.

We were always late back. He came to the library and followed me round. Get one for me, he said. And later we would find a place on a stair landing where I'd read his story. He liked adventure stories, boy detectives. That's what we'll do, he said. We'll find this great mystery and solve it then we'll get a stack of money and be rich and live some place nice.

I'd go back to Fife. Or Oban.

What's it like?

And I'd tell him a little.

What's a cow like? he asked. Is it maybe about the size of a horse?

So I told him about farm animals and railway journeys that ended at the sea.

Is it just water? And are the ships like in pictures? Do boats have sails? How come the Forth Bridge doesnae collapse? All at once, one question after another. He had never been further than Springburn Park, had never heard a radio and thought tramcars went on forever, round the world. He was used to his fathers disappearing.

We could take a car to India and see Buffalo Bill, he said. Maybe your da'll be there when you go in.

So we'd find a quiet close, tiptoe up to the top landing and huddle together under the gas light. His favourite story was *Henrik's Forest Home*. When I finished reading he always wanted me to read the bit where Big Jacques, the French Canadian trapper laid dynamite in the mine. Francie would smile; all the time I was reading his face was fixed in a radiant grin.

More, he'd say. More.

I've to go in for my tea. I'll get a big row, roarin and greetin and everything.

One more page. Right? Just another page.

Then I'd have to run home, through streets almost deserted as shops were shutting and families had their tea, through a series of corners where ghosts lay in every shadow, in every darkened place, ready to pounce, making me jump over cracks and take the stairs three at a time. I always arrived home breathless, looking down the stairs from the door, in case I was really being chased.

One night my mother was embroidering a white tablecloth by the fire, coloured threads on the floor around her or hanging from her clothes, needles in her mouth. Miss McClure has asked to see me, she said. Do you know what it's about?

I shook my head.

Where were you anyway? And why are you out of breath?

He was being chased by they bad weekit buggers o' boys that throw stones in the dark, my granny said.

SEVENTEEN

Saved

HIS HAIR WAS parted in the centre. He wore a dark-blue double-breasted suit, a white shirt with a studded collar and a maroon tie. His shoes were brightly polished. He had a bluish growth on his cheeks and chin.

God Almighty. What a fright I got. I looked down at that man and thought it was your daddy, my granny said when Mister Smith, his wife and two or three others from the Gospel Hall came round the backcourts singing hymns and bearing witness on a Sunday afternoon.

That Lizzie Paterson would be better off cleaning under her bed than singing hymns in the backcourts of Glasgow, my mother said.

God love her. She's had a hard life, said Aunt Barbara.

There's plenty folk who've had a hard life, but don't all go round the backcourts shouting up at windows and singing hymns, Granny said. Marie. Is that man no like Archie?

Archie never went round the backs singing.

Here, my granny said. Come you here to me and tell me what that man's wearing.

His shoes are that well polished and his clothes well pressed. There you are now, she said in triumph. I told you. You know how Archie aye liked to be neat and tidy as if he'd come out a bandbox. And his son's taken after him.

* * *

It was raining. We had been to Springburn Library and took our books up Mrs Jamieson's close to keep them dry. She swept the stairs every day, wearing rubber gloves, an apron and a diamante brooch at her lapel. She complained about her neighbours.

We'll need to be quiet.

I know. Just stay over here and whisper.

Right, then. Read to me, Francie said.

No you read it yourself. I want to look at my own book.

Francie sang 'Five Minutes More'. What do you think that means? he asked. Five minutes more in your arms.

Shh.

Right. Sing this, come on:

> He always sings.
>> What does he sing?
> Raggity music to the cattle as he swings.
>> How does he swing?
> Back and forward in his saddle on a horse.

Mrs Jamieson's door bounced open.

Hooligans, she shouted. I will have a word with your fathers and don't think I won't. If you want to make a noise, do it outside your own doors.

We havenae any faithers, said Francie.

I'm not a bit surprised. Out of here, go on, down this stair immediately or I will send for the police. I have a telephone, you know and I will phone the police station immediately.

She watched us down to the landing below. If I see you back here again, I'll have you sent to a home, she said.

On the next floor, Francie said, Shh.

What is it?

Somebody's there.

Where?

Downstairs.

Where?

In the back close.

How do you know?

I can hear him. Listen.

Who is it?

Sandshoe Sannie.

Listen, she'll get the polis. She's got a cop phone.

What'll we dae?

He's murdering somebody. Listen.

We'll go and see, said Francie. Maybe we'll stop him and get a reward.

Okay, but listen; we'll only go downstairs and keek round the corner, then run like hell, cause if he finds us here he'll kill us too.

Francie looked round the corner. It's Joey Docherty and Wee Senga Thomson.

Senga drew her coat round Joey. Get yous away to hell out of here, she shouted. Cheeky wee buggers.

We ran into the rain and along the road, past the shops and closes to our favourite bit, up my Uncle Charlie's close, where I turned up the gas and settled down to read.

That's what Sandshoe Sannie's like, said Francie. He's got sandshoes so's he can creep up dead quiet, then he gets you and murders you, flings your body in the canal and you're never seen again. Honest.

Francie, you're no reading your book

If you tell anybody, I'll kill you. I know Sandshoe Sannie and I'll tell him to get you.

I could teach you.

What?

I could teach you to read.

Right, on you go then.

I'll read this and you can follow.

What's my book called?

What Katy Did Next.

That's an A, said Francie. Sure it is?

Uh-hu.

And that's And.

That's right. What's that?

But.

That's great. Can you write?

What do you think?

Want to learn?

If you like.

I've to go up for my tea.

Will we read tomorrow?

Uh-hu.

Promise?

Sure.

Swear on your Auntie Barbara's wean's life and hope to die?

I promise.

And write as well?

Aye.

A policeman was waiting at the foot of the stairs.

What were you pair of hooligans doing up there? he asked.

Reading.

And is that what yous were doing up Mrs Jamieson's close?

Uh-hu.

Well, I think yous boys are very naughty boys because yous've been reported for mischief, and if I catch yous again, or if I even hear of yous being up Mrs Jamieson's close readin books or breakin into hooses, which is what she said yous were doing, and creating a riot by singin, I will personally see that yous're hanged, drowned, burned and shot and fined when your library books are overdue. Do yous hear me?

Aye.

Sure Sandshoe Sannie's real? said Francie.

We caught him last week. He was raiding a blind hen's store of worms. Now, away hame the two o yese.

* * *

There were two black paraffin heaters on the stage of the Gospel Hall. Every Sunday they distorted the texts on the bare wall:

> The Wages of Sin is Death
> *Romans* 6:23
> What Must I Do to Be Saved?
> *Acts* 16:30

Looking through the heat was like finding substance behind the bevelled glass on Jimmy Delacourt's door or seeing shadows through the heavy, knobbled glass in the school entrance.

We sat on wooden benches.

Francie said his name was Frankie McDonald. They think I'm a Protestant, he said.

And finally, said Mrs Smith. Who has a testament? What boy or girl has an inspirational story to tell of the events in their life since they gave their soul to the Lord.

Please, Miss, said a girl with pigtails. I gave my soul to the Lord two weeks ago and he's helped me at school.

Wonderful, child. Your tea is poured.

And I have washed at the sink every night since my soul's been saved.

Join your sister.

Margaret McCrory's no my sister.

She is your sister in Christ, my child.

Aye, but that that's no real, sure it's no.

Anyone else?

How'd you cry her my sister if she's no my sister?

Anyone else? Perhaps a boy this time.

I prayed to Jesus every night since I've been saved to see if he'd save my pal as well and he's here to be saved the day, said Francie.

Wonderful, Frankie. Wonderful. What an example to us all. From the mouths of babes and children shall ye learn, said the Lord and how right that is. Tell me your name, boy?

Carl, miss.

And how long have you wanted to give your soul to Jesus?

I don't know.

He's wanted to gie his soul to Jesus every night since his da died, said Francie.

To lose a loved one is especially hard. But the Lord has called your father, and he has gone to prepare a place for you, as Jesus promised. And your daddy will be looking down on you now, rejoicing with the Lord that you've been saved. Our hearts are filled with joy and overflowing with love for the Lord that another child has been rescued from the clutches of Satan. Everybody sing the chorus with actions:

> Running over. Running over.
> My cup's full and running over.
> Since the Lord saved me
> I'm as happy as can be
> My cup's full and running over.
> Jesus wants me for a sunbeam, a sunbeam, a sunbeam.
> Jesus wants me for a sunbeam.
> I'll be a sunbeam for him.
> For I'm H-A-P-P-Y. I'm H-A-P-P-Y
> I know I am; I'm sure I am
> I'm H-A-P-P-Y.

Pray with me child, come and pray with me. Everybody close their eyes and pray with me and the newfound lamb that has been lost. Once again, dear Lord we thank you for all your many blessings, for the food we eat, our homes and families, our loved ones. And we thank you most especially for your dear son Jesus who died on the cross that we might be saved. God we pray that you will take and bless this poor sinner. What's your name son? Your name? What is it? This poor sinner, for Jesus sake. Amen.

Go to the back and get your tea.

Mister Smith shook my hand and said I could witness at Kirkintilloch in a week or two. He cannae, said Francie. He helps me with my sick mum.

Of course.

The cakes were stale, though you could take as many as you liked. The tea was milky, hot and sweet, made in the urn.

I might go and witness to see what Kirkintilly's like, said Francie. Is it far away?

I don't know.

Will there be horses there? Or coos?

It will if it's in the country.

How come he never asked me to witness?

Maybe it's because you swear and sing outside auld Jamieson's door.

C'mon, we'll go doon the canal and see if there's any hot water coming out the power station. Unless you're scared your blind granny sees you. And then you can read that bit of a story again.

The canal walkways were cobbled and backed by warehouses, some disused and crumbling, others painted and shining with promise. From Pinkston Road, across the canal bridge, before the railway line from Buchanan Street to Oban, lay Jack's Mountain the Stinky Ocean, Francie's favourite place. We sat and watched the warm water gush from the power station, making the canal eddy in a warm spiral.

We tethered our horses by the back of the mountain, then lay on the ash to see where the Indians were camped. Four of them over there, said Al. They want to parlay. Keep me covered.

I kept the chief in my sights while Al traded furs and rifles in exchange for a clear run through with the stage. I don't trust that chief, Al whispered when he came back. We'd better ride with the stage and make sure they don't attack us when we cross the river.

We sat by the ford, rifles cocked while our horses grazed and the stage crossed the river. Then they attacked, from everywhere, arrows whizzed past our ears and took off our hats. They charged us with tomahawks, regrouped and charged again till the stage was lost and there was just the two of us, with only a dead horse to shield us, till the cavalry appeared on the brow of the hill and chased the Indians back to the reservation. They thanked us for helping with the stage and we rode with the cavalry back to the trading post.

EIGHTEEN

Blood

GOD LOVE HER and keep her. What a terrible time; what an awful time for tragedy to strike. No that there's a good time, but this is an awful time, a terrible time of the year when we're supposed to be thinking about love and peace and Jesus. It's shocking, so it is; terrible shocking.

I was looking at the cakes on Delacourts' counter, waiting to buy some treacle for my cold: hot milk and treacle soothed a cough, after you had your eyes shut tight with a towel over your head, breathing in through the nose over a steaming basin of boiling water and ammonia.

There's my boyfriend, waiting for me to serve him, said Jean. I'll be with you in a second, Carl. I like your scarf. It's big enough; that should keep you rare and warm.

I blushed.

Aye. A deep cut's a sair cut.

You're not blushing, are you, Carl?

I'm fine.

I'll be with you in a second.

You can serve the laddie if you'd like.

I don't think he minds waiting.

God, but it's a sin and a shame. He maybe was never much of a man, but he was all the man she had and she must have felt something for him one time. And for him to have died like that is hellish. God love him, he must've wandered off. Lost his way, poor lamb, the same as us all. He was their weans' father and now they've nobody, nobody at all, except her, poor soul.

Was there anything else you wanted, Mrs Dickson?

Gibby Tolcher was dead. It was in the papers. The *Daily Record* said the body of an unidentified man had been found floating in the Forth and Clyde Canal by Pinkston Power Station. And the police had been to Mrs Tolcher's door. They'd taken her to the City Mortuary by Glasgow Green, where she identified her husband. He had a ten shilling note in his right hand.

Gibby worked in Macfarlanes and drank in the Cosy Corner. Every Friday and Saturday night he'd sing 'Bread and Cheese and Onions' outside the pub door.

Shush, my granny said. Shush till I hear him.

Then he'd cross the road and stand outside his close shouting for help. Francie told me, Take him up the stairs. Help him and he'll gie ye money.

We walked behind him, supporting his back while he held onto the walls, taking the stairs one at a time till he reached the top.

God bless the weans o' Keppochhill Road, he said. God bless them, one and all. Yous're all good weans to your mammies and grannies; and remember this, yous've all to be good weans to your mammies and grannies for yous'll miss them when their gone. Oh, yes. You'll always miss a mother's love. Yous're all good weans to your mammies and grannies, helping auld Gibby Tolcher up the stair.

When we reached the top he asked if we knew the words of his favourite song, then he'd sing, searching his pockets for pennies and ha'pennies, sometimes a sixpence or a threepenny bit:

> Take a toddle, have a nice long walk
> in the country every morning;
> Open your mouth and swallow all the air,
> and when you're tired yawning;
> Step into a nice wee pub, sit doon and rest your bunions;
> then call for hauf and a pint o beer
> Wi bread and cheese and onions.

Bring him in, said, Mrs Tolcher. Bring him in for the love o' God. By the way, do any of yous weans smoke?

Oh, bairnies, cuddle doon, said Gibby, taking off his boots. The finest poem ever written by any man or woman excepting Rabbie Burns and that goes without saying. The lad that was born in Kyle. Oh, yes. Listen to this, laddies: 'Bairnies, Cuddle Doon', by Alexander Anderson, an ordinary man, a working man who understood the working man's heart. Oh yes, the bairnies. That's no the right title, but it's what it's been known as from the day and hour I first heard it:

> The bairnies cuddle doon at nicht
> Wi muckle faught and din;
> 'Oh try and sleep, ye waukrife rogues
> Your faither's comin' in.'
> They never heed a word I speak:
> I try to gie a froon,
> But aye I hap them up an' cry.
> 'Oh, bairnies, cuddle doon.'

Did he gie yous any money? Mrs Tocher asked.

Gibby was usually asleep by the third verse and Mrs Tolcher wouldn't let us leave till we'd emptied our pockets.

Thank you, laddies. See yous next week.

Mrs Dickson waited while Jean served another customer.

It'll take two ounces of ham for their tea and that'll do me, said Mrs Dickson. It'll be a sorry Christmas in that hoose and no much of a New Year either. What is that poor woman going to do for presents and how'll she bury her man? A parish funeral, that'll be it. The parish. God save us all from the misery of a pauper's grave.

Was there anything else?

No, that'll do me. And would you put this in the book till Friday. God love they poor bits of weans.

By the way, we've started a sheet, said Jean Delacourt.

I'll need to be gettin over the road.

I said, we've started a sheet for Mrs Tolcher.

Aye, that's right, poor soul. God help her, that's good o folk. She'll need a' the help she can get.

There you are, Carl. Still waiting. I see you've got your eye on these cream cookies. I'm just going to have one with my tea and I'll give you a bite if you tell me what you're getting for Christmas.

* * *

Aunt Eva and Uncle Matt came up from Turnberry where she was working at the RAF Base as a canteen manageress. They brought two boxes of food, including a chicken, chocolates and cigars we'd to keep till Christmas, and when no one was looking Aunt Eva gave me my first bar of chocolate in the lobby.

Eat it all to yourself, she said.

After we'd eaten onions, steak, chips and peas, then apple tart and custard, Matt told us they'd leave when their passage was arranged, six weeks at most.

They were to live in Ontario which was red on the Atlas, one province in from Quebec which was green and along from the blue island of Newfoundland at the mouth of the St Lawrence River. They would sail up the river to Montreal then take the train for Toronto, eventually arriving in Matt's home in Brigden in the middle of nowhere with nothing much except the paper mill where he'd worked. Now he thought they'd be moving to Thorold on the Welland Canal, which takes ships to Lake Ontario, avoiding the Niagara Falls, where was sure he had a job.

You could come and see us, Matt said. When we're settled, you could come for a holiday, come and stay.

It's no the same as going to Millport is it, Granny said. Where would we get the money to send him to Canada?

Now, Jo, you don't know what lies ahead.

Are you going to get the money?

There's no use discussing it now. One thing at a time, we've enough to contend with.

Canada has great opportunities. Once we're settled and have a place of our own, we'll get you across there, all of you. You as well, Mrs Kaufmann.

If I go there, you'll have to bring me back in a box.

* * *

Uncles George and Charlie worked for Wilson Brothers in Pinkston Road. Charlie was a foreman brickie. I'd go down the road to meet them coming home from work.

School broke up on Christmas Eve. I couldn't find Francie who told me he would probably be in chapel all day, so when we left the church I walked down Pinkston to my Uncle Charlie's work. I used to stand outside the gates to hear the noise of George's machine, the way the sound changed, how the pitch became denser the further the blade cut into the stone; when the yard was busy, the noise of his machine rose above the rattle of the lorries. There was a ginger cat, cranes and pumps, a draughty office and men shouting above the noise. Only the sign spread above the gates, painted black with a red shadow, Wilson Brothers, Builders, seemed the same.

I arrived as they were leaving.

Well, Carl, and how was work today? Charlie asked.

Were you busy? asked George. Get much done?

No bad, a wee bit.

Do you think he's a good worker, George? Are you taking him on your squad?

Our squad's full. What about you?

I think we've a place in our squad.

Smart boy wanted.

That's it, you thinking of applying?

* * *

My mother cried on Christmas morning. She was sobbing by the front room window, staring at an already dreich day.

Did you get your present?

I haven't opened it.

I went back to the kitchen and sat by the fire while the kettle boiled, made tea and carried the cup into the front room. My mother hadn't moved. She neither acknowledged the tea nor my presence. We stared across to the coal ree and potato shed, the railway yard and piles of wood till she wiped her eyes with the corner of her apron.

I suppose we'll need to get on with it, she said.

Later, when I was reading my new books by the fire, she stirred the gravy, sobbing openly, her tears mingling with the water, the browning and the salt.

Marie, my granny said. Marie, for God's sake, will you pull yourself together.

Marie, my grandfather said, you'll have to learn to live for the sake of the boy.

A red glow in the chimney soot were fairies in the fire. If there were fairies you could send your letter to Santa, or make a wish. I had written asking that my father come home and my mother stop crying. Later, after my first taste of chicken, when they were playing a hand of whist, drinking beer and sometimes singing, one would start the snatch of a song and the others joined in, my mother asked Granny, Mother, what did Archie look like?

* * *

Every day it rained. Water ran down the Back Lawn Stairs, down Vere Street, through the backcourts, closes and onto the street.

We ran to school, huddled in the playground and ran home. When the rain stopped, dampness hung in the air. Familiar places became distant and it took a while for folk to come out of their dens, onto the street corners and closes. When Francie and I came back from the library the crowd had gathered in Uncle Charlie's close.

I can't understand why anyone would want to live in Canada, said Andy Walker. It's a Western democracy, with typical Western democratic problems. Why do they need people? Because they have little or no indigenous population. And why do they have no indigenous population? Because they've killed them all, which means, they'll take any Tom, Dick or Harry. Australia, South Africa, New Zealand, they're all the same; fine, big and open countries with no sense of identity because they're tied to the British Crown.

Don't start that sort of talk around here, said Davie Sanderson. I won't hear a word said against His Majesty.

If you had the ability to think for yourself you might actually be able to tell me if you believe in Scotland.

What do you mean?

Do you think Scotland exists?

If this isnae Scotland, where is it?

It's a close, part of a building on a street which is part of a district in a city called Glasgow which, it so happens, occupies part of a country called Scotland. This Scotland is interesting. Ask someone what it means and they'll tell you one thing while another person will tell you something else, but most of us are agreed it's an idea.

Don't talk bloody daft.

Where do you work?

You know damn fine where I work.

Allan Ure's, where you are a labourer.

A blacksmith's mate.

Fine. That's your Scotland, isn't it? Noise and a furnace. Mine is the railway. When I was young I went to sea and when I came back I was fit for nothing but the railway, so that's my Scotland, the railway; but, what was my father's Scotland? A farm and the First World War, unemployment, a job on the railway and a house in Springburn. My mother's Scotland was different: she's a Gael from Lewis, so she lives in a Scotland with two languages, one of which her children hear when her sister comes, when they speak this strange language and laugh. But her Scotland is gathering peats and harvest, washing blankets in the burn, same as my father. They met at a market in Stirling. He was selling cows and she was there with her mother and father. So what's her Scotland? Am I making sense?

Not to me.

That's because you see Scotland as a place rather than an identity.

If you're so bloody clever how come you're a railway fireman?

Because of the kind of Scotland I come from. I only managed to get a job on the railway because my father was already there. Does that seem fair to you, because it doesn't seem fair to me. How did you get into Ure's?

None of your business.

Same way; a nod, a wink and a handshake. Somebody spoke for you. So that's another part of your Scotland.

I don't know about anybody else, but I've had enough. I'm going upstairs.

Would you say your Scotland is the same as the Duke of Argyll's Scotland or the Scotland partially inhabited by their Graces the Dukes of Buccleuch, Hamilton and Atholl or just about anywhere else you'd care to mention, but take that trio, not a bad half back line.

I'm fed up with this.

Now is not the time to run away. Answer the question.

What question?

Is your Scotland the same as the Duke of Argyll's or even someone who lives in Milngavie or Bearsden?

I don't know.

Of course you know, but you've accepted your lot as a proud member of the lumpen proletariat, because one of your finger milking friends spoke for you and that was all right so to hell with everyone else. Do you know what their Scotland's like?

Whose?

Don't pretend you're stupider than you are. I know what the gentry's Scotland is like, because I hate this bloody city and I hate this street and I hate this condition because I know there's better and I want better because I deserve better because I'm as good as the next man and I don't mind privilege based on merit, but not on birth.

Is that the sermon finished?

He's talking sense, said Connor Flynn. And that's the trouble. It's sensible, but no very practical. Don't think some of us have never thought about this, Andy. We've thought about it all right, and reached the conclusion that things'll never change.

You'll never change, said Davie Sanderson. You'll never change because you think whatever the priest tells you to think. If the priest tells you to think it, then that'll be right.

Shows how much you know, said Connor. The priest can tell us anything he likes, but it doesn't mean we have to do it.

You do what the priest tells you and he does what Stalin tells him and then has the cheek to call himself a free thinker. He's a fool.

Comrade Stalin led the Soviet peoples through the greatest battle of their history, against the might of the German army.

We all faced that.

Not like Leningrad. Hitler's intention was to destroy the Soviet Union, everyone knows that. Instead, the Soviet people defeated him and are now struggling to survive in a world where they are no longer allies. Why do you think that is, Mister Sanderson? I'm sure you'll tell me. It is because the Soviet people are showing the working classes of the world that there is an alternative to the system of divide and rule, patronage and repression, that it is possible for folk to live in freedom and dignity without the say so of some leech who'll take whatever's going and give nothing back but condescension.

I will not listen to this traitorous talk. You're no better than a Nazi.

Apologise.

I will not.

Let me ask you again and this time I am very serious. Apologise, Mister Sanderson.

Where were you when better men than you were dying for their country?

I would willingly have fought Fascism.

Where were you? Where were you when I was at Arnhem? Perthshire, was it? The Angus Glens? Put away with the women and children because you refused to defend them, so I had to go and fight for the likes of you and your family as well as my own, so that you could come back here and call me stupid. You're no too anxious to talk about why you were a conshie or why they wouldnae let you fight. I don't know how you can hold your head up in this street or any other, far less come away with the traitorous nonsense you're allowed to speak here. If the Soviet Union's so wonderful, why don't you go there and see how far you'd get with that kind of talk. You're a traitor and no better than a Nazi.

Davie Sanderson was standing in the close, the gas lamp above his head and to the right, stretching his features, darkening half his face. Andy Walker was seated on a step with Connor Flynn above and beside him. Billy Carson and Junior Johnstone were behind Connor Flynn, I saw Francie with the other children perched behind the men, four or five in the dark, the broken stairhead windows blowing a continual draught.

Andy Walker stood up, and before he was erect, his right arm swung from below his waist. Davie Sanderson was too late. He jerked his head back, but the blow caught him on the chin, unsteadying him, throwing his weight to the left side of his body, where another fist was moving towards his head; again, his head swung round as the second punch connected and as his head swung round to meet the third, he pushed himself forward in a vain attack but met Andy Walker's right fist which connected squarely with Davie Sanderson's nose. His face crumpled. His eye closed as his nose was flattened into his cheek bone and blood squirted from his nose and mouth. Andy Walker stood back to avoid the chaos that scattered over the close, on the grey flags and stone stairs, across the walls and down Chrissie Anderson's flush panelled door with the terrazzo step.

Bastard.

Apologise.

Fucken lousy bastard.

Andy Walker stepped forward. A globule of blood hit him on the cheek. He winced and closed his eyes, shaking his head.

I'm sorry, he said. I'm sorry it came to this. Can we shake hands?

Fuck off.

Blood was spotted on my knees, down my legs and socks and shoes.

Connor Flynn spat on a rag from his pocket. Here now, he said. Surely to God your mother will think the blood is yours. You'd better get yourself wiped out of that before she sees it.

Chrissie Anderson threw cold water over the stone. It glistened in the gas light, turned a pale pink, became water and disappeared.

NINETEEN

Canada

Pinkston power station provides the electricity for the Glasgow tramway system. It is therefore an extremely important building and one of which we should all be proud.

I could barely read my writing. It was the first composition I had written in ink, using a new nib. The wooden handles of the pen were stained dark blue and the holder was rusty.

Thank you, Carl. That was very interesting, said Miss McClure, handing back our compositions. I'm not sure you covered the subject. What was the subject we were asked to write about? Yes, Mary.

Please, miss, A Memorable Family Event.

And what was your memorable event?

Please, miss. My sister had a baby.

That's memorable for all the family, isn't it? Now, what about you Andrew?

Andy McNair was a wee boy with spiky hair and a turned eye, whose father used to challenge the Cosy Corner to fight, get a doing then go home and batter his wife. The police were called, he left, came back, went away and came back till she took in a lodger, a roadsman from County Fermanagh who came home singing.

Andy told us his uncle was a cowboy. His auntie was a film star and his other uncle played for Rangers. His mother had been heard to remark in the Co-operative that Andrew's teacher thought he had a rare imagination.

Outside it was raining. Seagulls glided past the window. They landed on the ledge, stared into the classroom, sniffed the sea, turned and dropped in the air. I longed to see them land on the playground, three storeys below.

The school was on a hill at the top of Pinkston Road. A stone wall rose from the street. There were entrances on either side and the playgrounds were divided by a wall with high, green railings. The Boys' Entrance was on Scone Street and the Girls' Entrance opposite the park.

The view was dominated by the twin towered chimneys and the square, flat roof of Pinkston power station. Every day, smoke covered the city; the haze forced lights to fade in the street. This was when leaves were stuck to the pavements and shoes tinkled on the cobbles, when the back of the nose and corners of the eyes were thick and moist all day. It was worse at night. Fog cleared on Sundays and we longed for rain.

Or the city appeared like a flash through gauze, when a streak of sunlight brushed the roofs, or a cluster of slates sparkled in the rain.

Some time in the early afternoon the air would lift, as though a wind from below had cleared the smoke and a concentration of uneven turrets, towers and belfries shimmered in the distance. Flocks of starlings rose and turned like a skein of silk above a place I had never been, a city that was different to where I lived, as though Glasgow was imagined steeples and spires, magnificent distances and tree ranked avenues.

Some towers were stone, others brick. There were slate roofs, iron and glass decorations above the parapets and corbels. A continuous haze sometimes descended, dark and grey, occasionally shot through with sunlight which heightened the mystery, as though the roofs and towers had absorbed the light, abandoning the streets to whatever dropped below. I imagined they were dark and dank, filled with people who strained to catch sunlight and longed to rise to the top of the buildings.

* * *

Why didn't you write about your family? Miss McClure asked at lunchtime.

Please, miss. I didn't, I didn't know what to write.

I'm sure that's not true. I'm sure you could have thought of something. You understood the question?

Yes, miss.

And remembered it?

Yes, miss.

Then why didn't you answer it?

Please, miss. I could, I could, could; I couldn't think of what, what to write.

Am I right in thinking you spend a lot of time staring out the window?

I don't, I don't know, miss.

I am right, amn't I?

Yes, miss.

Do you know your mother's coming to see me this afternoon?

Yes, miss.

And you know she's been here before?

Yes, miss.

Do you know why I've asked her to come again?

Yes, miss. I think so.

Why?

Please, miss. Because, because I didn't do, didn't do my composition.

No. Carl; would you tell me if there was anything wrong?

Yes, miss.

Really wrong, I mean.

Yes, miss.

Do you miss your father?

Yes, miss.

I'm sure you must miss him dreadfully?

Sometimes, miss, but I don't think he's dead, not really. He might come back. My mum told me he was missing at sea three times and he came home from the war, so he could be away and might come back.

Do you believe that, Carl?

Please, miss. Can I go, can I, can I; please, miss, can I go for my dinner.

Let's walk down together, but before you go I want you to know why I've asked your mother to see me. I think you are one of the brightest boys I've taught, but your class work isn't good. There are lots of spelling errors, silly mistakes, as if you don't pay attention, or something is using up your time. Do you know what an IQ test is?

No, miss.

It's a test to see how clever you are. I'd like you to take that test. Do you think you would?

Yes, miss.

I think your marks would be high. And once we know that, we might be able to work out why you are not performing as well as you should. Now, I think you might be hungry.

After lunch we picked sides for football. I was late for the game. If I played had to be careful. Two weeks ago I'd gone into a tackle, turned and slipped on the wet concrete. I skinned my knee.

That's they bad weekit buggers o' boys tripping him up, my granny said, weighing the crowdie in the muslin bag that dripped into the sink. She gathered the sour milk and when it solidified she rinsed the contents in a muslin cloth, adding a little salt. Every day she squeezed the bag and weighed it in her hand. When she felt it was right she added toasted oatmeal; in summer, berries, sugar and the top of the milk to make crannachan.

She retied the bag.

You watch yoursel, she said. You watch when you run and don't let any of them near you.

He was probably playing football, my mother said.

Surely to God you don't let him play football.

The janitor, who picked the team, told me I was dropped. You were good enough for a while. You're a good wee runner and you can get in the back of a defence, but you cost us two goals cause you wouldnae tackle. You've got to tackle. So, that's it. You don't tackle and you're dropped.

You're out the team? Uncle Charlie said. That just means you'll need to play harder, need to be better than whoever took your place, unless they're only giving somebody a chance. That's what it'll be, they'll be trying out somebody new. Is that it?

I think so.

They came for tea on a Saturday night; Uncle Charlie and Aunt Cathie and my three cousins, Joseph, Charles and William, came from three closes away; Aunt Barbara, Uncle George and Michael came from down stairs and Aunt Margaret sometimes came down from Gleneagles. The fire was stacked and the lamps were lit. The windows were washed with cold water and vinegar, inside and out, clean curtains were hung; the house was scrubbed and furniture polished, everywhere the smells of disinfectant and polish, beeswax and vinegar, wood and cooking oil.

It was high tea, ham salad and chips with lots of baking and home-made jam. Some time around seven someone would go over to A and C Hanlon, Licensed Grocers, whose shop covered the corner of Masterton Street, with their name in green italics above the door. It smelled of wood and sawdust mingled with raw spirit, whisky and sherry.

The whisky barrels were behind a high wooden counter on the left as you went in the door, the smaller sherry barrels and food were straight ahead. There was a window to the right with metal advertisements, Fry's Chocolate Cream, Scott's Porridge Oats, Grant's Standfast. The whisky was measured in gills and half gills, filtered through a copper funnel.

We had beer, sherry and a gill of whisky. My grandfather would light his pipe and my mother would set the card table in the front room while Granny watched at the window and the others talked in the kitchen, my Uncle George shy and silent, Aunt Cathie awkward at first, smiling when anyone spoke.

They gathered partners and played a round of whist, my mother and Uncle George were especially favoured because they were good players, though when the cards were cut and they played my grandfather and Aunt Margaret, Uncle Charlie always sighed. We'll be late the night, he said.

The games were discussed at the end of each hand when the men drank their beer and lit cigarettes, through the continual tea and conversation above the Scottish country dance music on the radio. The men were always cheery and detached.

Charlie had a beautiful, gentle face, open and warm with wide, clear eyes.

His voice was low, with some of his mother's lilt. He smelled of soap and his straight red hair quiffed over his eye. His smile was all teeth. He had a lovely, amiable sense of humour.

I was asking Joseph, he said. He couldn't tell me, but I think you might know, just because you're older. If it takes a hen a week to walk a fortnight, how many apples are in a barrel of pears?

He danced with his sisters and sang with Barbara, everyone smiled when they heard his name and were always pleased to see him. He was the one member of my family people spoke of outside my home. One of the last times I saw Andy Walker, he said, Your Uncle Charlie's a fine man. He's got work for a few folk round here, and there's not many people can say that.

Charlie told me the poem of 'The Highwayman', where the moon is a 'ghostly galleon' and the road a 'ribbon of moonlight'. And I loved 'the landlord's red-lipped daughter', whom the highwayman promised to visit by moonlight; the redcoats knew and were waiting in ambush.

I read the poem to Francie. Just shows you, he said. That's women for you. Then he smiled. Here, he said.

Where'd you get them?

Knocked them. Some guy was in seeing my ma and I raked his pockets.

Four in a packet of five Wild Woodbine.

Francie let the cigarette dangle from the side of his mouth. He scraped the match down the close wall and cupped his hands around the flame, the smoke emerging in clumps. He took the cigarette from his mouth and grimaced, flexing his tongue as though dipping it in honey. With the cigarette in his hand and his eyes shut, he tried to remove the strands of tobacco from his lips and teeth by spitting along the line of his tongue; then he put the cigarette in the other corner of his mouth.

You don't want to get a big coosie on it.

What's that?

When the end gets wet, like a cow's erse. Here. You light up.

I'll see how you get on. What's it like?

Great.

He blew a line of smoke across my head. I coughed. He held the cigarette in his two forefingers and coughed. The tip was elongated and conical. He tried to flick the ash by snapping his fingers.

You okay?

He nodded, put the cigarette back in his mouth and withdrew it immediately, handing it to me.

You take it, he said, his face glistening. You take it. I'm going home.

He ran downstairs and over the road. I put the cigarette in my mouth and held it there, unable to breathe as the smoke closed my left eye, suddenly inhaling a handful that immediately made me dizzy and sick, sweaty and breathless.

In the street I watched the red tip soar through the air and hiss in a puddle, edging my way along the wall, head down, almost unable to see.

You all right? my mother asked.

I'm just tired.

Straight to bed then.

The ceiling moved through the light from the park.

I was afraid to close my eyes, scared of sleep. Often, I found my father standing by the bed, looking down and smiling. I carried him around with me during the day, asking for help when I was sure I'd stutter, asking him to calm me, to stop the hiss in my head, the feeling that my body was packed with air, that everyone was watching.

I'd meet him on the way home from school, in the street, or he'd be waiting in the close to see me upstairs. But mostly, he would come for a blether during the night, nothing like a nightmare nor even a dream, rather he'd take my hand and we'd walk through Oban, along the Esplanade, up Miller Road to Glencruitten Drive or we'd walk to Gallanach with my mother and Aunt Joey.

You can play football, but don't tell your granny, my mother said. You should be playing football, your daddy was a good player. And he played shinty too, for Oban Celtic. Did I tell you we met at a dance in the Drill Hall?

* * *

The woman in Possil library had her hair gathered on either side of her head, like earphones, which caused some weans to stick their heads round the door and shout, Calling all cars, calling all cars. Over and out.

She inspected every hand before a child was allowed in the library and inspected them again before a book left her charge, issued a single book to each child and gave instructions on its care, inspecting each item carefully on its return.

This was issued three days ago, she told me. You can't possibly have read it in that time. Come back next week and you can get another book then.

I have read it.

Don't be silly. Move along. There's someone behind you. Hands, please. Let me see your hands.

Would you like me to tell you what the story's about?

Don't you dare be so impudent. If I thought it would do any good I would send for your parent, but your father's probably as ignorant as yourself.

I see you're a great reader, said Andy Walker. You're never away from the library.

I'm in two libraries, Possil and Springburn.

Why's that?

I told him.

Get your library tickets, he said. Libraries are free and open to all and no bloody woman is going to change that.

Can I help you? she asked.

You can tell me why you refused to issue this boy with a book.

I trembled when he spoke, looked at his heavy boots and dungarees, his old jacket and bunnet and heard him quietly and reasonably state what he came to say: I understand these things, but I know this boy and believe he is telling the truth. He has, after all, nothing to hide. I wonder why you felt you should make a remark about his father?

When Andy asked to see the head librarian and was shown into a small office at the back of the main library, I felt her eyes on me in the hall. She walked past, first one way and then another. I looked at the black and white floor while she paced, stretching to see into the office, suddenly looking away, running behind her desk in a show of efficiency.

After no more than five minutes a tall, thin man with gold rimmed spectacles at the end of his nose came out the office with Andy Walker. He spoke to the woman, who clutched her hands in front of her stomach in an operatic gesture, her eyes skimming my ear: I am sorry, she said.

And I too would like to apologise for the fact that my staff were so inconsiderate, the man said. I assure you it will not happen again and I would like to thank Mister Walker for drawing it to my attention.

Andy and I walked home in silence, his hand on my shoulder.

Next time I went to the library she looked at me, looked at the book and sneered. When she handed me the book she said, I'm not at all sorry, you little guttersnipe. Whoever gave the likes of you ideas above your station deserves to be whipped. I'm not at all sorry. In fact, I'm glad your father's dead. Now go and tell that to your friend, if you dare.

I told Francie.

We'll get her, he said.

A fortnight later, when we were about to deliver the dead rat he'd found by the canal, she was gone. I never saw her again.

Have you ever thought when you stand even in Springburn or the Possil Library it would be impossible to digest the information that building contains in a single lifetime, Andy Walker said. I think I'd've enjoyed that, had circumstances been different, of course. I'd've liked to have been a librarian.

Maybe then you wouldn't be able to mock other people's ideas and opinions, said Davie Sanderson.

What I do is point out what I see as inconsistencies. For example: have you ever wondered why they lock up drink here. In every other country in the world they leave it lying around. Here they lock it up. Or, why do Glasgow pubs have mirrors behind the bar? Anyone been in a pub in Scotland which doesn't have a mirror in front of the gantry? Why are they there?

Light. They reflect the light and save on electricity.

It's a lovely notion, but I'm afraid the truth is rather more prosaic. The mirrors are there so's the barman can see what you're doing while his back is turned. What does that tell us about ourselves, the way we drink and the country we live in?

The trouble with you is you think you know everything.

No. I certainly don't know everything. I know more than you, which isn't saying much, but I don't know everything. For example, I don't know about glass, because I don't understand glass. I don't understand how a transparent substance can have a solid form. Do you?

* * *

Sometimes, my mother said. Only sometimes. I've seen me looking through a window and thought it was him, or I catch my reflection in a shop window or even a mirror and it reminds me I'm alone. You never get used to it. It's always there, but you learn to live with it. I suppose it's like everything else, you learn to live with it.

I wanted to tell her to take the black diamond from her coat sleeve, but she touched it whenever I asked, and mentioned Mister Henderson Stewart, Liberal MP for Central Fife: When Mister Henderson Stewart gets your daddy's pension sorted we'll be fine, she'd say.

He'd been a railway employee for less than six months and therefore had no pension rights. My mother had written to Henderson Stewart.

It's a terrible thing, she said, for a man to come all through the war, have been torpedoed and lost at sea three times and not get a ha'penny compensation, then to lose his life and find his widow gets nothing because he was a few weeks short of six months. God knows what we'll do if we don't get a pension. Waitress's wages would hardly keep me, never mind you as well. Do you know I saw Miss McClure?

We were by the flagpole in Springburn Park, the city stretching as far as we could see. It was Sunday and clouds scudded over the hills to the north.

She told me what's been going on. You don't seem able to concentrate. She asked my permission to see about Child Guidance. I agreed of course, but you'll need to let me know how things are with you. And you know your Aunt Eva's going soon, so there's big changes ahead for all of us. God, would you look at that sky. It feels like rain.

* * *

Matt and Eva were radiant. She wore a dark blue costume, a creamy blouse with a frill at her neck. Her hair was curled and bobbed at the back; her ears dotted with small gold earrings. I could not take my eyes away, trying to remember every detail.

I sobbed into her shoulder when she knelt to kiss me, Matt stroking my hair, the way my father stroked it when he called me Carlie. Eva held and rocked me.

Darling, she said. Come to the station. I looked at my mother, who nodded.

Matt shook hands with my grandfather, who held his daughter slightly and wished Matt good luck.

Thanks, said Matt. Thanks for everything.

And he hoisted me onto his shoulders, carried me downstairs, out the close and into the taxi. We waved up to the window, where my grandparents were watching. Everyone else was at the close, Aunt Cathie with a baby, William, at her arms, my Uncle George with Uncle Charlie.

My mother, Aunt Barbara and I sat on the back seat, Matt and Eva with their backs to the driver. There was nothing to say. The women cried and I cried too. Eva kissed me again, took a handkerchief from her pocket, wiped the lipstick from my cheek, the tears from the side of my face. Matt pressed me into him.

And then they were gone, with me waving, the white platform tickets in my left hand, standing on top of a barrow as the train curled round the station bend and they waved white handkerchiefs and we waved until we could not tell them from the other hopefuls leaning out the train and waving. After they had disappeared, we kept waving, while everyone sang 'Will Ye No Come Back Again', repeating the refrain over and again like a chorus:

> Better lo'ed ye canna be;
> Will ye no come back again.

I love to think of them, young and hopeful; finding their seats as the train crossed the Clyde, sitting down in the musty compartment, Eva wiping her eyes, Matt sniffing, then, in the crowded train, they'd look at each other and smile.

I dream of them sleeping in the compartment and stirring in their sleep, his arm round her, of the ticket collector coming to check their tickets, of being wakened and staying awake, of Matt buying tea and Eva shivering on the Preston station platform where they waited for the train to Liverpool, of Eva trembling and wanting to cry, looking again at this dark and handsome man for whom she'd left her family, the man who was becoming less of a stranger, the man who was taking her across the world.

Of Liverpool docks and the strangeness of the boat, of the tickets being inspected, then inspected again, torn, stamped and the stubs returned; of them finding the cabin and setting out their clothes; Eva lining the wardrobe and neatly filling the drawers; of them peering out the porthole, the sag of the hooter; of them rushing up the metal stairs and on to the deck as the hooter sounded again when the lines were cast away; of tugs on the Mersey, the boat turning in one channel then finding another; of lights on the shore and the moon in the sea around them; of Ireland to the left and the country receding, of the Mull of Galloway on the right, stars in the sky, Cassiopeia and Orion's Belt, going to bed with the smell of the sea; of Eva in her husband's arms, the sway and rock of water, of Matt and Eva waking, dressing for breakfast and finding themselves in the middle of the ocean.

TWENTY

Fight

DON'T TELL ME you've never fought.

Never.

Never punched anybody?

No.

You'll have taken plenty, but?

No one's ever hit me.

Not even your ma?

Just my da before he went away. And my grandad sometimes.

Francie wanted me to re-read *Beaver Lodge*. Kawlior the beaver had built a lodge and found a mate. Francie loved the bit where Kawlior defended his family and an Indian tried to get his pelt.

If you're scared, you don't show it. You never cry, he said. And don't let them know they've beat you. Get the first dig in and keep going. And don't fight fair. You never fight fair. If you fight fair you get beat. So what're you going to do?

Don't know.

Jesus. Do I have to show you?

Aye.

Why do you think they're after you?

Cause I cannae fight.

And why do they keep annoying you?

Because my name's Carl and my grandad's German.

My ma says your grandad's a nice old guy. He raises his hat when he sees her and says good morning. So, you do to them what they did to you and you never forget it. You keep thinking about it till you're mad and then you get them. The first rule is you deck them. Standing up they're the same size as you or bigger; so the first thing you dae is deck them as soon as possible. But even afore any of that, maist o' them'll crap it and gie in if you say you'll batter them and they know you've done it t'somebody else.

Down the canal bank, we wrestled the same moves until I could beat him, could wrap my arm around his neck and use my leg to force him to lose his

151

balance. Then he'd trick me, try to dummy the throw, use different ways of blocking my grip, forcing me to think on my feet. In the end he ducked and threw himself at my stomach, winding me and we almost landed in the canal. For a while we lay on the cobbles, sweating and laughing. I had trouble breathing and my head swirled when I closed my eyes.

Five or six boys appeared on the other side of the canal. They stripped naked and stood with their arms round their shoulders, shivering. The ground shook, the sluice gates opened and a rumble of water poured into the canal, filling the air with steam. We heard the splash and through the haze the boys jumped into the water, diving and surfacing yards away, splashing and steering themselves through the wrack and detritus, breaking through the steam, their shouts quivering in the early evening air. They swam towards the swirl in a line; inches separated them from each other and the draw of the whirlpool.

It lasted till the swirl diminished and the water was broken only by their bodies. They shivered on the bank and dried themselves with their clothes.

We'll have to learn to swim, said Francie, as we ran up the road, pushing and jumping, bringing each other to the ground, passing Wilson Brothers and stopping, as we always did, at Huggies.

Jas Higginson and Sons, Fleshers.

I swear to God, my granny said, they horses know where they're going.

The fat man with a bloody leather apron and wellington boots, dried blood caked down the front of his jacket and the peak of his bunnet, chased anyone he caught hovering by the gate.

George told me, They've to shut the gates when there's a killing. If they leave the gates open the horse can escape. And they've to be exact. If a horse went mad in that wee yard, somebody'd get killed.

Could they no shoot it? my mother said.

Of course they bloody shoot it; why in the name of God d'you think it's there in the first place, for a fish supper?

Don't you be so bloody smart, I mean could they no shoot it before it gets out the yard, otherwise it's some poor old buddy with her shopping that thinks she's on her way home who's going to get a horse chasing her up the close and landing on her lap.

George had kept his accent. He never spoke about the war; all I knew was he'd left Dunkirk with a pair of left boots two sizes too small. I loved it when he said words like wee, but my favourite was, Och tae hell. I'd ask him to say it: Och away tae hell, you wee scunner you, he said, giggling, his eyes alight.

Francie looked in Huggies' gate: Hey, Carlo, he shouted. Shush.

We lay beside each other, peeking from the gatepost, on the ground by the wall. The Killer had a cigarette at the corner of his mouth. He stood on a box. The horse was dragged from the shed, a skinny Shire or a Clydesdale, chestnut, with a white forelock and mane and ruffles at its feet. Two men and a boy held the reins taut and moved the horse forward. It stamped and shied, refusing to move towards The Killer, who shifted the cigarette from one side of his mouth to the other with his tongue.

Come on, he said. We havenae got aa day.

The horse would not move. It stared at The Killer.

God. We'll need to move the bloody box, he said, stepping down.

The horse shied slightly and tried to creep backwards, but the reins were tight. With its front legs stamping the ground, it shook, evacuating its bowels and bladder. Now, said The Killer.

He placed a metal object on the plate of the face, below the forelock and above the eyes. There was a snap and the horse's legs twitched then trembled as though they could no longer bear the paltry weight. Blood spurted from the wound, spewed over The Killer's head, splattered the wall at the back, then trickled down the horse's face, over the eyes and gathered below the jaw where it dripped onto the yard the boy had started hosing. The Killer lit another cigarette from the end in his mouth, stepped down from the box and threw the dout into the blood where it hissed before being swept into the stank with the blood and water and anything else in the yard.

Then, with no one around, alone and trembling, the horse, already dead, unable even to blink, crumbled as the legs gave way and it toppled onto its side. The men put chains round the twitching legs and hauled the meat into the shed.

* * *

Every day Alex Irvine came up to me at playtime with the two others beside him. You're a bastard, he said.

I turned away.

I said you're a lousy fucken German bastard wi a fucken German name. Heil Hitler.

Sometimes the three of them chanted, We won the war, often joined by others, following me round the playground, hissing rather than shouting.

German.

Miss McClure was ill. Someone said she was bad with her nerves, but I heard no more because Rosa McCance, who lived in Coldstream Place and was called Big Big Rosa, was talking: My sister, her that's in America and lives in a big big house, well her daughter's a very very clever girl and she goes to this very very fancy big big school, well she told me that they were at this big big wedding. Thousands of people there. Well, you know what it's like in America.

We had a new teacher. Mister Thomas Thomas walked into the classroom one Monday morning and told us his name. I thought of the man who said everything twice and was about to laugh. He was looking at me when Alex Carson laughed.

I'll see you after, boy, he said.

Tom Tom kept Carsie in at playtime. His hands were red with the belting.

I believe in belting, he said. I believe to spare the rod is to spoil the child. But I am a fair man. Some of you boys do not have fathers and I would like you to think of me as a father rather than a teacher. And I hope to be fair in the way a parent is fair. A parent chastises the child for the child's own good and does it in the child's best interest; and so you will find it is with me.

I thought about it. I didn't know what the word meant, but knew it was something I shouldn't know, something deeply harmful and insulting.

Please, sir, I asked one playtime when no one else was around. Please, sir. Can I ask you a question?

Of course.

It's about a word, sir.

What word is this?

It's a word I get called and I don't know what it means.

Then it may have no meaning in the same way as a word like scallywag has no meaning. Is it scallywag?

No sir.

Then what word is it?

His face turned pale. He gripped the sides of his desk, lifted the lid and took out a belt. He grabbed my hand by the wrist and belted me repeatedly without speaking. I screamed and eventually heard the door open.

That'll do, Mister Thomas, said the new headmaster.

Mister Campbell took me to his office. The secretary filled the sink and I sat with my hand and wrist in cold water till the swelling subsided and the redness dulled. She put cream on my wrist.

Well, Carl, he said. I think we can work together on this, don't you?

Yes, sir.

Good. The thing is, Mister Thomas has had a very difficult time; the war. He is trying to find his way back into his old profession and is here on a temporary basis, till Miss McClure recovers. Given that, we wouldn't want anything to come between a man and his family's livelihood. We wouldn't want to deprive his family, would we? So why don't you tell me what happened?

I found it difficult, and thought I might stutter.

Who said that word? he said.

I heard it.

Where?

I can't remember.

It's a terrible disgrace, he said, a terrible disgrace to hear a word like that from the mouth of a child. I don't think you need mention Mister Thomas's actions to your mother. I'll have a word with him and we'll sort it out, surely.

That night, Francie told me what it meant.

Next day at playtime I approached Alex Irvine by the gate. What do you want? asked Reggie Smart.

I want to see him, I said pointing to Alex Irvine.

Fuck off, he said.

I'm not a bastard. My mother and father were married and my daddy was killed.

Oh my, your daddy was killed, said Alex Irvine.

You're still a bastard, said Smartie.

I hit him. My schoolbag was by my side and I could not swing it back properly, but when it hit him on the face, he stumbled back, held onto the railings and fell with his hands to his face and his nose bleeding.

I dropped my bag. The more I thought of what they'd said, the more I thought of how I felt, the more I wanted to hit him. I closed my eyes and was absolutely focused, aware of nothing other than what I was doing, swinging my arms uncontrollably, sometimes connecting, till I was jerked off my feet and held by both arms. Then I heard his sobs above the chanting.

Clear off, all of you, shouted Tom Tom, his arms wrapped around me.

He took me to the headmaster. Waiting in the corridor, the feeling stayed with me. I knew I wouldn't stutter. I could do anything I liked.

Up, said Campbell. Both hands.

I'm not taking it.

I beg your pardon.

I'm not taking the belt from you, I said. I got the belt already and I'm not taking it from you. Tom Tom belted me because I asked him what a bastard was and I was fighting because I was fed up being called a bastard and fed up being called a German.

Every time I said it, he winced.

I'm not a bastard. If I tell my mother I got belted for saying bastard because I was saying what somebody else said and that you told me not to say anything, she'll come up to see you. You told me not to tell her because you didn't want Tom Tom to lose his job.

I'm going to overlook this matter this one time. You are obviously very upset, not at all like you. But I do have to say that if we ever catch you up to any of that sort of hooligan behaviour again, nothing and I repeat nothing will save you.

That night Mrs Smart came to see my mother, who took me to the door and made me apologise. Reggie told her Alex Irvine had been giving him money. Mrs Smart said that when she went to see his mother, she burst into tears and left the house while his uncle belted him. Then she asked who he'd been stealing from: It was me, she told Mrs Smart. He stole from me. He knows we've nothing but he stole from me and gave it to other kids for sweeties. He didn't take any himself. He gave the money away to others; so, at heart, he's not a bad boy.

Francie and I sat up Alex Irvine's close, reading *Beaver Lodge*. When he saw us, he ran into the street. I caught him at the Back Lawn Steps.

Hit me if you like, he said.

* * *

We made a kite with bamboo canes, brown paper, string and sticky tape. We painted a face on the side and launched the kite from the top of Keppoch Hill. It soared and looped, with the pigtail flapping behind. Francie tied the bits of string together as it flew, looping the end to a piece of Bugsy's kindling. It rose when we tugged, till the string almost snapped, then dived and spun upwards again with a final tug before giving up on us, turning its nose downwards, ending in a spectacular crash.

Is that your kite broke, boys? asked Davie Sanderson.

Can you fix it? asked Francie.

Let's see. No, the main cane's broke. The spine's gone. Yous'll need to get a new cane, the first tug of wind and that'll snap again. Where did yous get the cane?

Mister Walker.

Aye, well, yous'll no be getting cane or anything else off him.

How no?

He's in Russia. He's emigrated, off to the Soviet Union leaving his wife and weans to starve in Keppochhill Road.

We knew Andy Walker had gone alone. Some said his wife would follow when he was settled, others said she refused to go. Then they said he wasn't in the Soviet Union at all, that he was in Newcastle, Dundee or somewhere in England, probably London.

Well, said Billy Carson. He always was a man of principle.

And a man of his word, said Connor Flynn.

He's a daft bugger, said Davie Sanderson.

He'll be missed around here, said Junior Johnstone.

He's deserted his family, said Davie Sanderson.

Not at all. Of course, he didn't, said Connor Flynn. He's a missing person.

I don't give a damn what he is, his rent's no paid. His wife and kids'll have to leave their house.

He would never desert his family, said Junior Johnstone. There's some misunderstanding.

It's because he's a communist, said Billy Carson. Mrs Walker told my wife. The rent man said he wanted no communists or families of communists living there.

Quite right, said Davie Sanderson.

She says she's been victimised. If we organised a rent strike, he'd change his mind.

Everyone looked at the ground.

Does she honestly think that we'd help her by no paying our rent? How in the name of God can that be right? asked Davie Sanderson.

We could put a sheet round, said Connor Flynn.

She wouldn't take it.

We could give it to the factor.

Then we'd need to keep doing it.

It's worth a try, said Connor.

Then we heard she'd been rehoused. The ragman refused to do the flitting. Someone said Andy Walker had stopped him beating his horse. Mrs Walker and the children were last seen on a Saturday morning by the Somerville Memorial Church at the corner of Pinkston Road, with shopping bags and suitcases boarding a tram for town. By night their house had been emptied. Her neighbours took what furniture and fittings she'd left. Connor Flynn said, They even took the gas mantles.

Two weeks later Joey Docherty and Senga Thomson, who had recently married, moved in with their new baby.

Where'd you get the wean? Francie asked her. Is he no a wee bit young for his age?

You're a cheeky wee bastard, she said.

* * *

We climbed the dyke, walked along the top of the cars and squeezed round a lorry into the back of the Masterton Street garage where a small black and white cat was feeding three kittens. She turned and lifted her head.

There, said Francie. There now. Who's a good mammy; who's a clever girl.

And from inside his pullover he produced a piece of fish: Knocked it, he said. From Daisy's Dairy. Two bits for my Maw and a bit for the cat.

Within minutes the fish had gone. Francie pulled the newspaper from her as she tried to stick her head beneath his jumper.

Nothing, he said. There's nothing there. Go back and feed your weans like a decent mother should.

Two nights later, coming back from football, we heard the wails. The cat was by a zinc bucket filled with water. Her kittens floated on top.

Francie smashed every windscreen in the yard, climbing into the scrap yard next door and over on to the top of a midden, eventually coming out at the end of the lane, near Pinkston Road.

* * *

Tom Tom wrote the subjects on the blackboard in a copperplate hand, thin up-strokes, thick down-strokes, his chalk parallel with the board: What I Want To Do, A Happy Memory, My Perfect Day. I asked if I could write about a cat and was told to do what everyone else was doing. Later, he gave me an extra piece: Do that composition about a cat, he said.

I missed out the windscreens and finished with her sleeping on a chair in Francie's house, writing first of all in pencil, eventually, when I thought it was right, copying it out in my best writing.

Two days later, at the end of the day, when the other pieces had been marked and commented on, he stared at me, dangling two sheets of paper like a dirty rag.

This piece of trash has been done by someone who thinks he's better than the rest of us, he said, someone who thinks he's too good for this place and what we do here, the way we live and the way in which God has ordered us to live; someone who would rather write about his own ideas than do what everyone else does.

I stared at the desk.

Listen to this, he said. This is the opening sentence, The cat had no name. What kind of opening sentence is that? Rubbish. For homework you, MacDougall, have been given a round zero and you will write a proper composition for tomorrow.

He tore up the paper and theatrically dropped the pieces in the waste bin, piece by piece.

By the way, he said when he had finished. Miss McClure is coming to see you tomorrow.

She was pale and thin, her face was flushed and she was wrapped in warm clothes. When she came into the class, Mister Thomas was belting a boy who asked if it was possible to add a long division sum. Tom Tom stared for a while without blinking. Then his head shook: Out, he said.

My dad told me to ask you, the boy said. Please, sir. It's a joke.

I'm sorry, I won't be coming back, said Miss McClure. Sorry not to be seeing you all again.

Please, miss. Where are you going?

I'm taking a wee rest, she said. I understand Mister Thomas will be with you till the holidays and you'll be getting a new teacher at the end of the summer, when you move to a new class.

She'd asked if we could have a word in the corridor. Take as long as you like, he said.

Well, Carl, she said. How's your stammer?

Fine, miss. Thank you. My stutter, my stutter's fine.

I'm very glad to hear it.

Is everything well?

I think so, miss.

Good. Perhaps you'll be going to see the Child Guidance people soon?

I'm not sure, miss.

I hope so. I'm sure you'll get things sorted. It must be a problem for you, but I know they'll find the answer. Stick in and you'll do well. I have every confidence in you, every confidence.

She came to see me, my mother said. That woman isn't well. She's had to give up her job and she climbed these stairs to see me and ask about you. It's her lungs. Pleurisy. I thought it was good of her coming to see me. She just came up to the door and said, I do hope I'm not disturbing you. A very polite woman.

* * *

The following Monday, a small, dark-haired woman came into the class. She was wearing a thick purple coat, a yellow and black Dress MacLeod tartan scarf and a red hat. She took off the hat, put it over the chair by the desk and started talking immediately.

I didn't even have time for a cup of tea, she said. These tram cars; I'd be quicker walking. Now, what would you like to do today? Who'd like to draw? Are there no paints around here? Well, we'll need to find some. Now, if I ask you to be on your best behaviour, by which I mean silence while I go and get myself a wee fly cup of tea, do you think you can manage that?

Please, miss, where's Mister Thomas?

Away, far away.

Are you our new teacher?

My name is Mrs Docherty and I'm your replacement teacher, though I'm only supposed to be temporary because I have children of my own, but the way things are shaping up it looks as though I'll be here for some time yet. Now, I need that cup of tea. I've seen the headmaster and he knows I'm here and you know I'm here, but I wouldn't like anyone to know I wasn't here, so if you keep absolutely still as a wee crowd of mices, then I can have a cup of tea and we'll do something nice when I come back. And this is the way we'll do it, every day we'll begin with something nice, then we'll get the rotten stuff over with and finish the morning with something nice. The afternoon will begin with something nice and end with something nice, but we will, I am sorry to say, have a dreary bit in between. Now, I am going to make that tea because it is, you will have noticed, a very chilly day, very cold for the time of year, and when I come back I will tell you all about my family.

She closed the door and we watched her head move behind the frosted glass, bursting into chaos when she disappeared. The door was flung opened. Mrs Docherty was crouching by the handle.

All right, she said. Get your arithmetic books out. Long division, I'm afraid. Where were you? Had you done page 17?

Yes, miss.

Page 23?

Yes, miss.

In that case you won't mind doing them both again.

How many sums would you like us to do?

All of them.

Then, when she'd seen us settled and had walked up and down the four rows, she said, I think you might be quieter now.

No one spoke while she was gone. She had left the door open and we stared at Tom Tom's writing on the board. Mrs Docherty came back with a cup of tea in her left hand. I didn't bother with the saucer, she said. I hope you won't think me rude. By the way, did you all have a cup of tea this morning?

Yes, miss.

And a breakfast?

Yes, miss.

Well, I know that may not be the case, but we'll find out soon enough. Now, put these books to one side and I'll tell you about my family.

* * *

The flurry of snow turned to slush, then rain; frost in May. Every day we thought it would improve, but by Saturday morning everything was white.

The snow was in the air, floating rather than falling, like fog, or the haar that settled round the Kettle chimneys, slowly dropping like a ghost. The air was powdered, particles stuck to your hair and eyelashes; fresh on the breath, it narrowed your vision, seared the roof of your mouth and inside the nose.

Just before we reached the canal, a cloud crossed the water. It rose into the air like smoke, stronger and heavier than the other snow, then clung to the atmosphere, changing the landscape, dimming and softening the canal and its contents, the surrounding path and buildings, wrapping them in an ivory cloud.

The surface was pale and clear below the mist, a beautiful pale green rising from beneath the ice, the debris changed to charcoal and brown, their form distorted by ice; everything paler and softer in the ambiguous light.

Sure it's like this in the frozen north, said Francie, suddenly turning to a paltry noise.

A bird was locked in the ice, something like a crow, as big as a seagull and black. It had lost its voice. It opened its mouth and cried, but no sound came. It flapped a raggedy wing, the other frozen in the ice with its yellow feet. It turned to the sky and yelled again. No sound came.

We could save it, said Francie.

I hit the water with a stick and the ice disintegrated. It'll go when he water comes, he said. It'll go when the warm water comes. Try, he shouted. Try. Go on. Try to fly.

The wing flapped. Again the bird raised its head and opened its mouth.

TWENTY-ONE

Oban

MY MOTHER SAID there was nothing else for it. We've no place else to go and somebody needs to be around, so we're staying in Keppochhill Road.

Mister Henderson Stewart's letter had been forwarded. He sympathised, but my father had not been a railway employee long enough to warrant a pension and since his death had not been caused by company negligence, no other payment was due.

But the waitressing job with the railway gave her privilege tickets and a few free passes, which meant we could go to Oban.

The more he receded, the clearer he became. Trivialities sharpened and ordinary actions, deeds and opinions took on audacious proportions. It became uncontrollable; from something that comforted me before sleep to a daily fixation, like a wave I wanted to watch and maybe even feel its spray, but did not want to wash over me.

I dreamed of seeing him walk down the road with Willie or have them sit by the fire in their stocking feet with screw-topped bottles of McEwen's India Pale Ale.

I had watched him shave, stood by the sink while he filled the old teacup with the broken handle and pink peony rose transfers half full of water from the kettle, dip the brush and scrub the soap into his face.

I have to do this every morning, he said, every morning God sends. And so will you. If I'm going out at night I have to do it all over again, scrape my face and powder it up.

More than anything, it was the voice I tried to recall. His accent was softer than the speak of Fifers or rapid Glaswegians. And I tried to summon it, tried to speak without rolling letters at home till my granny could hardly make out what I was saying.

Marie; are you sure that wean's all right? That's that reading for you, she said. Nobody knows what words are in these books.

* * *

The only place it sounded right was Oban. Every summer we went for a week, sometimes a fortnight, to tend the grave.

I'd buy a comic from the Buchanan Street Station news-stand. The train left from Platform One and we were always early, finding seats and closing the window for the haul through the tunnel, past Jack's Mountain and the Stinky Ocean. I had the comic finished by Stirling and tried to conjure faces to see if I'd remember them, the way I sometimes did before sleep, wondering how they remembered me.

Or I'd read till Crianlarich, where the wait while the engine took on water was punctuated by the wheel tapper's hammer.

Then the landscape took over. Kilchurn and the awful sweep of mountains by Loch Awe, the vibrant greens of bracken, yellow gorse and silver birch flurried through my imagination.

Francie and I became marooned on the shores of Loch Etive; or we were stranded in the hills above Balquhidder, living alone on plants and berries, learning to trap, hunt and fish. We'd live in a small, stone cottage with a turf roof, sleep on heather and bracken beds, burn wood and peat, staying alone, where friends would visit with news of the fairs and markets, where we would take our dogs into civilisation, admired for our daring deeds and rugged life, dependent upon no one. We would become mountain men, conversant in more than one language.

In Possil library, while I pretended to be waiting on an adult, I found a small paper guide book to Oban. It spoke of hill forts and brochs, of cinerary urns and axe heads excavated at Glenshellach, a stone on the road to Ganavan where Fingal tethered Bran, Dunstaffnage Castle where the Stone of Destiny was kept, smugglers running brandy ashore, illegal whisky stills, the cleared township of Balure in Glencruitten, where Scotland's oldest uncontested human remains were found. I put the book away in case the librarian caught me.

* * *

My grandfather was always waiting by the station: You are how? he'd ask.

He smelled old, a dry sweet smell of soap and food. His face was smooth and shiny, tight, as though the skin had been drawn downward, moulded over the contours of his face and gathered below the chin. His hair was white and straight, cut short and his eyes seemed filled to overflowing when he saw me, standing there, barely taller than myself and smiling through the language I could not understand.

We stayed in Glencruitten, walking through the town to Combie Street and up the hill, past the big houses, past Mossfield Park and into White City, where Joey was always waiting by the gate, crying with her arms outstretched when she saw us.

I loved to waken in the bedroom at the back with the photograph of my Uncle Michael in his sailor's suit on the dresser, with my Aunt Joey seated in her good dress, Katie and Margaret standing awkwardly, their hair in bunches. A photograph of Joey and my father was above the bed.

On the first evening if it was fine after tea, we'd walk through town, up the brae to Pennyfuir, along the main path and over to the right, Loch Linnhe in the distance, to the second row and along and the little stone that looked as though as though it had been left by mistake, more a boulder than a headstone, my father's name and the span of his life:

TRAGICALLY KILLED
SADLY MISSED

I never knew where to look or what I was supposed to do. I stood with my head bowed as though in prayer, staring at the clipped grass, occasionally lifting my eyes to see if anything had changed, waiting for my mother's hand to slip into mine, for her to touch my shoulder and the repeated shudder of a sob that overpowered everything till she removed her glasses, her face tattered with tears and saliva, and trembled, repeating my father's name.

Look at me, she'd say. And I've to walk back through the town like this.

She'd go up to the lavatory and leave the door open, running the tap to wipe her face. Come on, she'd say. Joey'll have a cup of tea ready.

And though she would talk of going, she'd seldom visit the grave until the afternoon of the day before we left. With a bunch of flowers from the garden, or whatever she had picked on her walks up the glen or along the road to Gallanach, wild scabious, honeysuckle, daisies and red campion which she mingled with fern, reeds and grasses by verge of the road.

I did this when I was a girl in Muir of Ord, she said, staying with my Auntie Kate at Balvaird. Going to school or on the way home, I'd pick a posy from what I found and keep it for myself. Or when I was looking after the cattle; I'd lie there reading, then get up and pick the flowers. I'd get lost in a book and God alone knows what happened to the cattle, so I'd have to get up and find them. I never thought, not once, no, never did I think that I'd be picking a posy for my husband's grave, my laddie beside me. God knows when we'll be back here.

This was when I would cry, as though it had been waiting to happen, sobbing into her, my temples scraping the buttons on her coat.

* * *

There was an undrained bog near the head of Glen Cruiten, a godsend of grasses, rushes, reeds and sedge where small flowers bloomed as a dark as cocoa. There were flowering stems with leafless stalks and hard pink blossoms. There were reeds in water all year round. There were frogs with coloured backs and toads that jumped and rested and walked on three legs with the fourth tucked somewhere underneath. There were newts who wrapped their eggs in leaves.

Dippers walked the glen. They ambled up the midstream using their tails as a rudder, circling the mosses and ferns with thriving islands of activity beneath the boulders. After a rain the stream overflowed and came to rest somewhere at the back of the hump I thought was a hill. There were strings of underwater weeds and roots, stones and logs. I imagined beaver lodges and platypus instead of herons and bitterns that jumped into the air. I found a reed warbler's nest, a deep cup woven round the stalks and every day heard a curlew call.

* * *

Why we saw some folk rather than others, I never found out, but always imagined there were too many relatives, that if we tried to see everyone, we would do nothing ourselves. Anyway, there were always relations who'd stop in the street.

Of course there was talk about folk falling out, about Highland sensibilities being disturbed because my mother usurped a male prerogative by insisting on taking not just a cord, but the first cord at my father's funeral.

I'd be sure to see my Aunt Annie. She was always perjink and knew my tastes exactly. There's a bit of cake there I'm sure you could finish, she'd say, looking away from me, turning back when I'd cleared the crumbs to ask about school or relate some item of town news she seemed to have saved just for me. She was the only person I knew with a refrigerator and in summer made her own ice cream. When we got back to Glencruitten, Margaret Boyd always asked, Did you get ice cream?

Two big platefuls. I'd've had more, but my mother said I'd had enough.

What kind?

Strawberry.

I'm coming next time you go.

We'd usually go in the afternoon, walk through the town to the prefab in Longsdale Road with the little green wireless on a table by the fire. We'd usually leave when Uncle Ronald came in from work. If I closed my eyes, he sounded like my father.

You have your father's way about you, he'd say. You have your father's way of standing and his big spades of hands. But you have his mouth and nose, as well as the shape of his face, though, of course you have your mother's hair and eyes, but it's got a twist to it, your hair, the same as your Dad.

Granny's house smelled of soup and cooking. She was a big woman who frightened me at first. Everyone said my father was the favourite, her youngest child. If that was true, I never felt the privilege extended to me. I suppose she was like the folk who have to do what they have done all their lives, who can hardly snatch a moment's peace; I suppose the prospect of another child, a boy with no Gaelic, did not please her. I think she saw me as another kind of burden.

She had taken Uncle Peter's bairns when their mother died. She had taken Charlie Boyd, who wasn't related at all. And there was my grandfather, a Free Church of Scotland elder for forty years while she remained Roman Catholic. Neither spoke much English, my grandfather hardly any. If he started a sentence in English, it was usually finished in Gaelic.

He was a small man, even as a child I thought him tiny. My granny said his office was in the Lochavoulin Bar. His obituary in the *Oban Times* said he was a Gaelic scholar, though he barely read English, but enjoyed a good comic, especially Biffo the Bear: *Tha e droch muisa bourach that Biffack Bear*, he'd say, giggling.

Margaret Boyd, talks of being told: You go Joe Boney's and get a stalk of sugarally and a comack. They still tell stories about him, Ally Feeteran who expected everyone to understand Gaelic. He told an English tourist to bring his car into the side of the *rathad mhor* because it was *fliuch* in the middle. He disliked Glasgow and said he wasn't going back because the folk were very rude. He did what he did in Oban: walking along Argyle Street, he lifted his hat to everyone and said, Good morning. No one answered.

My grandmother insisted he take me to the evening service. He would pech a bit climbing the brae to the High Free Kirk. He always had toffee or peppermint balls and during the sermon was known to break the toffee on the wooden seats. We always sat to the left at the back, standing to sing, staring at the worn grain on the back of the pew in front while the women's voices rose like gulls.

Their house at 2 Miller Road was in the close, first on the left. Monday was cleaning day, when the place was stripped from top to bottom, the woodwork washed and linoleum polished. The range was small and to the right by the door. The living room was dark and small; there was a table by the window, which was covered in white net curtains. There was a gas mantle, an armchair by the window and a brass bed in the recess. There was a continual fence of heat from the range.

My grandfather's allotment was opposite the house. There were huge cabbages and cauliflowers, stalks of rhubarb and rows of potatoes shaded by foxgloves and lupins. Granny stewed fruit from the garden, served with sago, semolina and tapioca.

Ask who he's talking to? Margaret asked me. When the *boddach* goes in the garden, ask who he's talking to.

Who are you talking to, Grandad?

Wheesht.

Grandad. Who are you talking to?

Can you see I'm talking to the fairies?

He squatted among the vegetables and whispered. If anyone showed the slightest hint of scepticism, my grandfather told them the story of his brother, my father's Uncle Ronald.

When they were boys on Belnahua, Allan MacDougall saw a mermaid. It was a summer evening and the sun was sinking behind Mull. He was at the far end of the island and saw her sitting on a rock. He knew a fishing trip was planned for the following day and told his older brother Ronald what he had seen. Ronald did not believe such things. Next day, he was drowned.

Ronald MacDougall is buried with his parents on the island of Luing. Their grave is marked with a headstone of slate from the Belnahua quarry. Every summer my grandfather cut lupins from the clumps that bent over Miller Road and with a heuk to trim the grass, walked from Miller Road to Luing to tend his mother's grave, as he'd promised.

The graveyard on Luing is packed with MacDougalls, many from Belnahua, most with slate headstones. It's easy to recognise the family names. My great-grandfather, Peter MacDougall, died aged fifty-two, in June, 1879. His wife, Christina died in February, 1894, aged fifty-five. Their wish was to be taken from Ballachulish and buried in sight of Belnahua and my grandfather carved their headstone in a language he did not understand.

* * *

The tinkers came to Glencruitten every summer. Horses and carts came up the drive; heavy at the back like the ragman's wagon, their clothes and blankets covered by a tarpaulin, cooking utensils, tools, wood, canvas bags, scrap metal and some furniture piled behind. They'd drive past the houses to the plod of the horse, with squeaky wheels, a clatter of tin and a man on the moothie. The men in front held the horses' reins, but someone walked with his hand on the bridle, like Paw Broon, bunnet, moustache and pipe. The women were dark with small, brown faces wrapped in heavily checked or tartan shawls. They sat beside the driver, smoked pipes and smiled; young men and women walked at the side and children were seated at the back of the cart; the girls had already gathered the privet and were making roses from pink and yellow crepe paper. By evening their bow tents were scattered up the glen, fires lit and the horses grazing.

A smell of woodsmoke came from their clothes and rose in pockets along the glen. The men tied their scarves across their chest and always seemed to have heather in their bunnets or lapels. The young women's hair shone in the sun. They smiled in their short-sleeved dresses that buttoned down the front; they flirted, giggled and sang.

All summer, they'd be in town, playing the pipes by the pier, jaunting their melodeon tunes around pub doors, telling fortunes, selling waxed or paper flowers, heavy baskets of lucky white heather tied with Royal Stewart tartan ribbon, collecting old clothes, asking for junk, cooking over fires in heavy iron pots, drinking and singing, fighting, getting barred from pubs and soaked in the rain, the children with bare feet, running and calling to each other in a language that was neither English, Scots or Gaelic but could have been all three:

*The manashies are deekin for gadgies an peeve and the hantle dinnae
jahn the cant sae ca awa, laddie, ca awa, doon the road for a pliskie,
some penan and a wee tait slab.*

In early September, the carts would rattle in the early morning rain, as though you'd heard the noise in your sleep. They'd leave with neither sound nor warning.

When I got back to Glasgow they'd ask where I'd been. Where was that, Carl? Jean Delacourt asked, and laughed again when I said, Ho-baan.

TWENTY-TWO

Eva and Charlie

I RAN HOME from school. I'd written an essay Mrs Docherty liked and had known all the geography answers. I was hungry and Francie would want to play up the park.

In the close I felt I was passing through snow. When I ran up the stairs I was sure something followed me. If I dawdled, looked out the window or tied my laces, I'd be lost. I had to reach the doorbell quickly.

Aunt Barbara opened the door. She was crying. I could hear sobbing in the kitchen. Barbara could not speak. Granny was at the fire, muttering. Tears streamed down her face as she rocked back and forward in her chair.

Jo, my grandad said. Jo, for goodness sake.

He turned to the fire when his bottom lip trembled.

My mother had a handkerchief twisted round her fingers, pulling at the fabric. She stared from her mother to the fire to Barbara to her mother. When I came into the kitchen, she looked at me and shook her head unable to speak.

What's wrong?

Go out and play.

What is it? What's wrong?

No one spoke. Then someone said, Eva.

When Charlie arrived in his working clothes they showed him the telegram:

EVA DIED THIS MORNING STOP
LETTER WILL FOLLOW STOP
MATT.

This was Thursday, 15 December 1949.

She had written to me since going to Canada, little notes slipped into her letters telling me how she had settled in Thorold, that I had a new cousin, John Miller, who was ages with Michael. At Christmas a box of presents arrived with her cards; and lined along the bottom were a bag of peppermints for my granny, chocolates for her sisters, White Owl cigars for my grandfather and a bag of peanuts wrapped in chocolate in a candy shell. When we went to the

Kelvin Hall circus we ate the nuts.

I dreamed of my Aunt Eva, imagined Thorold, poured over the photographs of her and Matt outside their bungalow, Eva with the baby in the garden, standing beside their car in a print dress or wrapped in a warm coat with a hood, gloves and scarf beside a snowman. I imagined leafy streets and expensive houses, wondered how I'd go there and what I'd do; would I simply get off the train and walk to her house, turning on the corner and look at the numbers walking up the street, or would she meet me at the station, come running down the platform and say: My, how you've grown.

Slowly, they remembered silly incidents: the time she was dancing to a tune on the radio and kicked the shoe off her foot and it smashed the window. She said a boy had thrown a stone, but the glazier told her the glass had been broken from inside. Or the time she threw a stale piece of cake to the monkey in Wilson's Zoo. The monkey sniffed the cake and threw it back.

On Sunday night my mother said, The funeral'll be tomorrow.

How do you know?

If she'd died in this country, that's when it would be.

Not unless they have an inquiry about sudden death over there.

I expect they'll have that, said Charlie. I think their laws are much the same as our own.

He'd been round every night, usually with one of the boys. He came round on his own on Sunday night. We thought he wasn't coming, but he turned up at half past eight and laughed because he thought he might not have to work tomorrow. He was working at Greenock, building St Joseph's Chapel. There was a gale blowing up and they might be rained off.

I was playing on the bunker at the end of the lobby, and as he passed on his way to the door he told me to be careful. What is it tonight? he said.

I told him the stagecoach was being attacked by Indians.

Watch out for the arrows, he said. See you tomorrow.

He smiled and waved as he closed the door.

Next day, Monday, around five o'clock one of the Wilson Brothers came to tell us there had been an accident. The wall he was building collapsed in the gale. They thought it was serious.

He died at half past five in the Greenock Royal Infirmary. His heart gave out during an operation.

Matt's letter arrived on the day of Charlie's funeral.

It was sudden. There was nothing anyone could do. They think it's a heart attack, he wrote, but the results of the post mortem have not been released. The funeral went ahead as planned. He had photographs of Eva in her coffin and would send them on to us.

I asked if I could go to Charlie's funeral, and my mother said, We'll see.
It would do no harm.
I think Cathie said Joseph is going.
I polished my shoes the night before, then polished them again. It had been like this for days, wandering around looking for something to do. In school, I stared out the window and no one seemed to mind. Mrs Docherty smiled when she saw me. She touched my hair and asked if I was all right.
I said I was fine.
I don't think you're fine. It'll take a while, she said. It'll take a while for you to adjust to the loss and you've been through loss before, but I want you to know you are special in God's eyes and that is all I am going to say. You have been gifted and now you are asked to use these gifts to their full advantage, to carry a cross few have borne, except perhaps in time of war. Do you understand, Carl?
I nodded and ran away.
I knew how to deal with this. I had dealt with it before and this was the same, here again. I had upset everyone when my daddy died. I had upset them by telling them I knew he was dead, that time on the stairs in Kettle.
My daddy's dead, isn't he?
If I hadn't said that they wouldn't have been upset. So I had to be good, say nothing and make sure I didn't cry. I was fine. I knew what to do, knew how to deal with it, knew what it meant, go out and play, carry on as usual.
Maybe, I could cry at night. When I was alone in bed and supposed to be asleep, perhaps I'd cry when no one would know. But I would know and God would know. It was difficult to think of Eva without crying, or the way Charlie's face keeked round the door, his hair flopped across his face.
For a while I carried Eva's picture, the one she had sent from Canada, a studio portrait taken with Matt, her hair gathered as I remembered, with combs at the side of her head, a two-piece costume and blouse, Matt behind, his hand on her shoulder. And from the bottom left corner, slanting upwards to the right, she had written in fountain pen with blue-black ink:

> *For Carl*
> *With love*
> *Aunt Eva & Uncle Matt*
> *XXX*

I'd trace my finger round the shape of her mouth, the comb in her hair and wondered if the one on the other side was the same; it would hardly be otherwise with Eva, but had she made a mistake that day? Did she know they would only photograph the one side and so she only put one comb in her hair? And what did the photographer say as he took the picture? Was she pregnant when it was taken?

My granny had Charlie's Highland Light Infantry battalion picture on the mantelpiece above the fire, smiling in a kilt, beside a small studio portrait where he is also in uniform. He looked bemused, as though he had been taken by surprise or was seeing something only he imagined, his mouth slightly gaping, his eyes bright, his cheeks approaching a smile.

She took the battalion picture down. Can you find your Uncle Charlie? she asked. Where is he?

There he's there. In the second row.

She held the picture close to her face.

He came through the war, Granny said. He was at Arnhem and then went through Germany; he even brought back that copy of Hitler's book for your grandad. He came back here and was killed by the wind. All those men, she said. All those men in the war; look at them. Some of these men'll be dead; but he survived. Your Uncle Charlie came home, got married, had three of a family and was killed. Where is he again? Let me see if I can find him. Where is he? Which one's Charlie?

* * *

My black shoes were polished. I had never worn a tie and the collar was tight.

A stillness had settled over the house. My granny wandered around with photographs in her hand, moving from one piece of furniture to another.

My grandfather stared into the distance.

What's going to happen to these boys with no father?

Cathie'll hardly be able to manage on her own.

But she'll be provided for. Charlie'll have seen to that.

If no Charlie, the Wilsons'll see to it.

He'd served his time with Wilson Brothers and been with them since he came back from the war. It was common knowledge the Wilson Brothers thought the world of Charlie.

Cathie wouldn't go to identify the body, wouldn't leave the house, so my grandfather went in his dark-blue three-piece suit, black woollen tie, his homburg hat and good grey coat, polished shoes and grey woollen socks that were darned at the heel.

Again, in the morning I watched him shave. He blew out his cheeks when he brought the razor across his face. It tinkled in the cup with no handle that sat by the sink. He looked different with his teeth in place. I was so used to seeing him slumped in his chair by the fire, but when his teeth were in place, I glanced at his stomach to be sure it was him. His bottom waistcoat button was unfastened.

Weary work, he said as he closed the door.

You'd think Cathie would have gone, Granny said. You'd think she'd've gone to see her man.

And someone said, Shush, Mother. Shush.

I liked my Aunt Cathie; she always smiled, seemed interested in me and in what I was doing. But there were differences, holy pictures on the wall and attendance at St Theresa's. Charlie became a Catholic to marry her.

His front room seemed incandescent. Everyone blinked and lowered their heads, turned their faces to the wall or put their backs to the window, away from the light that distilled through cotton. The mirrors were covered and there was a heavy smell of chrysanthemums.

He lay by the window, in a dark-stained coffin, a white shroud across his chest, his face covered with a satin mat, embroidered with a radiant crucifix. His hair sprouted from below the mat. I expected his hand to free itself from below the cloth, to pull the mat and shake his face, then to run his hand through his hair and smile his smile that tucked his face up at the corners, the way light is stored in water.

We had tea in the kitchen and moved to the room, squeezing in as best we could. The priest with his back to the light, facing the coffin, his voice occasionally overtaken by a shunting train or tramcar, the sweaty folk uncomfortable with the service and the space. He had a thin, grainy line round the rim of his collar. His jacket was frayed at the edges and a button was missing. Small pockets of hair gathered beneath his chin. Cathie's brother Joe McGuinness had cut himself shaving and had a piece of newspaper stuck on his chin. During the service, his wife turned him to her and swiped the fragment from his face. A dribble of blood seeped through the congealed edges and trickled in two uneven lines down his chin, gathering below the Adam's apple and disappearing behind his shirt.

And later we stood in St Kentigern's cemetery where Aunt Carrie and Uncle Willie were buried; I remember thinking Joe McGuinness's tie had been knotted by hands other than his own.

The day was cold and fresh, without rain. A small breeze seemed to rise from the city, carrying the taste of Possil Loch. Somewhere, a bird sang. Then there was nothing; a silence so intense it could have been a sound.

TWENTY-THREE
Miss Fernie

ONE MONDAY, AFTER playtime, we had a new teacher.

Miss Fernie slapped the desk with her ruler. Eyes front. Backs straight. Hands on desks. And no talking. Her cheeks flushed when she shouted.

Later that week, she told me to pull myself together. I've been told about you, she said. It's not as if this is the first time such a thing has happened. You have, I believe, lost a father. Rather than sit around moping, you should get yourself a hobby, do something useful, instead of staring into space.

* * *

Francie asked me to read to him. I put the book down after a page.

Do you want a cuddle? he asked.

I stood up.

Come here, he said. Put your head on my shoulder.

He sat on the stair and I sat beside him. He leaned across, put his arms around me and rocked me back and forward, my head on his shoulder.

See when my da was killed in the war, he said, I was wee and my Maw just kept cuddling us and telling us to cry. We thought he was coming back and then he was killed.

His breath on my neck, his arms and face felt warm. The wind through a broken window made my legs cold.

Maybe the next time, he said. Maybe you'll cry the next time. See instead of reading a story, make one up for us.

Our arms and legs around each other, we made up The Story of the Stanks, where the manhole gratings and sewer covers led to tunnels and passages of gloom, populated by dwarves and ravens, a place where rats and beggars congregated.

See when you're down there and you die, they just leave your body and the rats eat you.

They gnaw your bones.

Pick out your eyes.

Would they eat your hair?

Don't think so.

Or your bum?

And we laughed till Mrs Jamieson chased us. From then, I imagined the world through keyholes, trying to see what used to be, to imagine the broken machinery, torn wallpaper or bare floorboards repaired, constructing, events that gave the desolation meaning, trying to imagine what they might be in the future.

There were times when I'd stand by the wall and wait for a familiar face, or I'd pretend I knew someone and follow them, walk behind someone in the way I sometimes dawdled behind my mother, near enough to be called.

* * *

Miss Fernie clapped her hands. Sit up straight, she said. I want you to paint a busker or a barker. She distributed paper, brushes and small blocks of colour, while the girls filled small, clear jars with water from the sink in the corner. Do you know what a busker is? Or a barker? Hands up, please, anyone who knows. Yes, Wilma.

Please, miss. Is a barker a dog?

Sit down. Stupid girl. Of course not. Who knows what a barker is? Or a busker? Very well then. Since no one seems to know I will have to tell you. A busker is a street performer, usually a singer or musician; a barker is a fairground salesman; and you should paint either one or the other.

Please, miss.

Yes, William.

Please, miss. Can we paint something else?

Very well then.

I wanted it to be a landscape, hills, a river, trees and sky with darker colours at the bottom, gradually becoming lighter, moving through grey to a pale blue sky with a yellow sun in the centre.

What's this? she asked, tore the paper, then ripped it again until she had a wad she could no longer shred. Rubbish, she said, repeating the word with every tear. I hope no one is as foolish as this silly boy who refuses to do as he is told. He will stay here until he paints a busker or a barker and paints it properly, a happy fairground scene with colours and light. Though I have to say, I am not too sure why we are teaching art to the likes of you. No one around here knows anything about art.

Next day she told us the first astronomers saw patterns in the stars and named them after mythical people, beasts and gods. I knew that as the earth moved around the sun, constellations appeared, disappeared and reappeared at different times of the year. I did not know why, or what one star's position was in relation to the others.

I asked.

Miss Fernie narrowed her mouth. The edge of her lips turned white. What do you want to know something like that for? she said.

* * *

Francie found the story of Tutankhamun's tomb.

Teacher told us. Imagine, but; imagine what was on Keppochhill Road afore people.

Maybe there was nothing.

There must've been something. We cannae be the first. There has to have been something here afore us.

What I don't understand is where to look.

Maybe you look where other folk've dug.

What do you think we'll find?

Skeletons. And stones and plates. Maybe we'll find a house. Would we find plants? Know how they found food with the pharaohs? Maybe we'll find something like that.

So we wandered the park, looking for fossils, digging for clues of an earlier habitation. We imagined finding food, wooden and pewter plates with bread and fruit, or sunken bushes, an apple tree, raspberry or gooseberry that had grown into the ground, whose fruit was covered with the Keppochhill clay. Or a labyrinth, a network of underground passages abandoned by a previous people, but their wide rooms and narrow corridors lit with flaming torches remained.

When we found stones, we kept these as possible clues, as though they could indicate the beginning of a trail, the corner of a building, the edge of a wall. And scraps of habitation were also kept, cup handles, plate and saucer chips, the bowl of a teaspoon.

I told Francie about the skulls I'd found in Fife and Patch's cemetery in the corner of the garden. So we dug a hole, lined it with a panel of bricks with slates and placed wood across the top. We sealed the entrance and covered the hide with clods of grass. We had a trail of smaller stones leading to the entrance, beginning with a single stone, then two together, three and so on to six, when we worked the numbers downwards.

We kept what we found in a tin box and roamed Keppoch Hill, digging in the ground, looking for treasures to add to the store; or damming the streams with stones and divots, building the dams bigger and wider, covering the facing with mud so no water escaped, not even a cupful trickled over the top, then diverting the water into rivulets which flowed from the dam, allowing a controlled trickle to run from a channel in the side, a small waterfall from each of the dams, cascading down the hill and into the steady stream that flowed from the hill down Vere Street into the syvers on Keppochhill Road.

* * *

Francie went to the Springburn Baths with the Gospel Hall's summer scheme, Suffer The Little Children. He learned a kind of dog paddle, then was told to leave.

It's not because you're a Catholic, it's because you lied. You lied about your name and you lied about your religion.

I'll need to get someplace else to swim, he said.

You could go to the baths on your own.

There's a swimming club that meets at the baths, Davie Sanderson told him. But you're supposed to be able to swim before you go.

For half an hour we shivered by the poolside while the instructor shouted at the swimmers.

Skinny pair of buggers, i'n't yous, he said, when they were exercising.

Will you teach us to swim?

Can yous no even swim?

We came to learn.

Come back when yous've learned and put on two stones each.

We spent the tram fare on sweets and walked home.

Come into the cemetery, I said. There's lights on the road. If we go into the cemetery we could maybe see the stars.

There's no lights in the cemetery.

I know. And that means the stars'll be dead clear.

But it's creepy.

No it's no. We'll be okay. Honest. See if it gets creepy, right; if it gets too creepy we'll go by the road.

I knew my father would want to see me, knew he had no time to say he was leaving, so I assumed he would return. I imagined he might not return to his body in Oban, or to Lambhill or St Kentigern's where his in-laws were buried. Sighthill was the nearest cemetery and I thought if he was coming back it would be to the nearest place and would come back there at night when no one could see him, when he wouldn't scare me as much as during the day. I'd introduce him to Francie and ask if he knew Francie's dad or could find him.

Francie took my hand. We walked along the pathways shaded by angels, veiled urns and obelisks, with shadows moving between the tombstones as we walked.

This was where I thought my father would appear, as I had seen him, standing in the Kettle churchyard. I thought he would not want to be seen from the road. I ran onto the main path and started climbing the hill into darkness.

Where are we? Francie yelled. Where are we going?

At the top of the hill I stared across the city, beyond the river and its fringe of hills, beyond railway yards, factories, parks and buildings, hidden beneath the ribbon of streetlights, pale in the moon or red from the Dixon's Blazes fire.

This is great, said Francie. He smiled and turned himself round, sometimes staring into the sky.

Come on, I said, running down the main path towards the Keppochhill gates where I stood while my breath came in handfuls, trembling with the thought that something could jump from a grave and grab my ankles.

And Francie came behind me, shouting and slapping the side of his horse, Come on, he shouted. We need to get over afore the redskins catch us.

Walking back along the road my legs still trembled as I imagined the spirits who might be following, waiting to drag me back to the cemetery, hiding in a close or backcourt, where anything could happen. I ran in front of Francie and when I'd left him at his close, where he said he'd catch some shuteye, I ran across the road and up the close, climbing the stairs, two, three at a time.

Is that you back? my granny said. Running, running and always running.

Leave him alone, Mother, my Aunt Barbara said, nursing Michael by the fire.

If he's no father and his mother's aye working, somebody has to tell him. What if he falls, if he breaks a leg or falls on some broken glass, what'll yous do then?

Barbara smiled and raised her eyes.

Now listen you here to me, my boy, I want you washed and ready for bed in ten minutes flat with no books or wireless for you.

I stripped and washed myself every night, but lately I could not be bothered and often missed brushing my teeth. I knew they would rot, but didn't care. We used Gibb's Dentifrice, which came in a tin, but more often than not when she couldn't afford the toothpaste my mother told me to brush my teeth with soot from the chimney. I liked the taste of soot.

* * *

At first she pretended not to see me, then asked a question I could not answer. Stupid boy, she shouted. Stupid boy. Whoever sent you to the top of the class?

Out of there at once, this instant.

Her face was red and her limbs shook. Someone giggled.

She ran to her desk and, in a single movement, snatched the belt and threw it at me as I was rising to my feet. The belt caught me full in the face and I burst into tears.

Baby, she shouted. Baby. Out of there and into the corridor where you will stand until you learn not to cry. Stupid boy, always crying.

There was a swelling on the side of my face.

What did I tell you? Granny said. How many times have I said it; I've said it before and I'll say it again. Stones, that's what did it, bad weekit buggers o' boys throwing stones. It's a helmet he needs. Now he's getting bigger he's easier to hit.

Shush, Jo, my grandfather said. What happened, Carl? Was it a stone?

I told him what had happened.

My mother left before me in the morning and I was usually in bed by the time she got home. That night I thought I heard her step on the stair. She touched my cheek, followed by the sharp coldness of the flannel on the side of my face.

Next day, just before the morning interval, I heard her voice on the school corridor followed by the sharp click of her heels. Mister Campbell opened the door.

Sorry to disturb you, Miss Fernie, he said, I wonder if you could spare us a moment.

It's not convenient, she said, looking at my mother, turning her back on the door and glancing at me.

In which case, my mother said, entering the classroom, you'll have to make it convenient or I will say what I have to say in front of the children.

How dare you interrupt my lesson.

How dare you throw the belt at my child.

I think this would be better settled in my office.

Miss Fernie doesn't have time for that and neither do I, my mother said. I have taken a morning off work and that was scarcely convenient.

I refuse to have my classroom invaded in this way.

Do you deny throwing the belt at my son?

Please take this woman out of here.

Can you explain the swelling on the side of his face?

He's not the only child I belt.

But he is the only child you throw the belt at.

Now we're not actually sure that took place, Mrs MacDougall.

Then tell me how the swelling occurred. Carl says his teacher threw the belt at him. Is he lying, Miss Fernie?

I think this what we have to establish.

Correct me if I am wrong, Mister Campbell, but it seems as though you are siding with Miss Fernie. I would have thought it would have been in your interest to have this matter dealt with properly. You surely don't want someone like that on your staff.

Mrs MacDougall, I think you can leave it to me to deal with this. I'll write you a letter and let you know what action we've taken.

That's not good enough. Everyone knows you will take the easiest route with the least amount of fuss. I want an apology, and I want my son moved to another class where he won't be beaten by someone who cannot control her temper.

I don't think that will be possible.

In that case, I will write to my MP. I am already in touch with Mister Henderson Stewart, who was our MP in Fife, and will have no hesitation in consulting him on a matter like this.

I have no intention of apologising, Miss Fernie said.

I'm sure you will do what's necessary to save your job, though I will certainly make clear this goes on your record. I do not believe in hitting children. I have never hit my son and certainly do not intend to allow someone like you to do so, far less allow this man to justify it.

I don't think there's any call for that sort of insult, though I do think we should discuss this matter in the privacy of my office.

Mister Campbell took the class after the break, that afternoon another teacher came and two days later Mrs Docherty was back.

TWENTY-FOUR

Brothers

WE'D BEEN BARRED from the Minors.

Get yous two t'fuck out of here, Uncle Tommy said when we turned up for our birthday treats on the fourth successive week.

We'll get in next week, Francie said. But we never did. They put a man on the exit and when we went to the box office the woman in the yellow overalls told us we were barred.

We roamed the streets or sat on the hill. Everything was in for a week or two, coloured elastic bands joined together to fire paper pellets, catapults, bows and arrows made from bamboo canes, crossbows from chair legs, steelies and jauries.

The woman still kept us back from the library and things got so bad we watched the girls skipping games and sang with their rhymes, though we gave up on playing houses and shops with earth and tin cans.

I'll be the faither and come in drunk, said Francie.

No in my hoose you'll no, said Agnes Dineen.

Every Saturday morning the rent man came with a rose in his lapel and Mister Brown collected the insurance. Francie was fascinated. Nobody ever comes to our hoose, he said, except my uncles and they tell me to fight for Scotland and die for Ireland.

Then because I'd been to the baths with Francie, Mrs McDade made my tea. I hope you like banana sandwiches, she said.

The house was small and lit with gas, the kitchen dominated by a range. There was a table in the bed recess and chairs round the table. I assumed the other room was the bedroom. There was nowhere for me to sit, so I shared a chair with Francie. There were perhaps four other children, all girls.

Remember we have a guest, said Mrs McDade. Please, Carl, help yourself, son.

I took a sandwich from the plate. The others packed their hands with two or three, taking a bite from each then leaving them on the table. Mrs McDade slapped the back of their heads, took two sandwiches back, sliced away the missing corner and put in sandwiches in front of me.

I'm fine, thank you, Mrs McDade. I'm not hungry.

Someone snatched the sandwiches.

Why do you stutter? a girl asked.

Don't you be so cheeky, said Mrs McDade.

Are you teaching Francis to read? asked another.

Is it true yous were caught reading up a close?

Shush, said Francie. Listen. There she's there. It's Jessie Anderson.

And from the close a woman shouted, Come on, rats. Your tea's oot. There it's there. Breid and jam.

The children ran from the table and came back eating the bread and jam.

She's a poor old biddy that's lost her mind, said Mrs McDade. She puts bread and jam oot for the rats and my weans eat it. She says she wants to catch a rat and put it in a shoebox.

Why?

God knows. Maybe she's lonely and wants a wee pet.

Come on, said Francie. We're going out.

Now I want you back on time, said Mrs McDade, running her hand through his hair.

Mammy, chuck it.

And I don't want you to get into any bother.

She kissed the top of his head. I love you, Francis McDade, she said. You're my boy and you'd better be good.

He smiled and wiped the top of his head.

Does your mammy do that all the time? I asked.

What?

Kiss you.

Aye. She usually cuddles me, but she didnae because you were there. I think she knew I was embarrassed.

What's it like?

What?

That.

Nothing. It's just ordinary.

Later we lay on top of the hill and tried to see the stars, stopping off to read before going home. When I got home I could tell my mother had been crying.

Nothing, she said. It's nothing. Nothing's wrong. Nothing at all. Did you enjoy your tea at Mrs McDade's?

Then she told me, Mister Henderson Stewart had written in response to her appeal. He'd investigated the matter fully, had spoken with the railway authorities and was sorry to have to confirm the previous position: that because my father had been a railway employee for less than six months, there were insufficient payments to his pension.

* * *

Every day, sometimes more than once a day, Mrs Docherty asked if I was all right.

You don't seem fine to me, she said, ruffling my hair. There's something bothering you, isn't there?

No, miss.

And how is your mother?

Fine, thank you.

And everyone else is well?

Yes, thank you.

I've noticed your work is falling behind. I know your mother's busy, but it would be good if she could find the time to come and see me, say after school. In the meantime, I'll see what I can do.

She mentioned it to the headmaster on his weekly round.

Everyone's fine, Mister Campbell. Things are going along quite smoothly, aren't they children?

Yes, miss.

Though, I have to say, Mister Campbell, there is one boy whom we feel could do better. He has done very well in the past and could certainly do well again.

She was looking at me.

Yes, I know about this boy, Mister Campbell said. I'm afraid he's heart lazy. He seems happy to lie beneath the tree and wait for the plums to fall. I don't think he's a worker. Rather, I feel he's an idler and as such is a disgrace to himself and his family, a bright boy who refuses to apply himself.

* * *

Have I just to go and see Mrs Docherty? she asked. See that bloody man Campbell; I don't know what your father would have made of him and I don't know what to make of him myself. It's the war, you know. People like him get jobs like that because they survived the war. Decent folk who could do the job are dead or wounded and just because he can get to work they think he's fit and able, same as that other nasty bitch. But any more nonsense from him and I'll be having a word with his superiors, for he's not only incompetent, he's impertinent as well. But I don't think he'll be impertinent with me in a hurry. What are you laughing at? Adults can be impertinent as well as you.

I saw more of her now. She saw me off to school in the morning and was back when I came home. She'd taken a permanent job with the railway.

It was silly not to. When you think about it, I'd be better taking that job, even though the pay's not great, rather than the jobbing work here and there. Jobbing's all very well, but it's not enough to raise a family. It's all right for a woman who has her man working and maybe wants to earn a wee bit more for their holidays, but it's not for me. Not now any roads.

We'd take the tram and wander; go out on Saturday afternoons, doing pretty much the same as we did on Sundays, except that the shops were open. Saturday walks were never planned; she acted on impulse. This'll never do, she'd say. Come on, you and me are getting to hell out of here.

We'd wander through the big stores like Copeland and Lye, with the massive staircase, or down Buchanan Street and into Rowan's, which was her favourite shop, though she never bought anything: A very superior store, she'd say after the man in the morning coat held the front door open.

Which department, madam? he asked.

Just looking.

Then we'd cross to Fuller's tearoom. Don't breathe a word about this, she'd say. Not a word. Not to anyone.

God, this is terrible, she'd say, ordering a pot of tea and a cream puff.

And with the last drop of tea drunk, we'd cross Buchanan Street to stare in the barber's window with four men working, where I could have spent forever watching the men being shaved, bathed in white, with towels around their faces, white foamy beards, removed line by line.

And on Sundays we'd visit the Cathedral and Provand's Lordship, maybe the Necropolis if the weather was fine; otherwise, we'd go to the Art Galleries.

She'd stand in the main hall and look around her, as she did in Rowan's, hold her handbag into her body and suddenly decide: I think we'll look at that Armoury today. You like that man on the horse, don't you?

And she talked all the time, talking about everything till she pounced on the subject. Mrs Docherty's worried about you, she said. What's been going on?

I tried to tell her what I could, but found it difficult. Often when the stammer came I had to stop talking.

She says she's sending you for a test. I think it's a good idea. You should take it. It's what Miss McClure wanted, an IQ test, and it's a disgrace that nothing's been done since she left. Mrs Docherty thinks you're performing well below what you should be doing, so we'll see how we get on with that.

Two days later, I took the test. On the Friday, Mister Campbell came into the classroom. I'm afraid it has to be now, he said to Mrs Docherty.

But the first test was accurate, she said. You know as well as I do, he had no preparation.

Nevertheless, they seem to want it again.

I sat in his office, using the far end of his desk. He smiled when I looked up and, when I finished, told me I could take more time if I wanted, or I could revise the paper, for there were still 20 minutes to go.

I've finished, thank you.

That was very quick.

I've done the test before, I said.

He put the papers in a brown buff envelope with a handwritten note and told me to go back to class.

* * *

We went to the Theatre Royal for a Christmas treat, sat in the gallery watching the Carl Rosa Opera Company singing *La Bohème*; walking home, across the Phoenix Bridge and up Craighall Road, my mother was crying.

What, do you mean they sing? asked Francie.

They don't talk. They sing. And there's a big orchestra as well.

I'm no sure I like the sound of that, he said. See when my uncles start singing, it's no very good.

It's no singing like that.

What kind of singing is it?

Do yous get a music teacher?

Aye, sometimes.

Well, it's a bit like that, except it's no tunes, just a long bit of music with singing.

And do yous pay to get in?

I told him the story of Mimi dying in a garret. What was her name? he asked. I told him.

Come on, he said, and we ran along the road and up Scone Brae past the school, along the path to St Theresa's and the pitches to the plank, where he carefully took away the clods and divots, removed the stone and from the tin took out a new jotter and pencil.

I bought them, he said. I went shopping for my mammy and she gave me money and told me to buy them. What was the woman's name again?

And when I told him how to spell it, he opened the jotter and wrote MIMI in capital letters near the top, licking the tip of the pencil before every letter.

Going home, we met them at the foot of the Long Stairs.

Where're yous going? asked Alec Irvine. Alex Carson and Willie Simpson were with him.

Baths, said Francie.

What're you doing playing with Fenians? said Davie Sanderson.

I can play with anybody I like.

Naebody else'll play wi' him, said Willie Simpson. So he's forced to play wi' a lousy fucken German bastard.

Come on, I said to Francie.

No, he said. We've got to face them. They'll go for you cause they think you're no much of a fighter, so I'll take Sanderson. He's like his big blue nose faither, all fucken talk. See if you can handle Irvine. Kick him in the balls. Ready. Now, mind what I told you, the only thing you need tae know is get the first dig in and keep going. They're gonnae crap it anyway. Cause I've beat every one of them and they know what I'm saying's true. Come on, Carlie son. Don't let them scare you. Okay then, who's first, come here Sanderson and let's have a look at your big blue nose.

I went for Willie Simpson. As we tumbled over I felt a jab in my side. When he landed, I fell on top of him. He squirmed from beneath me and kicked my face as he went. Only then did I see the other two running. I was the only one injured. I had a sore side and a kick in the face, but we won.

And we sang all the way to the Kay Street Baths, where Francie showed me his dog paddle and taught me to float, firstly with my feet attached to the rails, then with his hand supporting my chin and me screaming for him not to let go. He did let go and I swam for two or three strokes. After that, we could do anything. We ran round the pool and splashed in from the side, jumped from the diving dale and swam the breadth of the baths.

Later, on the corner of my Uncle Charlie's stair, I was reading a Children's Classic version of *The Last of the Mohicans*.

Francie put his hand inside his jumper. Here, he said. I've nothing else for your Christmas.

He had drawn a Christmas tree with coloured candles round the edge and a robin at the top and Merrry at the top and Crismos at the bottom. Inside he had written, 'To Crl From Francis'. The C and F's were written backwards. I gave him a card I'd written which more or less said the same and I also gave him a bar of Fry's Five Boys chocolate, which I'd bought with money saved from going messages.

We should make a list of the books we've read, he said.

You write it then.

We'll write them another night, said Francie. That was some fight, eh.

We won.

They ran away.

Did Simpson kick you?

No.

I thought he hit your face.

He just missed me.

Know something?

What.

You havenae got a brother and I havenae got a brother either. But we should be brothers, you know, like Thingme.

Who?

Him in the book with the name you cannae say.

I can so say it.

What is it then?

Chingie.

That's what I said, Thingme. Some name. How could they not call him Red Eagle or something like that.

Or Willie.

That's right. Me Francie Red Eagle. You Carlie Swift Hawk.

Is that us brothers?

No. We've still to become blood brothers.

You mix your blood. I seen it in a picture.

We cut our thumbs on a broken pane and rubbed the cuts together, our blood mingling on the skin. We should let it join, he said, smiling at each other while the blood ran down our hands, dripping from the wrist onto the stone stairway.

I know, he said. We ran along the road, up the Long Stairs to the plank where he tore a piece of paper from the notebook where he'd written Mimi. His blood went on first, then mine.

That's it, he said. That's proof. A blood brothers' record.

He folded the paper, carefully placing the notebook, pencil and blood brothers paper along the bottom.

TWENTY-FIVE

Child Guidance

I MOVED MY leg from the warm hollow in the centre of the bed, across the colder rim, dangled my foot over the side, then swung back into the warmth. It was some time after six; I had Toby at my feet, listening to stillness.

I got up around seven and shivered on the linoleum, rubbing my skin, jumping from one leg to the other and dressing simultaneously, trying to retain the warmth. My feet were always cold. If I put my vest, shirt and trousers on first, I often could not feel my feet. If I put my socks on first, I shivered till I'd eaten something warm. I put my head out the window. The morning light was dim and blue. Across the tram and electric cables, across the phone lines, the drift of rain.

You're up, my mother said. You'll be wanting tea and I don't suppose you've forgotten it's Christmas.

My stocking was pegged to the washing line under the brace of the range. There was an orange in the toe, an apple, a banana, a torch, a packet of Rowntree's Fruit Gums and a bar of chocolate. I knew my presents would be clothes. Everyone got clothes for Christmas and were wore them on Christmas Day or to church on the Sunday between Christmas and New Year.

Open your parcel, my mother said.

It's clothes.

There's more than one parcel.

I had an *Oor Wullie* annual, a Buffalo Bill Wild West annual and a *Beano* Monster comic, Children's Classic editions of *Gulliver's Travels*, *A Tale of Two Cities* and *The Legend of Robin Hood*. I got a pencil case and a rubber.

I sat on the floor beneath the clock by the bed, reading while my mother and Aunt Barbara roasted the chicken, then George did the potatoes in the fat, while the peas were shelled and boiled with sprigs of mint my mother found growing by one of the Springburn Park ponds. She nipped a spring and it sat in my daddy's shaving cup with the peony rose transfer. The jelly was put on the window sill to set and we had mandarin oranges and custard.

We sat down to eat after the King's broadcast. My grandmother emptied her food onto my plate.

188

Did you enjoy your dinner, Mother?

The chicken's lovely, beautifully done.

The peas are nice.

And so are the potatoes.

I put small pieces of chicken breast and gravy back on my granny's plate, carefully avoiding the places she tapped with her fork to find the food.

When dinner was over, we sat staring at each other. Barbara and George smoking, my grandad in his chair.

It's terrible to think of it, Granny said.

Mother, don't start.

I'm only saying it's terrible to think that this time last year we were all here and there's a new year no far away though poor Willie and Marie's man, what's his name, never saw last New Year.

Mother, please.

And who knows how many of us'll be here next Christmas, or maybe somebody'll go before the New Year.

Barbara picked up Michael and left the room. George lit another cigarette.

Jo, for goodness sake please. Let the dead rest in peace and let us get on with our life.

What kind of a life is this? You bring children into the world and watch them die. You see their children left fatherless, poor innocent bairns. Are we no supposed to talk about it?

My mother put the kettle on. My grandfather lit his pipe and stared into the fire. My mother leaned on the sink and stared out the window.

George looked at me and smiled.

Marvellous, he said. I'n't it marvellous.

* * *

A couple of days later, my mother and I walked part of the way into town. A horse had shied in Garscube Road, spilling its load of potatoes, cabbages, carrots and turnips across the street. There was a line of trams back to the Astoria. We'll just get off, she said.

When we passed, the horse was feeding from a sack of oats, the carter trying to save his load.

Things'll be different when you go back to school, my mother said. Mrs Docherty will have the result of that test and that should make a difference.

We should have gone to Oban, she said in the Del Oro Cafe, beside the bakers in Cambridge Street, where the smell of bread and coffee, the steam and the noise came on to the pavement. Every time we passed my mother told the story of me in town, crying and anxious to be home. I want an ice cream, I shouted when we passed the cafe. Shush, she said. We'll soon be home. I want a piano, I shouted when we passed Cuthbertson's music shop.

Joey wanted us to go to Oban. She sent a card, but you know that. She's always asking us to come up. Come and bring Carl, she says. He'll be getting big. She wanted us to come at Christmas, then she said New Year. I don't know that I could face it. We'll see. The weather's not too great. I wrote and said we'd be up in the spring, maybe Easter would be good.

That night by the window watching the stars and frost on the stone glitter like mica, neither one seemed nearer nor more important than the other.

* * *

Hogmanay meant an early rise: The busiest bloody day of the year, my mother said. Housework; all day, nothing but bloody housework; then you're supposed to have a party when you're too bloody tired for anything except your bed.

Everybody worked; my grandfather was obviously in the way, so he and his newspaper moved from room to room while Granny supervised.

Carpets were lifted and beds were stripped, curtains and lampshades taken down and washed. Lightbulbs changed, windows cleaned, floors washed, the front step scrubbed, brasses polished, stairs swept then washed and the stone flags finished with wet pipeclay that dried bold and white, with a freehand border the women worked round the edge of the wall. A running loop was easiest, but there were other, more intricate patterns.

Then, around two o'clock, my mother would rush out for the last of the messages. A bone from the butcher, a bit of lamb neck with meat on the bone was best, carrot, leek, onion, turnips, dried peas and barley, with a wee drop parsley for the broth; potatoes, cabbage, a wee bit lamb, stewing steak or chicken and everything leftover for the stovies, and mince to do us because we never knew when the shops would open. We always took more vegetables and meat than we needed. And with the broth on the go, the baking began. She usually bought a bit of black bun, Madeira or Dundee cake to go with the shortbread, pancakes and scones. And, of course, there was a bottle of whisky, screw-tops of beer, sherry and perhaps a half bottle of port.

My job was to wash the plates, cups and saucers, polish the glasses and lay them out along the sideboard. We ate when George came in from work some time around five, then the house was reset, the newly cleaned and ironed curtains were rehung, the beds remade with clean sheets and blankets, mirrors washed in a vinegar solution and polished with wet newspaper, the clocks were reset, a fresh cloth was spread across the table, the fire was lit and stacked, the food and plates placed on the table.

Then we all washed and changed and at 11 o'clock put the wireless on to the Scottish Home Service.

This was my favourite time, everyone sitting round the room all dressed up, light bouncing from the glass, the smell of warmth and baking, soup and bread, staring at the fire, listening to Jimmy Shand, waiting.

At five to 12 we opened the windows to hear the horns from the boats on the Clyde that always sounded at midnight, behind the chime of the clocks, and the noise of the city. My mother always said she could hear the cheers of the folk gathered at the Tron steeple at the foot of High Street.

At midnight, Jimmy Shand struck the opening chord of 'The Gay Gordons', the compère shouted Happy New Year, the foghorns sounded, cheering came in from the street, we opened the whisky and everyone burst into tears. We went round the room like strangers, shaking hands and wishing each other a Happy New Year.

With a drink in our hand and nothing to do we were suddenly awkward, nothing to say till the singing stopped and the cheery compère introduced his guests. We waited on our first foot, always someone from the stair, who came in with some whisky, food and a lump of coal. Drinks were exchanged and they would take a bite to eat. Then we would first foot someone else, going round till all the houses were visited, eventually settling somewhere for a song.

Peter Keaney always sang 'Biddy Mulligan the pride of the Coombe'.

Thank God, it's no one of his bloody shut-eyed songs or that would be us here for the night, my mother would say. We should have brought a loaf and made up pieces.

Barbara had to be coaxed to sing, George only sang in front of the family, so that meant my mother sang 'The Green Hills of Oban'. Then when she'd finished, fighting back the tears, someone would start a chorus, what my mother called a vulgar song, which she also found funny:

> Who was doon the dunny?
> Who was doon the dunny?
> I was there and so were you,
> You'd a bottle and I had two.
> Then the polis tried tae capture us
> And we had tae dae a runny,
> But we'd a rerr wee time, swallyin the wine,
> Doon in the dunny.

> I love Eldorado,
> I love Lanilique,
> Four Crown wine goes down strong
> Try it once, you can't go wrong;
> If you need a morning pick me up
> When your guts is feeling chronic
> Start you day the Buckfast way
> With Scotland's favourite tonic.

We never left the close and some New Years didn't leave the house, dancing till the wireless stopped around one, then singing to ourselves till I fell asleep and George carried me in to bed.

Then, on the Saturday before school restarted, we went to the circus at the Kelvin Hall, where the smell from the elephant stalls filled the hall. They stared from the menagerie, their trunks foraging in the straw, next to the tigers, Cossack horses, camels and llamas that spat if you went too near.

We ate the Canadian sweets and chocolate, the candy-coated nuts and sticky popcorn, laughing at the dwarves with their funny hats and noses pretending to soak the audience, then soaking themselves. The camels ran round the ring, the tigers roared from their boxes, their claws slashing the air, the elephants danced and women stood on the horses' backs, bouncing from the floor to the horse on either side, waiting for the horse to come round then jumping on its back again, while the ringmaster cracked his whip. Finally the trapeze artists: two men and two women swinging from bar to bar, letting go and just when you thought they'd tumble, they were caught, sometimes by the wrists, sometimes by the ankles, even when they did handstands on the bar and swung as though they'd collide, eventually dropping into the others' arms, they never tumbled, though you thought they might.

* * *

Mrs Docherty asked which book I'd enjoyed.
　Buffalo Bill.
　Did you know he came to Glasgow?
　Yes, miss.
　I think Geronimo was here as well.
　Sitting Bull.
　Annie Oakley was here.
　Yes, miss. And Vicente Oropeza.
　She smiled. Who was he?

The bullwhip king.

She looked long enough to make me uncomfortable. It was break time and the shouts rose from the playground.

You don't mind being here, do you?

No, miss.

It's warmer than the playground.

Yes, miss.

I wanted to have a word with you for a couple of reasons. The first is that you're going to have to take the test again. How do you feel about that?

Fine.

They want you to take the test this afternoon. And this is a letter for your mother. Do you know what Child Guidance is?

No, miss.

Your mother will explain. You've to go for an assessment. Your school work doesn't match the test results. They'll be training you to write the tests for them, the way they're carrying on. It's ridiculous.

Francie told me Jessie Anderson was getting a new corporation house. She took a rat in a shoe-box down to the City Chambers.

Just shows you, he said. We thought she was daft, but she's got a house oot o' it. We should do that. My mammy should dae something like that; after a', it's the same rats and if she can get a hoose and she's on her ain in the same size o' a hoose as us, there must be something we could dae.

I'm going to Child Guidance.

What's that?

Don't know.

You might get a house. See if you tell them you're needing a new house to get on with whatever it is they need to guide you for, I bet you'll get it.

* * *

The clinic was on the corner of Royal Crescent, part of Sauchiehall Street with columns on either side of the door. We waited in the hall, on chairs so tall my legs could not touch the floor, my mother in her good hat and coat, her handbag on her lap. When I spoke in a whisper, my mother said, Shush.

A door opened and the tallest woman I had ever seen emerged. My mother's head scarcely reached her bosom.

Mrs MacDougall, she said.

She led us into the room, her bracelet jangling, sat behind her desk and smiled, her hair simultaneously piled on top of her head and rolled to the back. She wore a cream, high-necked blouse with a gold brooch at her throat.

She had a gold watch on her left wrist, and later, in Ross's Dairy at Charing Cross, where my mother insisted we have a cup of tea before going home, I asked about the smell, then blushed.

Did you like it? she said.

It reminded me of Aunt Eva and Aunt Barbara too sometimes.

It's perfume, my mother said.

She did not introduce herself, but told my mother I was performing well below my capability, asking where I was born, what my father did, how did he die and so on. And while my mother told our story, I was taken to a table in the corner and given another test.

Would you mind, Carl? Just a question or two. She indicated three questions with red ink and when I had finished called me over. Just a second, she said, and checked the answers.

You know, she said, putting the paper into a folder, the problem is; well, I'm sure by now you know the problem, Mrs MacDougall. I think Carl would benefit from care. We'll tell you about that nearer the time, when you'll have a chance to raise and discuss the case. Have you any friends, Carl?

I told her about Francie McDade. She asked my hobbies, was I in the Wolf Cubs or the Life Boys, what books I had read and how did I like school? She rose to indicate the interview was over and showed us to the door, telling my mother she'd be getting a letter.

Next day, Francie was waiting by the Scone Street gate. I've something to show you, he said.

He'd found a cat with three kittens. She was wild and lay at the back of the midden. She spat when we went near. We tried to move her, but she arched her back and bared her claws.

We brought food, which she eventually accepted, never eating while we were there, but the dish was always empty when we returned.

She'll have to go when they empty the midden, he said.

The middens were emptied at night, and one morning she was gone.

She's deid, he said. They men'll've killed her.

We searched the basements and the middens, trailed around the washhouses and back closes, looked in dark and empty places but never saw her again.

After two nights, we knew we'd never see her.

She must be deid, right enough, he said, when I left him at the close.

* * *

Jockie Craig was the talk of the place. Even my mother shook her head when his name was mentioned. Whatever you do, she said, I hope to God you're never a drunkard. Drink's a curse.

He'd been barred from the four pubs in Keppochhill Road. Austin's, Benson's, The Auld Hoose and the Cosy Corner wouldn't serve him, so he was forced to drink in Possil, then Springburn, where he sang 'The Protestant Boys' and was barred from the Vulcan Bar.

He lost his job, I'm bad wi' my chest, he said, and shuffled round Keppochhill Road. He sang 'O Salutaris' and 'Faith of our Fathers' round the Catholic backs on a Sunday morning and was seen begging in town.

He did all right with the first house of the Empire coming out and the second going in; so he started off in Stevie Taylor's and ended up somewhere in Townhead. Coming up Pinkston, the street lights out, a cloud covered the moon and he stumbled into the canal. Two men heard his shouts and fished him out the water.

It was the moon, he said. It went dark.

Then, dripping wet by the canal bank, he turned to the sky and shouted: If I was a moon, I would be a fucken moon.

* * *

When I came in from school one Friday, the house smelled warm and fresh. My mother was ironing. Shirts and pullovers, socks, vests and pants were arranged in neat piles along the sideboard. My shoes were polished with a pair of new, unlaced sandshoes beside them, one toe in the heel of the other

I've been back and forward to that place, she said. I've seen God knows how many folk and they've told me all sorts of things about you. My head's full of it, I don't know what to think. All I know is that everyone says it's for the best. It's not for long, just for a wee while. I don't know how long. It depends on how you do I suppose. A while. Just a wee while. And we'll come and see you.

It's a home, isn't it?

It's a school. A residential school.

Where is it?

East Kilbride.

Where's that?

Not far. Near enough to visit. God almighty, son, she said. Things are no right. They're awful. I've done what I can and this will make them better. I'm trying to help you and I don't know what else to say.

We stared at each other, unable to move.

Now, listen. You've to be good. You've to stick in and do your class work and you've to behave. You've to concentrate, everybody says you've no concentration, and you've always to be honest, tell the truth. God knows what all's there, but you've to show them you come from a good home.

I need to see Francie, I said. And she sighed, as though I had struck her, as though she had no more energy left.

Hurry back, she said.

Francie panicked, then started running. I followed him into the house, where he searched below the sink and beneath the bed, taking scraps from here and there, and with his bundle under his arm he ran across the road, up the Long Stairs, past the Back Lawn towards the park.

We'll plank the lucks that mean the most, he said, taking the stones from the hide. We'll put away the special things and they'll be there when you get back. You get yours; on you go, go and get them.

When I got back, the biscuit tin was on the ground. I put my map of the stars and a picture of my father in the tin. Francie put in a picture of the sea and another picture of a wooded glade lined with bluebells and light shafting down through the trees, torn from a magazine. The jotter, pencil and the blood brother paper were placed on the top.

We sealed the tin, covered the plank and ran home.

PART THREE

c/o Nerston Residential School, Nerston, East Kilbride, Lanarkshire

One stops being a child when one realises
that telling one's trouble does not make it better.
The Business of Living: Diaries, 1935–50, Cesare Pavese

c/o Nerston Residential School, Nerston, East Kilbride, Lanarkshire

TWENTY-SIX

Nerston

I WAS AWAKE when she came in with the tea and toast.

Grandad was dressed and in his chair, Granny by the window. Barbara, George and Michael were in the kitchen. Barbara had made porridge.

You give yourself a good wash, Granny said.

We ate while Mum busied herself, washing each plate as soon as it was emptied, pouring tea, making and buttering toast, continually looking at the clock. Twice she stuck her head round the bedroom door. Nearly ready? she asked.

Dressed, I sat in the kitchen.

We'll write to you, my mother said.

And we'll come and see you, said Barbara. George and Michael and I will come and see you as soon as we can. They said we might not be able to come right away.

They said you'd need time to settle in.

But as soon as we can, we'll come and see you.

And don't worry about us.

No, don't worry about us. We'll be fine. We'll write and come and see you as soon as we can.

This is for the best.

Granny stood by the window, repeating what was said.

Carl, said Grandad. This is for your own good. You are going to get better, and get on with your studies.

I nodded, at first unable to speak. Everyone was on the verge of tears, so I couldn't cry.

It's important you understand what's going on. You'll have to stop dreaming: knuckle down. Everyone says you have it in you, but you don't seem able to produce it, and that's what this place will do, it will help bring it out of you.

My mother came in with her handbag, coat over her arm, hat in hand. The clock chimed ten and the doorbell rang.

A tall man in a gabardine coat stood behind a stern-looking woman whose hat was squint. She was carrying a folder.

We'll wait in the car, she said.

They left us with the awkward fragments. Mum cried as though she was going. Barbara and my granny cried, George and my grandad stood up. My grandfather touched my head, bent down and kissed me. George nodded, then suddenly kissed me. Barbara and Granny held and kissed me.

Come on, my mother said.

A small crowd had gathered at the close. The family was waving at the window. The man was at the driving seat of a grey Wolseley; the badge on the bonnet was lit. The woman held the back door open and as I went into a car for the first time I caught the smell of leather, cigarettes and heat. I looked to see who was in the crowd: mostly women with children in their arms, a couple of men with scarves and bunnets standing at the back. Jean Delacourt stood at the door of her shop. Mrs Anderson stretched across the Post Office counter and Wee Annie followed us from the Chisholm's door singing:

> For we're no awa tae bide awa,
> We're no awa tae leave ye;
> We're no awa tae bide awa,
> We'll aye come back and see ye.

I was so excited, I almost forgot to wave to the window, though my mother waved when she got into the car. A tramcar rattled past and we pulled away, down Keppochhill Road towards the Mosshouse.

Just by Uncle Charlie's close, I saw Francie at the Vere Street corner, swinging a stick and staring at the ground.

There's Francie.

I rapped the window, turned and stared out the back, leaning across to rattle the glass.

Shush. My mother lifted my wrist and held onto my hand.

Francie walked away from the car, while we carried on; past the Mosshouse to the Round Toll, along Garscube Road, down Cowcaddens and through the town, past George Square where the Christmas lights were being dismantled, along George Street and down the High Street to the Tron Steeple. I fell asleep somewhere past the Saltmarket, crossing the bridge at the High Court, my mother's arm around my shoulder, waking outside the city on a road with empty hedges and bare fields stretching into the distance.

Are you all right?

I felt sick and clammy. The man was smoking and the car was too hot. I rubbed my eyes as the car turned into a narrow road where the hedges seemed taller, interspersed with gates and trees. We drove down a hill, up the other side, past some houses with a shop on the corner, then down a drive towards what looked like a big house.

No one spoke as the car stopped by the door. The driver and the woman got out. My mother looked for the handle and rapped the window as the couple walked up the steps. He turned and opened the car door and I felt a sharp blast of wind and a heave of the sickness that started in the car.

Come on, the woman said and we went up the steps into a hall that smelled of lavatories and polish.

A small woman came out of an office to the left of the main door. Her hair was pinned in a bun at the back. She wore a blue cotton blouse and a brown tweed pleated skirt. She smelled of perfume and wore a gold watch.

Mrs MacDougall? I'm Janet Hassan.

She took the file from the woman, showed us into the office and closed the door.

Did you have a pleasant journey? She smiled at me. You look tired. Do you feel sick?

I nodded.

Just a wee bit? Well, the fresh air will do you good. The other children are out for a walk, but if we get you settled in, the others won't be long and I'm sure you'll feel better by the time they arrive.

There was a black telephone on the side of her desk. Beside her handbag on the other side was a small bottle of Tweed perfume. Her desk seemed ordered, with the files neatly piled, a glass paperweight on top of each bundle and a fountain pen and two pencils on a glass tray by the blotting paper. She swivelled her chair to the window and said, We'll see if Miss Joyce's around.

There was a moment's awkwardness. When Miss Hassan opened the door, Miss Joyce tossed her head and smiled. Miss Hassan tilted her head backwards to see Miss Joyce's face.

Miss Joyce smiled and said Hello to my mother. You come with me, she said, but first you need to tell me your name.

Your number is 14, Miss Hassan said. Remember that, Carl. As long as you're here, you'll be number 14. It's the first available number. As you'll discover, we have more than 13 other children with us at the moment. Numbers come and go. I think there may be 24 or 25.

Twenty-seven, said Miss Joyce.

So it's a bit of a squeeze. Now, I'm going to have a chat with your mum and Miss Joyce will show you round.

I stood up and my mother touched my sleeve. She waved her hand in front of her face and stared out the window.

* * *

Miss Joyce took me into a large room with windows to the right, a landscape painting of a distant town on the far wall and Mabel Lucie Attwell girls on the left between children's paintings. There were chairs round the edge of the room, a piano and a row of locked boxes on the wall behind the door. The boxes were white with black numbers above the lock.

This is your box, she said, pointing to the number 14. This is where your sweets and biscuits are kept. I presume your mother has brought some?

I don't know.

Well, if she has, this is where they'll be. We usually make a call around four or four thirty every day and this is where you come to get your stuff out the cupboard. This is the common room, which is also the games room and it's where we meet in the evenings after dinner, which is always at six.

I followed her down the room to a door on the left corner, down a flight of stairs past a smell of lavatories and disinfectant into a small, damp corridor. She switched on the bare light and ducked through a door.

The cloakrooms are through here, she said, and this is your peg, number 14. All your outdoor things will be kept here or in this cubbyhole, which again is numbered 14. We wear sandshoes indoors at all times; outdoor shoes, boots and wellingtons are kept in the cubbyhole; coats, caps and scarves are on the pegs, which are also numbered, so your outdoor stuff should be on your peg. Now, if you change into your sandshoes and leave your outdoor things here, we'll move along.

She waited, arms folded. While it seemed odd leaving my clothes beside a stranger's clothes, I liked the idea of having things in more than one place. I felt suddenly attached to my raincoat and my scarf seemed necessary. I turned the coat and caught the red name tag my mother had sewn on the collar.

This way, said Miss Joyce. We'll pick up your suitcase in the hall and go upstairs.

We walked back through the common room and into the hall, where I could see the shape of my mother's head on the chair in front of Miss Hassan's desk. Miss Hassan was talking and my mother nodded.

This is the dining room and the kitchens are through here. Trays are collected here, then you file up to the serving hatch, where the meals are served. There is a lavatory over there, through that door and down the corridor, boys on the right, and I forgot to tell you there are lavatories down the stairs from the cloakroom, going towards the back door. Do you need the toilet?

Yes, miss.

Very well then. On you go. I'll wait here.

The corridor was dark and smelly. The lavatories comprised a standard urinal and six cubicles with wooden edging on the top of the porcelain and no doors.

Miss Joyce asked, Did you wash your hands?

She carried my suitcase up the stairs, past the classrooms on the first landing to the dormitories on the top floor, boys on the left and girls on the right, divided by the stairwell. My dormitory was second on the left. There were half a dozen beds and lockers, numbered.

What number are you? she asked.

Fourteen.

And where's your bed?

By the window.

And your locker is by the bed. You'll find the washrooms and lavatories across the way. You will be wakened every morning and are expected downstairs in the dining room for morning prayers and grace. That's as much as you need to know for now. I'm sure you'll pick the routine up as you go along. I'll leave you to unpack your case. Bring it with you to the office when you come downstairs. Socks and pants, which you will change every morning, are to be placed in your top drawer. You will fold your shirts correctly and put them in the second drawer with your vests. Pullovers and personal items will be placed in your bottom drawer. Your washbag will be hung on a peg in the washroom. What's your number?

Fourteen.

You'll find our system is slightly different from what you've been used to: there are three teachers, myself, Miss MacLaren and Mister Scott. We teach different subjects and other teachers may visit from time to time, depending on holidays and the like, but we won't bother with that for now. One more thing, we have a way of doing things here, as well as a process of continuous assessment. Points are very important, but you don't need to bother about that; we find those who continually strive for points rarely achieve them. Your locker, bed and personal effects will be subject to regular inspections. Strip the bed and I will show you how to make it properly. You will make your bed every morning, immediately after you wash.

The sheets and two blankets were tucked below the mattress, the blanket corners tucked in and folded, the counterpane hanging regularly down each side, the pillow fluffed and placed on the top.

Now, take each item out the drawer and I will show you how to fold them properly. I will do one and you will do the others. I see your mother has sewn nametags on your clothing. Very necessary; no one wants to wear someone else's clothes.

I closed the bottom drawer and was sitting on the bed when I heard the engine. I stretched across my bed to the window and saw the car glide down the drive, my mother at the back window, waving to no one.

* * *

The sky was still, patches of grey flecked through a darker grey, and the only noise was a pigeon's call. Smoke rose straight into the air from the half-dozen village houses and the landscape was a patchwork of bare fields and hedgerows, with sturdy, desolate trees and the roadways hidden.

I sat on the bed, a draught on my cheek. There was a small radiator in the corner but the room was cold.

Up from the road, through the hedgerow and across a field to the left, a group of boys ran and suddenly stopped, pushed each other and jostled, breaking into a run to jump the ditch.

Then the house was suddenly alive, filled with voices. The boys must have used the door to the right, opposite the kitchens. I wondered if this was the sort of school I'd read about in comics, a boarding school for boys only, when the screech of girls' voices rose from the other side of the house.

I did not know what to do when a man put his head round the door.

Come on, he said. We'll dump your case in the office, then get you settled in. There's tea and scones in the dining room.

He left my case behind the office door, walked into the dining room and clapped his hands. Quiet everyone. Settle down. You'll remember at this morning's roll call we said there would be a new boy coming today. Well, this is Carl, who arrived about an hour ago and is feeling very strange. I think he'd like some tea and a scone, so you've all to make him very welcome.

A woman behind the hatch poured tea into an earthenware mug and pushed it across the counter. There were two plates, with half scones, buttered or topped with jam. I took a scone and turned to face the children. A large boy with cropped ginger hair said, Here, there's a place here. I walked over to his table, sat opposite him and smiled. He reached across and took my scone. Thanks, he said. The other kids laughed.

I drank my tea, staring at the pale blue Formica table top. The boy opposite reached behind him and lifted a scone from the plate, put it into his mouth whole and stared at me.

Miss Joyce came into the room and clapped her hands: Someone's taken a scone, she said.

The room went silent.

Did anyone see who took the scone?

There was some shuffling. A girl at the back stood up then sat back down.

Were you going to say something?

No miss.

Well, then. Somebody. Who took the scone?

She moved across and stood beside me.

Did you see it, Carl?

No miss.

Did you have a scone?

Yes miss.

Very well, then, we'll deal with this later. Stuff out the cupboard, she said and the dining room cleared.

My cupboard door was open, with a tin inside. My mother had left three bars of chocolate, two bags of mixed sweets and a packet of milk chocolate digestive biscuits, more than I had seen at any time before, including Christmas or my birthday.

I took a bar of chocolate and put the lid back on the tin. The ginger-haired boy snatched the chocolate.

Thanks, he said. And anything else in there's mines as well.

I sat by the door while kids milled around, sometimes in pairs. Others sat on the floor, stared out the window or just stood still. There were boys who put their face in their hands and rocked back and forward on their chair. A couple of girls wandered around with the hem of their skirts in their hands and their hands in their mouth. When Miss Joyce took the hem and let the skirt fall the girls joined others outside who played games I recognised from the school playground. The boys played football.

I did not know what to do, or what I was expected to do. I was sure that if I sat still and waited, someone would approach me. Miss Joyce locked the cupboards and swished past me.

Finished already? she asked. Gosh, that was quick.

She stopped in the hall and turned.

You did eat your chocolate, didn't you?

I nodded; and as she turned away a sudden fear gripped me, something like I'd never known, enough to make me tremble. I tried to stop shaking, but the more I tensed the muscles, the more violently I shook. The tremor in my legs subsided when I walked across the room. I stood by the window and turned back, gradually getting used to the fear, hoping no one could tell how I felt.

I felt like Abdul the Water Carrier in *How the Sheik Won his Bride.* When he went to the bazaar, he thought eyes were everywhere, could feel their stare and only slipped the piece of paper or whispered the message when he was absolutely certain no one was around, when he felt safe. And from then until he was safely home, with the door bolted and the windows shuttered, he lived in fear of being caught, was sure someone would tap his shoulder and ask why he was there.

Well, said Mister Scott. How's things?

I smiled.

I expect you'll be quite lonely and maybe a bit confused. Don't worry, you'll soon get used to it. You'll have to make yourself known. I'm sure you'll soon make friends. Do you have friends in Glasgow?

Yes, sir.

Lots or just the one?

One friend.

Is he special?

Yes, sir.

So you'll miss him?

Yes, sir.

I was wondering. Miss Joyce sat beside me and took my hand. She and Mister Scott exchanged glances and he moved away. You did see who took that scone, didn't you?

I looked at the floor.

And I think the same person took your scone too, didn't they?

Another cold wave of fear cut through me.

And I wouldn't be surprised to hear that they took your chocolate, for it vanished very quickly. This person has no stuff in his cupboard and I saw him eating a bar of chocolate.

I was afraid to move. We sat still. She held my hand and I could feel her staring at me, frightened in case I trembled again, or stuttered.

I don't think you're used to telling lies, she said. I think you're a little confused. You are in a strange place with new people and don't know how to react. Have you told lies before?

No, miss.

But you did know you were telling a lie, didn't you?

Yes, miss.

Are you shy?

I think I'm going to stutter.

So you won't know how to go up to people and make friends?

No, miss.

I'm sure you'll soon learn. One of the things about being here is that it forces you to do the sort of things you might not usually do, things which might not come naturally to you. So, let's see how you get on. And we'll keep this conversation to ourselves.

I had developed a habit they called dreaming. My grandfather said I was wasting time or idling, but it never felt that way. The actions in my head were real and I could sit, outwardly passive and inert, while battles raged and worlds tumbled.

My mother's stories made the world seem like a novel. She made a story out of everything, was incapable of going to the shops without finding something that could be turned into a story; her childhood and marriage were constant themes, staying at Auntie Kate's, the men at the sheep sale and working in the garden at Balvaird.

I must have been in a dwam, seeming to sit and stare at nothing, when a boy I'd never seen before kicked my foot.

Are you a German, aye or no?

No.

You've either got a lassie's name or a German name.

So what? I'm no a German.

Come on, he said. I followed him to a washhouse by the side of the house, across from the dining room.

It was filled with boxes; there was a bench propped up with bricks and a threadbare carpet. The ginger-haired boy stood in the centre with three others round him, whispering.

I turned to go and was grabbed from behind. A hand was put across my mouth and someone held my arms. The ginger-haired boy who took my chocolate sat on the bench. He didn't speak, looked round the room and landed on me without speaking.

How come you've a German name? he said.

I didn't speak.

Get him.

Someone else grabbed me from behind and they pulled me to the ground. When I landed I felt a kick in the small of my back and another near my stomach, then on the head. Someone sat on me and put his hand over my mouth when I started screaming. While I was held, the others punched and kicked me.

Leave him.

And it stopped.

I couldn't stand. My face was wet and I felt the sobs would take my breath away. Two boys hauled me to my feet. When they let go, I thought I was going to fall. I staggered towards the table and held onto the edge. The one they called Jaymo brought his boot down on my hand. I screamed and turned to run, but someone barred the door.

Fill the sink, he said.

The drain was stuffed with clods of earth. I stood in the middle of the room. The only sound was running water. No one spoke. Someone hit me from behind and Jaymo grabbed my hair and hauled me over to the sink.

That's for you, he said.

I held onto the sink, using my arms as a barricade, while the sink slowly filled. I closed my eyes and saw shapes and pin points of light. Again, I was sure I was going to faint.

Right, he said. Turn roon. If you dinnae dae what I tell you, he said, I'll smother you when you're sleeping. He snapped his fingers. You. Come here.

A small boy, younger than me, got up from the bench.

Jaymo smothered Wee Renchie, a skinny boy said. He's an enuretic. He fell asleep in Jaymo's bed and pished it.

Right, said Jaymo. Who's next.

Four boys stood up.

Watch, shouted a boy by the door. And they transformed themselves; emptying boxes, pulling the divots from the sink, books and comics appeared on the floor.

Everything okay? Mister Scott was standing by the washhouse door.

We're showing the new boy the scout hut, sir, said Jaymo.

When Scott left, Jaymo asked: Are you an enuretic?

I don't know.

Do you pish the bed?

No.

Then you're a looney. You're here because you're daft. Now, get to fuck. And don't think about shopping us. They don't want to hear about bullying and they don't want to hear about me. I've been here for ages and I don't want to go hame.

He reached into a box, took out a packet of five Woodbines, lit one and inhaled. Then he stared at the cigarette, turning it between his fingers.

You can do a fair bit of damage with this, he said. You could blind someone when they're sleeping or set fire to their bed. Cigarettes are terrible things. They should be banned.

And the other boys laughed. Someone grabbed me and shoved me out the door.

I went round to the back of the washhouse and sat in the middle of a patch of rhododendron bushes. The smell of the earth reminded me of the garden in Kettle. I thought of Patch and started to cry. I don't know how long I stayed there, but I was holding a branch when the bell rang. I came out from the bushes and saw the lads from the washhouse running into the house.

As I went in the door, a woman I'd never seen before stopped me.

Are you Carl?

Yes, miss.

We wondered where you were. Have you been crying?

No, miss.

I think you have, she said. Come on. We've a few minutes before tea. Let's get you cleaned up. I'm Miss MacLaren. Don't tell anyone; my real name's

Isobel, some of the girls call me Izzy and think I don't know, but you can call me Miss.

She took me into a toilet by the side of the office. There was scented soap and a white roll of cotton towel with Corporation of Glasgow in white letters on a red stripe down the middle.

Miss MacLaren filled the sink with warm water and took a face cloth from the side of the sink. She undid the top of my shirt and wiped my face, undid the towel roll and dried me.

That's better. You look much more handsome like that, though your clothes are mucky.

She cleaned my jersey and trousers with the damp cloth, took my hand and let it fall as we went into the dining room. She smelled of perfume.

After dinner, we gathered in the common room. Miss Joyce played the piano and we sang 'The Quartermaster's Store'. She told us a ghost story and at half past nine we went to bed.

TWENTY-SEVEN

Boxing

MISS HASSAN'S OFFICE seemed disorganised. Single sheets of paper were scattered across the desk and three folders lay open. She was reading and waved her hand in the air, signalling for me to sit. Then she sighed and put the folder to one side.

And how are you settling in? she asked.

It was my second day.

Fine, thank you.

Did you sleep well?

I'd lain awake, listening to the heating move along the pipes, or the ways wind crept through the window frame, the rush of noise behind the wall. Trees swayed, owls hooted and moonlight crossed the flimsy curtains. I had been glad to have a bed by the window, but it turned out to be the draughtiest place in the room.

Jaymo came into the washroom: Who's in wi me the night? Any volunteers? He stopped at the door. Don't worry, he said. I don't fancy you. Too skinny.

* * *

Miss Hassan rolled a gold propelling pencil between her palms.

You may find some children a bit strange, she said, and one or two could even be difficult. Some backgrounds are different to yours, some have no mother or father, scarcely any home to speak of, for some this is the nearest thing they have to a home. Now, I believe Miss MacLaren found you crying last night. Had anything happened?

No, miss.

You're sure?

Yes, miss.

None of the other boys were rough with you?

No, miss.

Mister Scott says you were with them in the washhouse, then the next thing we find you alone and crying. But according to you nothing happened. Why were you crying?

I wanted to go home.

That's understandable, but I don't think it's entirely accurate. You'll be lonely and in a strange place, but I want you to know that if there are any difficulties, you must, for your own good and for the sake of others, report them to me or to another member of staff. We treat bullying and abuse of any kind very seriously and offenders are severely dealt with. You do understand this, don't you?

Yes, miss.

Now, one other thing. Visiting is at the weekends, but we feel it's best to leave things for a week to two, for newcomers to settle in.

I thought my mum was coming up.

We think it would be better if you got yourself settled.

She said she'd be here.

We understand you've been through a very difficult time, but everyone agrees this is for the best. I don't know how much you know about your condition, or what we expect to happen. Would you like me to tell you?

Yes, miss.

From the reports I've read and the assessments that have been done, I think it's fair to say you've had something like a nervous breakdown. Do you know what that is?

No miss.

It's when something terrible happens, or when a series of awful things happen, tragedies really, and you feel you have no one to turn to, or no one to talk to; when you think no one will listen; when you feel alone and troubled and don't know why; when you can't be bothered doing anything, when you can't even be bothered taking your food, brushing your teeth and often can't sleep. It's when you want to cry and feel you can't, or you start crying when you hadn't even thought of it. Have any of these things been happening?

Some.

Such as?

Maybe them all.

Good, though I noticed you said, maybe. Does that mean some haven't been happening?

I don't know, miss. I don't think so.

You see, it's important you recognise what they are and more important for you to admit what's wrong. You must say you want to be better, which I am sure you do.

Yes, miss.

It's all very well for you to want to be better in here. I could imagine if I was in your place and my headmistress asked me a question I'd say whatever

I felt she wanted me to say, just because she was my headmistress. But recovery is something that happens outside this room, with others such as yourself. These children are from a number of places and are here for a variety of reasons, but they are very much the same as yourself. You may find some behaviour a little odd, but don't let that bother you and if one of them does something that bothers you or wants you to do something, no matter what, that you don't want to do, I want you to promise me you'll come to a member of staff straight away, because it could be for the other person's good too. Will you do that?

Yes, miss.

As you'll remember, we did some IQ tests. Some teachers thought you were clever, but your schoolwork was poor. Some of this could have been carelessness, but there could have been other reasons; so we'll also be looking at your schoolwork and see how well you get on. We'll be looking for signs of improvement, not just in spelling or sums or any subject really, but overall, we'll be looking to see if your concentration is returning, if you are settling in and getting on with other people. I also see some say you are lazy. I don't know how they know that and I'm sure it's not the case, but these are the things we'll be looking at here and, as I say, we'll see how you get on. Now, off you go and have your lunch, then I believe you are going for a nice long walk.

* * *

I soon learned the way: straight out of school and through the village, up the hill and down the road to the left towards East Kilbride, up and down two hills, then on the brow of the third hill, through the gate and along a hedgerow, over the gate and across a field, round the side of a burn and across the field to the school, or along the burn to the side of the woods at the back of the school, then up the bank, onto the road, down the hill, into the village and home.

The route was regular, meals were on time, classes started promptly and evening activities were divided into handicrafts, concert party (which included choir), scouts and guides, sports and personal recreation. Everyone knew where they should be and what they should be doing at any time of day.

We were wakened at a quarter to eight and were washed, dressed and toileted by half past. Breakfast was over by a quarter past nine, when we were divided into classes. There was a break for milk and exercise at half past ten, back to the classroom at a quarter to 11 with lunch at half past 12. Classes resumed at a quarter past one and were finished by three, when we went for a walk or did gymnastics in the common room if the weather was wet. The cupboards were opened around four o'clock and we were free till dinner at six. Evening activities were from seven or half past till nine and lights were out by ten. There were no classes at the weekend. Visiting was after lunch, when those who had no visitors had longer walks, recreational activities and, once a month, were taken on a Saturday morning outing, sometimes to the pictures, sometimes a museum.

We went to church on Sunday, had visiting in the afternoon and what was called social activities in the evening. This was board games, quizzes, puzzles and singing.

On the Sunday night I had my first bath, two in a tub, me and Alexander Brown from Edinburgh. Sandy told me his daddy had died and his mammy ran away, so he'd been brought up with his granny who had died last year so he'd stayed with an auntie but never got on with his cousins and came here.

I don't know where my mammy went, he said. I wish she'd come and get me. I went hame frae school and they told me my grannie had dee'd. Then they gie'd me ice cream and took me to the pictures, a woman like, and then I was ta'en tae this big place where I pished the bed and didnae mean it. I never mean it, but it happens.

What does Jaymo do?

When?

When he comes in your bed.

Nothing. He doesnae ken whit tae dae. He just lies there.

We washed each others' hair with Derbac Soap, were shown how to wash our feet and hands and were moved in twos from the bath to the fire where we dried ourselves and had our hair fine-combed. In our pyjamas, we brushed our teeth. My mouth was checked night and morning, fingernails and ears.

I'd been in Nerston a week and it rained all Sunday, turning into a cold and frosty night. Boys crept into each other's bed for warmth. Sandy Brown came in beside me.

I need a cuddle, he said.

* * *

Miss Joyce was teaching the eight times table. We chanted in unison, then she swooped down on individuals.

Eight sixes?

I'd been thinking about Francie, wondering if I'd get a letter. My mother had written twice and sent a parcel. But she never mentioned Francie.

Miss Joyce repeated the question. You're supposed to be a clever boy, she said. I wouldn't call someone who didn't know their eight times table very clever, would you?

No, miss.

Well then? Tell me. What is it?

There was a constant buzz of whispered conversation. All the time, in every lesson, children talked or hummed, sometimes the same tune over and over. Some of the girls talked to themselves, rocking on their seats. Boys talked behind their hands. Girls ducked under the desks, passed written notes and giggled.

Please, miss, I. Please, miss, I.

Everyone laughed.

Will you all stop talking.

There was silence. A girl giggled.

Latrine duty, Miss Joyce said. What we have here is dumb insolence. We find the same laziness that brought him here is very much in evidence. We find a boy who can't be bothered. Do you agree with that?

I started at the names carved on the desk.

Speak up.

Someone had carved my initials.

There we have it. Dumb insolence. Stand up. Put out your hand. Let this be a lesson.

She gripped me by the wrist, drew the ruler back and was about to hit me, when I pulled my hand away. The ruler whacked onto her leg. The class cheered.

I stared across the fields, waiting outside Miss Hassan's office. Smoke drifted and a car passed the end of the field.

You can go in now, said Miss Joyce.

Would you like to tell me what happened? Miss Hassan's desk was tidy.

Carl, you'll have to realise that when I ask you to speak, I would like to hear the sound of your voice. Miss Joyce has reported you for a very serious offence, which is tantamount to striking a teacher.

I didn't hit her.

But you caused her to hit herself, isn't that right?

Yes, miss.

Now why did you pull your hand away?

I was only stuttering.

Tell me what happened.

I told her what Miss Joyce said.

This is not the end of the matter, she said. I want you to come and see me tomorrow morning after breakfast and we'll discuss the matter then. In the meantime go back to your class and say nothing to anyone. You are, I need hardly tell you, in very serious trouble and I wouldn't like to think you'd do something to make matters worse. It's Scouts and Guides tonight after dinner.

You can go if you want to, but I would not like you to discuss this matter with anyone.

* * *

The scoutmaster arrived in a black Ford Prefect. I joined the crowd of kids who watched from the common room window as he pushed the car door open and struggled out of the small seat, supporting himself by holding on to the door frames, his legs apart, his kilt tucked beneath a dark brown sporran. The kilt hung like a blanket from his belly and the children nudged each other. When he reached into the back for his hat and box, his kilt popped up at the back and the children cheered.

He had the washhouse set up when we arrived. The place had been tidied and was lit by four or five oil lamps hanging from the rafters, with a flagpole in the corner.

Right troop, he said. Who's going to call the roll and break the flag? And who's this?

A new boy, said Jaymo.

Well, I hope you're all being nice to him. You can be in the Beaver Patrol.

This is Tommy, said Jaymo.

We lined up in patrols and he called on someone to break the flag, then we saluted. The time passed quickly enough, playing games, learning knots and planning expeditions. Tommy moved from patrol to patrol, supervising. He had a whistle attached to his lanyard, his khaki shirt was covered in badges and his false teeth moved when he smiled.

You are a silly boy, he said, hugging one lad to his stomach and smiling broadly. He then took the boy's hands in his own and showed him how to tie a reef knot: left over right and under, pull.

After a little over an hour, he shouted: Nerston Troop Ra.

Ra-ra-ra, said the boys.

Campfire, said Tommy, blowing his whistle.

We sat in a circle on the floor. Tommy started singing and the boys joined in:

> We are merry round the campfire,
> Bright and breezy round the campfire,
> In the evening round the campfire,
> In the shadows.
> We are merry
> Round the campfire
> Hear the echo of our campfire song.

There were mostly chorus songs, which Tommy led; then, at a point everyone but me understood, Tommy started singing and the boys joined in:

> By the blazing council fire light
> We have met in scoutsmanship tonight.
> Round about, the whispering trees,
> Guard our golden memories.
> And so before we close our eyes and sleep
> We shall bless each other as we keep
> Scouting friendships strong and free
> Till we meet again.

Let us pray, said Tommy. God bless us all as we make our way home. Bless us and our troop, dear Lord, and keep us safe till we meet again in scouting friendship. This prayer we ask in Jesus's name. Amen.

We tidied up the washhouse. Going out the door, I saw him give chocolate to three smaller boys and cigarettes to Jaymo.

* * *

Next morning, after breakfast, Miss Joyce told me to wait outside Miss Hassan's office.

I have thought about this, Miss Hassan said, and I have spoken with Miss Joyce. In sentencing you to a week's latrine duty, I have to say I am very disappointed. You have not made a very good start.

Yes, miss.

I think you are going to have to learn to stand up for yourself, to fight back. I think you accept things too easily. You're far too timid. Now, do you do any sports?

I've played football.

Are you a good runner?

I don't know.

Well, there's a boxing match tonight, so we'll see how you do there.

I've never boxed.

Best way to learn, I'm told.

* * *

I think it's a sin, said Martha. You shouldnae be daein this. D'you know what tae dae?

No.

I'll show you. It's supposed to be a punishment. But is it fuck a punishment. I love it. It's dead quiet. You get the place to yoursel, it's rare and quiet and you get to think.

She was on latrine duty for swearing and fighting with other girls. Bammy cows, think I'm daft, she said.

She had curly hair and amber eyes. She often seemed sullen, when she spoke to no one and walked around sucking her thumb.

Have you never had the belt?

Aye, but no like that. No wi a ruler.

What, just one or two?

Aye.

It's best to think of something else. See if you think how sore it's gonnae be, it's sorer than it should be. So, think of something else, something nice.

When you're getting the belt?

Aye. Think of, I don't know, ice cream or being at the pictures, something good.

And it doesnae hurt?

No, it hurts. But it doesnae hurt as much as if you think of how sore it's gonnae be. Know how you staun there thinking it's gonnae be sore? Well, don't. Think about something else. Anyway, do you know what to do here? You don't know anything, do you? Come on and we'll get a mop. You can help me do my bit and I'll help you do yours and that way we'll finish quicker.

We mopped the floors and checked the toilet rolls, then disinfected the pans and urinals.

I've never been in here, said Martha.

You have so.

No I havenae.

You must've been if you've done this wi other guys.

I'm usually daein this on my own. I never do the laddie's lavvy cause I've never had anybody t'dae it wi and I never wanted to dae it mysel, in case I was caught. Is this where yous dae it?

Uh-hu.

How?

We stand and do it.

Show's.

What?

Show's how'd you dae it.

She giggled, her hand at her mouth, then she stopped and giggled again.

Do men have to dae it like that?

Uh-hu.

Show's again.

I don't need. Are we nearly done?

We've to tidy the coats and put the shoes in the boxes.

Miss MacLaren arrived as we were finishing.

Come along, she said, clapping her hands. Out of here. Time for play.

The rain was incessant. We sat in the common room till dinner. The other children had their stuff out the cupboard; part of the punishment for those on latrine duties was that by the time we'd finished the cupboards were locked.

The girls had drawn peever beds on the floor, while some of the boys played draughts or snakes and ladders. Jaymo and a group of two or three sat in a corner, till Mister Scott came into the room.

Please, sir, he asked. Can we clean up the scout hut?

Isn't it clean already?

Yes, sir, but what we really need is someone to look after it all the time, a scavenger, someone who'll sweep the floor and keep the place tidy.

Off you go, but be back in time for dinner. And take your coats, it's freezing.

We sat till the dinner bell rang. Mister Scott looked round the common room, counting the pupils as they passed.

Run and see if they're still in the washhouse, he said to me. And you'd best slip on your coat.

The rain was strong. I could barely see. The wind and the shower stung my face. I ran out the front door and round to the washhouse, throwing the door open.

It took a while to adjust to the candlelight. The four boys were round the sink filled with water. Three or four frogs were in the water and two of the boys had frogs in their hands. They had inserted straws and were blowing into the frogs. The membrane of the frogs' stomachs had expanded. There were the bodies of five or six dead frogs on the floor.

What do you want?

I was sent to tell you it's dinner time.

Okay, said Jaymo. Clean this place up.

They left me. I closed the door and ran back to the dining room.

Jaymo shouted: Hey, Carl, Carlie, here, over here. Sit with us.

There was scarcely room. I squeezed in at the end.

Did you tidy up?

I never made the mess.

You are gonnae wish you'd done what you were telled.

* * *

After tea, when we'd changed into black shorts and a vest for boxing, I told Mister Scott my gloves didn't fit.

We've seen that one tried before, he said. I'm sure you're exaggerating. He pulled the glove on to my hand.

We were graded by height and weight. The smaller boys fought first. I won my first bout against a boy who constantly followed Jaymo. We walked around each other with our hands protecting our faces. His friends were shouting. He threw a punch and missed. I swung blindly and caught him off balance. He dropped his hands and burst into tears.

My second match was declared a no contest, because the other boy tripped over the carpet. By the third bout, I had no idea what was going on. We walked round each other, pretending or trying to throw a punch now and again, but nothing happened. I thought he was about to punch me, so I ducked and almost fell.

That'll do, Scott said. That's the semi-final over. I am going to toss a coin to see who'll fight the Nerston champion for the title. Heads or tails?

Tails.

Tails it is. You win. Good evening, ladies and gentlemen, this is Raymond Glendenning once more welcoming you to Harringay where tonight we have a mismatched contest for the championship of Nerston Residential School. These two lads are a couple of bruisers and I am sure we are in for a thrilling contest.

Most of the kids were laughing. There was some cheering. My opponent was Jaymo. One or two wee boys jumped up and down. The girls stopped talking and faced us. Martha's mouth was open.

That's no fair, sir, she said. Jaymo's bigger than him.

In the blue corner, we have the challenger. From Glasgow, nine years old and coming in at slightly more than a wet Woodbine is Carl Something or Other. And now the champion. What is there to say about this boy that he hasn't said himself. All the way from somewhere else, weighing in at 28 stone, the reigning champion and resident fly man, James Donaldson.

Come on, Carl, Martha shouted.

I didn't last a round. He came out and took a swing. I stepped back and, with his guard down, let fly with the right. I connected somewhere with his head or neck.

The kids were cheering. Jaymo swung, missed me and I swung again, connecting this time with his body. He staggered back, then lunged at me. His head smashed into my nose, his left hand got me in the stomach. I started to cry.

Contest over. No new champion. That'll be all, so it's goodnight from Harringay. Cocoa and bed folks.

My nose was bleeding. I could not get my glove off to fix it. Everyone was walking round me, putting the chairs away, talking.

You all right? asked Martha.

I can't get my glove off.

She took me to the cloakroom, sat me on a bench and unlaced my boxing gloves, smiling when our eyes met.

You sit there, she said. I'll fix you.

She came back with a rag soaked in cold water and held it against the bridge of my nose.

You'll be all right, she said. I thought you were great. You nearly killed that bastard. And you're gonnae kill him. Next time. Sure you'll do him next time. By the way, I go with you. Do you go with me?

What?

I'm your girlfriend. We see each other whenever we can, go for walks that that. And it's a secret. I'll no tell anybody.

Neither will I.

Do you want to kiss me?

No.

You're supposed to kiss your girlfriend. Have you never kissed anybody?

My granny and my aunties, folk like that.

This is different. It's the same as the pictures. You close your eyes.

Her lips were sticky. We sat with our lips together, breathing from the side of our mouths, our eyes closed.

Is this all we do?

What else do you want to do?

I don't know.

There were footsteps in the corridor. By the time Jaymo reached the door, Martha and I were apart.

What's going on?

None of your business.

Shut up, cow.

I am not a cow.

You're a bun and an enuretic as well. Imagine a lassie that pishes the bed. Is this your boyfriend?

Is he fuck.

Aye he fucken is. What are yous doing here if he's no your boyfriend?

I'm taking his gloves off.

Martha looked at me and left. Jaymo spat in my face.

If you hit me again, I'll cut your throat, he said.

He grabbed me by the shirt collar and banged my head against the stone wall. He stumbled when I pushed, pulling me with him. As he fell he hit his head off the wooden bench seat. I swung the glove Martha was going to remove and connected with the side of his head.

Three others came into the cloakroom. A boy with a turned eye they called Cockeye Bell jumped on my back and the other two pushed me against the wall.

Jaymo's face was red and his eyes glared. A spray of saliva hit my face as he talked. It'll no be me, he said. It'll be all of us. But I'll be first. I'm gonnae give you the biggest doing you've ever had and it might happen when you're sleeping. You better fucken watch your back, for I'll be waiting. Every one of us. We'll be there.

TWENTY-EIGHT

Night Walk

NIGHTS WERE FILLED with sobs and screams and there was a roll call every morning. Everything was done in groups of no less than four and in the late afternoon, between classes and dinner, a child on its own was watched.

It was easy to stay out of someone's way, even at night. By mixing with another group and being involved in separate activities you could carry on for days, unaffected by anyone.

Change was never far away. Friendships were fleeting. Children disappeared, then came back for a few days, or a black car arrived; they left and were never seen again.

Wee Renchie was missing for four days. He was found sleeping in a back close in Portobello, having been sighted in Leith and Musselburgh where he tried to steal food. He arrived in a police car, was taken into Miss Hassan's office then left immediately, one policeman carrying his clothes, the other holding a buff manila folder.

Others were discharged, then appeared at the home weeks later, initially for a visit, then they'd appear at tea-time. They'd be around for a day or two, till the black car came.

Don't go, said Martha. Promise me you'll stay.

I was brushing her hair.

I've nowhere to go. If I went home my mother'd bring me back.

We're fine here, sure we are. We're okay. We don't need to go anyplace, sure we don't. The only thing I'd like is, you're my boyfriend, so I'd like us to cuddle each other. No just now, after, when we're done. Just to hold each other. We'd feel better, closer. I used to get cuddles all the time. I miss them. Do you never get a cuddle?

I think it used to happen when I was wee, but they stopped when my daddy died.

She stood up, put the hairbrush on the bench and stretched out her arms. I stepped towards her and she put her arms round me. We stood still.

This isnae right, you're no very good at the cuddling.

I don't know what to do.

Jesus Christ, Carlie, for fuck sake. You haud me as if you mean it, just let go, let go and haud me, dead close.

I pulled her towards me, she dragged us onto the floor and we knelt on the stone flagging, holding on tight, our heads on each other's shoulders, swaying slightly till our knees were sore.

We sat on the bench rubbing our legs, then standing, suddenly awkward.

That was great, she said.

I know.

You really meant it.

I did mean it. I didnae know till we did it.

We should dae it, you and me, just dae it.

Martha smiled: Cuddle each other, she said, and moved towards me. I touched her hand and she held it, stretching across to kiss me. She pulled away and I reached across and kissed her cheek.

She turned towards me and we giggled when a stream of snotters brushed my cheek.

You kiss my cheek and I wipe my nose on your face.

And we stood, laughing at each other.

You should have seen your face.

When?

When I said you were nae use at the cuddling.

You nearly stood up.

When?

When you dragged us down to the floor.

I know. It was cold.

And sore.

Dead sore.

There was a noise, something like a door closing.

We waited, expecting it to come nearer.

When do we go back?

We don't. We stay here till they come and get us. Wherever we are, we stay thegither till they come and get us.

We often had no more than five minutes, sometimes saying nothing. Martha often stretched across, took my hand and smiled when I looked up.

I had hardly spoken to a girl and sometimes talked about things Martha found boring. She'd put up with it for a wee while, smile and say, I've got to go. At first, I found most of what Martha said was difficult. Her life was crammed with incident, what she thought of such and such a girl, what they'd said to her or what she'd said to them. Nothing was too trivial. Her whole day was recounted, sometimes even her dreams.

At first it was dead, dead dark, then it got dead, dead bright and I was sad cause I wanted you to see it, but you were away playing football and you managed to header in a goal; then it got better and we were here and you told us your team won and I was telling you about my Auntie Sadie in America who'd written to say she wanted me to go over and see her and to bring a friend and I wanted to take you. And when I wakened I was dead, dead sad because you werenae there and I wanted you to be there to be in bed with me the way I used to be in my mammy's bed when I'd waken and she'd be there.

I never remember dreams.

You must remember something. Try, she said. Try and see what you can remember.

Falling and running, being stuck in the mud and unable to move, struggling and lashing, sweating and choking. Then I remembered my daddy and Jesus at Kettle Church.

That could be a sign. It could mean your da's with Jesus. Dreams are great, she said. Especially when I dream I fly.

Often when she told me what she dreamed I didn't believe her, but couldn't say so, the way I'd have said to Francie. Something stopped me. This was different.

It's only cause we're here, she said. If we met outside, you wouldnae like me.

Aye, I would.

No you wouldnae. You'd be with your pals and I'd have t'be wi my ma.

Most of the day we ignored each other, though I'd sometimes find her looking at me, if something good happened. If I got a letter from my mother, I wanted her to know. A letter usually came at the weekend and a parcel arrived on the Monday or Tuesday.

Mother's letters were filled with news, how everyone was doing; they all sent their love, including Toby. She told me where she was working and that she was saving to get the front room done. She wanted a new suite; she fancied one of those fold-down bed-divan things, with new wallpaper and a decent carpet. That old thing in there's done, she wrote.

I showed her letters to Martha, who seemed puzzled at first, then looked forward to them almost as much as I did. She never got a letter, though she sometimes had visitors on a Sunday, people she never spoke about, a man and a woman.

If the weather was fine, we went outside; round to the back of the home, by the middens or the coal sheds, beside the woodpile we'd find a place to talk. If it was wet, we sat in the cloakrooms, aware of every sound; sitting talking, we listened in case we were caught. If we heard a rattle or a footfall, one of us would run into a cubicle, while the other flushed a pan and walked to the sink.

We sat in the bushes at the back of the midden, where we could see anyone coming. My hair gets dead tuggy, she said. My mammy used to comb my hair. I like it when you do it.

Where's your mammy now?

I don't know. I think she's still in hospital. When she took ill, me and my brother got split up. I don't know where he is and I'm here.

Where did you go?

I was sent with him and her. I hated it. Fucken hated it. I ran away and ran away and kept running away till I came here.

She took a strand of hair and twisted it round her finger, staring at her muddy shoes. She put her thumb in her mouth.

What happened? I asked.

Nothing.

It must've been something.

It was nothing.

That's not fair. You've made me tell you things, and I've never said I wouldnae tell you.

It's nothing.

If it's nothing you can tell me what it is.

I got lost. Right. I got lost. There. Are you happy now?

What happened?

Is that all you can say? They sent somebody to find me.

Were you okay?

I couldnae sleep. Sometimes it comes back in a dream and I hate it. It's as if I'm stuck again, except it's worse in the dream. I get caught in the branches and they tear my clothes and scratch me; there's animals howling and everything. See when I get that dream I pray it doesnae last long, that it just comes and goes away again.

What happens at the other times?

She climbed onto the top of the midden, swung herself down and ran into the house, leaving me with the hairbrush. By the time I got down, Wilma Anderson, a tall, thin girl with deep brown eyes, said, Martha wants her brush back.

* * *

Test your torches, Mister Scott said. Test your torches, turn them on and see if they work, then settle down. Quiet, everybody. Settle down.

We held the torches below our chins, making ourselves look scary.

It was odd; eight o'clock and everyone dressed for a walk in the rain.

It's a lovely night, so it's scarves and raincoats, gloves and wellies. Get yourselves ready and we'll meet back here in five or ten minutes. Everyone go to the toilet, get yourselves ready and come back here.

I need a cuddle, Martha said. She was suddenly beside me and touched my hand.

We ran to the back corridor and held each other.

We've too many claes on, she said and kissed my cheek.

Right now, everybody here. Mister Scott was standing on a chair. We've gone to some trouble with this, the teachers have put a lot of effort into this jaunt, so I want you all to pay attention. What's this?

Ribbon.

That's right. It's a yellow ribbon. Can everybody see that? Now, we've set the route, which has been carefully planned and is not at all dangerous, so there's no reason for anyone to get lost, fall down a hole, get into a ditch, or vanish in a burn so long as they remember to look for the ribbon and make their way round the route, through the wood, onto the road and home. And don't think you can go outside, wait in the washhouse, then come back half an hour later. There's envelopes with pieces of paper attached to trees beside the ribbons. These pieces of paper have a number, like this. What number's that?

Six.

So what does that mean?

There's other bits before it.

Correct. There are ten pieces of paper, each with a number and each at a certain location. Everyone must come back here with ten pieces of paper to show they've been round the course. And anyone who does not come back with the ten pieces of paper will have points deducted. And anyone who steals the pieces of paper from another boy or girl will be severely punished. Anyone who makes it difficult for another child, no matter how, will also be dealt with. Miss Joyce and Miss Hassan are at various points along the route and will check your papers to see you have completed the course. Now, are there any questions?

Silence.

No questions? Everything's as clear as mud. Then let's go.

He repeated the instructions before lining us up by the door, eldest first. He had a list of the order in which should leave. Miss Hassan and Miss Joyce, he said, had similar lists and would tick us off when we arrived. When the first girl left, there was a big cheer.

I was third last. Martha went two before me. I could see her shiver as she stood by the door. He touched her shoulder and she left, running down the drive with her hands at her side, her torch unlit.

There was a haze across the moon and the stars were clear, cold with a wisp of breeze. The houses were dark. Moonlight glimmered on the tops of the trees and sparked on the road, that looked like a river from the top of the drive.

I could see the torches disappear down the drive and reappear as they climbed the hill. The first ribbon was at the foot of the drive, another at the end of the village, with two more in the hedgerow before going into the wood, where there was no light or any sign of a torch. I had four pieces of paper in my left hand, the torch in my right.

The start of the wood was boggy where the other children had searched for their fifth ribbon, which was on a tree going into the wood. There seemed an obvious path; trying to avoid a thicket to the right, I got tangled in the bushes. I felt something rip as I pulled myself clear. There was what looked like a ribbon on a bush by the burn. As I approached I heard a boy sobbing.

Jaymo took my paper, he said.

What have you got?

I don't know.

He put the torch in his mouth, trying to break the sobs as he looked at his papers. I saw a torch approach.

Come along, said Miss Joyce. Who's this? Might have known.

She looked at her clip board.

Where's your papers?

She checked mine first and grabbed my collar as I was about to leave. Not yet, she said. Bennett has to go before you.

Tom Bennett was an enuretic who sometimes slept with Sandy Brown or Cockeye Bell. When he was in bed alone he kept us awake, turning till he slept. He often shouted in his sleep.

What's happened? You've no number five.

Bennett took the torch from his mouth. Miss Joyce shone her torch into his face. What's happened? she asked. Did you run into a tree?

Please, miss, I said. James Donaldson took his paper.

Is this true?

No, miss. I dropped it and hurt my face in those bushes.

Then why did Carl MacDougall say someone stole your paper?

Please, miss. I don't know, miss.

We'll see about this when you get back to the home. On you go, you first Bennett.

He ran off and suddenly stopped, shining his torch in a swirling movement that flared into the bushes. We stood, Miss Joyce and I, in silence. When Tom Bennett had disappeared, she tapped my shoulder.

On you go, she said.

Now they were everywhere, waiting, hiding behind the trees, on every branch of the trees, shapeless, nameless objects that would hurl themselves into me, tug my legs, haul my arms and pull me towards them, leap at me, reach down my throat and tear out my heart.

I tried running with my eyes closed, but that was worse. I preferred to see them, to know they were about to leap even though I could barely imagine their impact. Even by the fence on the edge of the field, I turned the cattle into objects of danger, wondered if they'd been frightened by the other children, that they were about to stampede, the sight of their tails as they flicked against the stars was as sharp as electric will o' the wisps, the noise of their hooves trampling the mud or their hides rubbing together became the sound of horsemen; their smoky breath was dragon's fire.

The houses in the distance, barns, hedgerows, fences, were places of refuge I could not reach, would never find. The noise of the breeze, its touch on my face, were hands of the nameless, empty dead who patrolled the darkness, waiting for a passing stranger. Perhaps this was death, moving from one life to another, gathering slips of paper where your sins were written, taking them to the gates of heaven where you'd be judged not on what you had or what you had done, but on what you did not have, the things you did not do.

If I was dead, where was my daddy? Where were Willie, Eva and Charlie? They'd help me. I scarcely stopped to gather the paper, pulling the envelope down from the tree, ripping the scraps, clutching them in my hand as I tried to climb a five bar gate and slipped on the mud, landing in a puddle.

The front of my coat, my face, arms and hands were caked in mud. I felt myself scream, but heard no sound, again and again as I tried to free myself from the clutches. I was sure I was watching myself; certain I was sitting on a tree looking at a boy scrambling through the mud.

What is going on?

Miss Hassan took a handkerchief from the pocket of her camel coat and wiped my face.

What a mess. But you're not the only one. It's nearly over and there's a warm bath for you when you get back to the house.

I was holding the edge of her coat, gripping her belt. She pulled me towards her. I could smell her perfume. She stroked my hair.

Did you think you were lost? she said. Well, don't worry. Back you go. The road's over there. Can you see it? Just up there. Back you go. Give me your papers. You've got enough, I'm sure of that. Let's see. You must have ten here. Will that do? Can't you speak? I'll tell you what, let's say it's ten. But not a word. Don't breathe a word of this to anyone or I'll lose my job. Do you understand? Carl MacDougall, ten slips of paper. There's it's there. Nice and official. It's in my record, so it must be true. Off you go.

Miss MacLaren took my coat and boots, washed my face and ran a flannel over the front of my hair, standing by the sink, her arm on my shoulder as I washed my hands, trying to make a lather with the Lifebuoy soap that was bigger than my hands. She took my hand in her hands, she had red varnish on her oval nails, washed my hands and dried them, taking me through to the kitchen where she poured a mug of watery cocoa from an urn on the range.

Can you speak? she asked.

I nodded.

Then let me hear you.

Thank you, miss.

She smiled and kissed my brow.

If you tell anyone I did that, we'll have to get married, she said.

Right we are, said Scott. Everyone's back safe and sound. One or two casualties, but you have all done extremely well. Some of you didn't get all the slips, but congratulations to those who did.

He put a record on the gramophone: The Weavers, 'On Top of Old Smokey'. One or two kids danced on their own, a couple of boys joined in with Lee Hays' spoken lyric, but we mostly sat in silence.

You all right? asked Martha.

I nodded.

What happened?

Nothing.

Did you get a fright?

I'll tell you tomorrow.

She walked away.

When the record finished its third performance, Mister Scott clapped his hands.

Just a second, he shouted. Quiet, everyone. Settle down. Miss Joyce has reported an extremely important incident. Now let me see if I've got this right: Tom Bennett, did anyone steal your slips of paper?

Tom Bennett, looked at me then looked away. Jaymo stood up.

No, sir.

You're sure about that?

Yes, sir.

You're not lying to protect anyone, are you?

No, sir.

Word of honour?

Word of honour.

Then why did I hear someone took your paper?

I don't know, sir.

Did anyone take Tom Bennett's papers?

Silence.

Did anyone take Tom Bennett's papers? I want to know. This is an extremely important matter. You were honour bound to complete the course in the way we agreed. One or two of you had papers missing and most of you completed the course in the order you set out. One boy was out of sequence and he knows who he is. Does he have anything to say?

Silence.

What happened, Carl?

I felt my face redden.

Take your time. Why aren't you speaking?

Please, sir. Please, sir. I think I'll stutter.

Everyone laughed. Jaymo sat down.

What's so funny? Would it be so funny if you stuttered? Tell me, Master Donaldson, would you find it funny if you had a stutter?

Jaymo laughed: I havenae got a stutter but, he said.

Take your time, Carl.

Please, sir, Tom Bennett was crying. He told me James Donaldson took his paper, and when I, when I, when I asked him what was, what was wrong, he told me, he told me Jaymo took his paper.

Tom Bennett gave me his paper, sir.

That's a fucken lie, said Martha. He took my paper as well, sir. He took two papers from me.

Martha Gilmour, two weeks latrine duty for foul language. Have you anything to say, Master Bennett?

Silence.

Master Donaldson?

Right then, bath time everyone, except Messrs Bennett and Donaldson, who will sleep in the single dormitories until further notice.

And will see me after breakfast, Miss Hassan said.

The locked dormitories were at the end of the house, beyond the staff quarters, two single rooms where Martha said you slept in a sleeping bag with the light on all night. There was a window in the door, which was locked from the outside.

How do you know?

Somebody tellt me.

TWENTY-NINE

Cinderella

WE SAW THEM in class and at mealtimes. Sullen, they ate and appeared to spend their time together or alone.

Rather than wandering round in groups of two or three, avoiding contact, the school suddenly unfurled. Boys played football, climbed and roamed. We tidied the washhouse, read, told jokes I didn't understand and dreamed of what had happened before we arrived and what we expected when we left.

Girls skipped and sang, danced and played shops, made raffia ornaments, brought their dolls down from the dormitories and played house, where children frequently misbehaved, the man was out working or, more usually, in the pub, and four or five were sisters, getting ready to go to the dancing.

At first, Martha and I sat with the others but, usually between stuff out the cupboards and tea, we ran down the back stairs, found a place to huddle and often spoke in whispers, piecing our way through things no one else knew. She thought her mum was dead.

She has to know I'm here. I keep asking and no one tells me. If she knew I was here, she'd come and get me and she'd get Wee Andy too.

Do you dream about her?

All the time. She's there, a clear sky, nice cold night when you know it's cold but you're warm, all happed up. Like when you're in bed and you stick your foot outside the blankets, well she's the warm bit and you're only putting your foot outside to see what it feels like, but when you pull it back in, she's the warm bit, her and you, and I want the two of yous there when I waken and when you're not there I feel sad till I see you. Do you feel sad till you see me?

Sometimes.

You're only saying that.

No. It's true.

Do you think they know?

They ask about you.

I tell them I can talk to you and you talk to me. I got asked if you stutter when you're with me and I said you were fine.

I get asked why I don't have any boy pals.

And what do you say?

I tell them the truth, I don't know.

I know where you sleep.

She closed her eyes, smiled and turned her head back towards the school. I looked, she said.

She turned towards me, her hand to her mouth, eyes alert, laughing.

I needed the lavvy and our bit was busy, so I ran to the laddie's bit and looked in. I knew your room was just about opposite the lavvy and your bed's at the windae. It was dead exciting. Do you want to see my bit?

She ran to the common room and I counted to 200. She had left by the time I stood beside Cockeye Bell's group, who were playing snakes and ladders. When the game ended, I counted to 100, slipped into the back toilet and ran upstairs where Martha was waiting.

My bed's over there, in the corner, she said.

Apart from a few dolls, fluffy toys and different coloured counterpanes, the rooms were the same, a mixture of single and bunk beds.

And what's going on? What are you doing here?

Miss Joyce was at the end of the corridor.

Please, miss. It was me. I was showing him the dormitory.

And why would you want to see a girls' dormitory, Carl?

His bed's draughty and near the windae and I was showing him where I slept.

Off you go. I'm sure Miss Hassan will want to see you in the morning.

* * *

Her desk was untidy. She waved me to sit down and continued reading.

Well? she said. She drew the papers to one side, stared and put the paper down.

I didn't even try to speak. Her voice sounded grim.

I believe you and Martha Gilmour were in a girls' dormitory?

No, miss. We were outside. We were only looking in.

Why?

Martha wanted me to see where she slept.

Miss Hassan sighed. She shifted the file and put her hands on the desk.

I know you like Martha and think of her as a friend and I'm sure she feels the same about you, but friendships can be confusing and we sometimes get dragged into things we may not want to do or might not even think of doing in other circumstances. I am going to speak with Martha and I think it would be a good idea if you spent less time together, for you to find a friend or two among the boys. I know Martha was friendly with a number of girls, so perhaps she can pick up these friendships. I think it's important that you reach out to other boys, talk to them, don't be shy.

We smiled across the common room and maybe twice a day ran to the back steps. We hardly spoke, laughed and said, We'd better get back, but seldom moved immediately.

I asked, she said, How can I no see him? And she told me, Naeb'dy's stoppin you fae seeing him, and I said, Aye yous are. Yous are aye being nosey.

What did she say?

Nothing, just what I said afore.

She'd go one way and I'd go another, usually into the back door.

On the Thursday night, Miss MacLaren told us to get our green work aprons and to prepare the table for shoe polishing.

Newspapers were spread, brushes, polish and dusters appeared. Most of the children had canvas black sandshoes, but, as usual, Mister Scott took us step by step through the process.

We're going on a special treat tomorrow afternoon, Miss MacLaren said. Everyone has to look their best and wear bright and shiny shoes.

It was raining when the buses appeared. We stood round the common room windows and cheered.

Jaymo and Tom Bennett had been around most of the day, avoiding each other, surly and brooding. Tom Bennet seemed nervous, frightened, but Jaymo bumped into children and pushed girls out of his way. They watched the buses load.

Miss MacLaren had an accordion and Miss Joyce led the singing. I had been told to sit with Sandy Brown. Martha made her way up the bus, changing seats.

Whit's she daein? said Sandy.

Here you, shift your erse.

She was with two other girls in the seat opposite.

Away you and sit beside Annabella Ross. She fancies you rotten, away and see.

Which one's Annabella Ross?

Away and ask: say, Excuse me, are you Annabella? And if she says Aye, say, Do you mind if I sit beside you? And move in afore she can answer.

She smiled and pressed her shoulder into my arm.

You all right?

I get sick on buses.

Then go to sleep. I'll see naeb'dy bothers you.

They were singing 'Ten Green Bottles' and I slept till the cheering wakened me outside the Art Galleries. Everyone, except Martha, was piling over each other, rubbing condensation from the windows, shouting, Please, miss. Where are we?

You all right?

I'll be fine when I get fresh air.

She led me down the bus. Miss Joyce guarded the door.

How did this happen?

Please miss, Alexander Brown, the boy from Edinburgh, wanted to sit beside Annabella Ross and he asked me to change places.

A likely story.

It's true, and you'll need to move. Carl needs fresh air or he'll be sick.

We stood on the pavement while the others lined up. Miss MacLaren counted the heads and Miss Joyce led the way. In the main hall we were split into two groups, who shuffled through the ground-floor galleries, with numbers counted every 20 paces.

We followed Miss MacLaren to the arms and armory where we silently admired the swords, daggers and armed horseman. We met the others on our way to the beehive. Stuffed animals, the display of mountain hares, weasels and ptarmigans in summer and winter coats took up most of our time.

The armory gave her the creeps, but Martha ran from one exhibit to another, smiling. I had seen them before and was bored by the time they were climbing the stone sarcophagus.

You all right, Carl?

Miss MacLaren was beside me.

Please, miss. I'd like to see a painting.

Which one?

I don't know, but my mum always takes me to see the paintings.

We've run out of time. Not everyone is as lucky as you. Some children haven't had your opportunities and haven't been before.

The bus was parked on Kelvin Way. Miss Joyce counted us on board. Mister Scott had arrived, there were two cardboard boxes on the front seat and the bus smelled of fish and chips.

Miss Joyce told us, No one gets a fish supper till we're all nice and quiet. Mister Scott distributed the food and Miss Joyce showed us how to wipe our hands with the paper napkins she distributed and Miss MacLaren gave us a beaker of lemonade or red kola.

Now we are going to the real treat, Miss MacLaren said as Mister Scott gathered the rubbish and the bus moved into Sauchiehall Street.

I see they're sitting together, said Martha. I'll bet they'll sit thegither in the pictures. Do you think they do it?

Do what?

Jesus Johnny, what do you think? He looks as if he fancies it, but she's no too keen.

How do you know we're going to the pictures?

Where else would they be taking us at this time of night? They wouldnae be giein us a fish supper to take us back to Nerston, especially since some people get sick on the bus.

We were counted outside the Tivoli, ushered into the main hall and told to go to the toilet, four at a time, then counted into the cinema that smelled of dead cigarettes and seated in two rows along the stalls, girls in front of the boys' row. When Miss Joyce and Mister Scott left the theatre, just as the lights dimmed, everyone changed seats. Martha came in beside me. Great, she said.

Small blocks of ice cream were passed along the rows, just as the trailers started. The blocks were frozen. Martha took mine and tucked it beneath her skirt.

What are you daein?

What dae ye think I'm daein? I'm meltin your ice cream wi mine. Look.

The two blocks of ice cream were lined between her legs, above her knee.

Martha Gilmour. Miss Joyce's voice was dimmed by the music at the start of *Cinderella*. She gave me the ice cream when the Fairy Godmother appeared.

We could do wi' one o' them, she whispered and put her arm through mine.

We were counted out the cinema, sat together on the bus going back and fell asleep holding hands. They were warm and sticky.

You were there when I wakened, she said when we reached Nerston.

THIRTY

Dream Angus

DON'T THINK WE'VE forgot, Jaymo said, getting ready for bed on the Sunday night.

We'd spent the day with Mister Scott's nature group, working on a farm, eating ham and tomato sandwiches, drinking tea from a flask and water from the well. We stacked the wood shed, fed the cattle and swept the yard.

Martha and I cleared the potting shed.

Is this like being married?

I don't know.

It must be; I mean, this, us working together, just you and me in a wee place, doing things. Sure it'd be great to stay here?

Aye.

I'd make curtains and put them on the windaes, but you'd need to clean them first.

There's naewhere to cook.

There's nae place to sleep or do the lavvy eithers, but we could make they places, if we lived here like.

The farmer's wife had piled the kitchen table with scones and crumpets, soda farls and pancakes, jams and syrup. We started with soup and finished with apple pie and custard with ginger perkin biscuits straight from the oven and wrapped in newspaper to keep them warm to eat on the bus.

We were bathed in pairs. On the other side of the building, girls ran up the stairs screaming and with Miss Joyce's voice rising above the commotion we splashed around till Miss MacLaren told us to stand by the radiators and dry ourselves thoroughly before putting on our pyjamas and going quietly into the dormitories: Be sure to dry your hair, she shouted.

That's what I like, she said, pulling over the curtains, nice clean boys. I think you should all say your prayers and thank God for having given you this lovely day.

There was a tightness in my chest. My arms were pinned and I struggled to breathe. I was lashing my legs and trying to find something to grasp, to cry and breathe at the same time. There was shouting and suddenly it was over.

I jumped out of bed as Miss MacLaren switched on the light. She was wearing a housecoat: Goodness, she said. What is it?

She wrapped me in a blanket, took me downstairs, made tea and held my hand.

Tell me, she said. Tell me what happened. Was it a dream?

No, miss.

What happened?

I don't know.

Were you attacked?

I think so.

Do you know who attacked you?

No, miss.

But there aren't many suspects? she said, pulling the blanket round me.

I must have slept but wakened with the taste of blood in my mouth.

On the Monday I saw Martha after the morning class.

You all right? she asked.

I nodded.

You sure?

Uh-hu.

You're not. I know you're not. Something's happened? What is it?

Nothing.

Do you no want to go with me anymore?

It's not that.

Then see us eftir.

We sat in the rhododendron bushes. I told her I was scared, that I wanted to run away, but couldn't because I'd be brought back and that would be worse.

We could run away, she said.

You like it here.

But I'd run away with you. If I talked to your mother she wouldnae send us back.

Tommy arrived with the badges we'd won. Jaymo won the sportsman and the pathfinder badge. He stood to attention, came forward, accepted the badge with his right hand, shaking Tommy's hand with his left. I was given my third class badge. Tommy told us badges were an honour, because we were too young to be in the Scouts and shouldn't have any badges at all.

There was no campfire because of the badge ceremonies and after prayers, while Tommy was putting his things away, Jaymo told me to clear the washhouse.

It's dark.

Tough luck, he said and put out the candles.

I fumbled around in the dark till Miss MacLaren arrived.

Who told you to clear the washhouse? she asked. Was it one of the boys? Tell me, Carl. Please, tell me. I won't do anything if you don't want me to. I promise. You can trust me.

I want to go home, miss.

Of course you do, she said. And you're getting better, aren't you? You're feeling better, you're doing very well and you'll be able to see your mother very soon, then it won't be long till you're able to go home. Now tell me what happened.

When I finished, she smiled.

I won't mention this if you don't want me to, but I'd like you to promise you'll tell me if there's any more trouble.

Yes, miss.

Word of honour?

Yes, miss.

They were waiting in the dormitory.

That shed better be clean, said Jaymo.

If not, you're in for a doing, said Tom Bennett.

I don't think he cleaned the shed.

Ne'er dae I.

I think he was talking to that cow, MacLaren.

Maybe we should go and see and if it isnae clean just do him now.

We could just do him anyway.

You do him.

No. You do him.

You.

You.

They pushed each other, giggling. Jaymo took a pillow from one of the beds, pushed Tom Bennett to the floor and held the pillow over his face, releasing it immediately.

Does that remind you of anything? he said.

* * *

Miss Joyce told us she was off to London.

Roger and Callum and Maggie and I. We won't be taking the car though. We'll leave it at home, and since we're only going for a few days, we may very well do a day here and there, go down at the coast or maybe into Perthshire, then into Aberdeenshire over the Cairn o' Mount road if the snow's cleared when we get back.

Miss MacLaren took our class while Miss Joyce was away. She came in every morning with her hair tied back, wearing a flared skirt and a jumper, sometimes with an amber necklace and earrings. She wore little or no make-up. I could have looked at her forever.

Miss Bainbridge took Miss MacLaren's class. She was short with straight black hair and stumpy legs. She wore flat shoes and always seemed to be running in and out of the classrooms.

On her first day we were surprised by the sound of laughter from the other class. Miss MacLaren was telling us about the Dutch system of dykes; when she was a student, she'd worked on a Dutch farm. She was telling us the story of the boy who saved his country by putting his finger in the dyke, when she was interrupted by laughter from the room next door.

She stopped talking. The laughter rose again.

They seem to be having a good time, she said.

Next day the classes were amalgamated. Miss Bainbridge read us a story about Wee Macgreegor. She showed us a picture, pointing out the way he was dressed, that his tammie, toorie, scarf and boots identified him as being from a working class family, because that was the way workers' children dressed when the story was written, before the First World War. Then she read the story in a Glasgow accent.

On the third day, Miss Hassan came to hear Miss Bainbridge.

D'ye think they weans know what Wee Macgreegor's on aboot? she asked.

Meybes aye, maybes naw, Miss Bainbridge said.

Wunner how that is?

Beats me.

Please, miss, said Yvonne Clark, who had arrived with her mother by bus.

Whit is it, hen?

By now there was a continual stream of laughter, so loud Yvonne had to wait, giggling herself and unable to speak.

Please, miss, she said. You're speaking the same as us.

Naw I'm urnae, Miss Bainbridge said.

You ur sot, said Miss Hassan.

I'm ur not.

Aye ye ur.

Och well, I'm only here a wee while. I can dae whit I like.

She took us for longer walks and helped us gather wild flowers. She took art classes and played the piano for country dancing in the evening. Martha and I danced 'The Gay Gordons' and 'The Valeta Waltz'. Miss MacLaren and I danced 'Strip the Willow'.

She fancies you, Martha said in 'The St Bernard's Waltz'.

There was no stuff out the cupboard the day Miss Bainbridge left. Just after three o'clock, a man she introduced as Mister Angus Farquharson, my intended, arrived in a pale blue baby Austin. He was a beefy, cheery looking man in a comforting tweed jacket, cavalry twill trousers and heavy brogue shoes. He wore tan woollen socks, a checked shirt and a dark blue club tie. He brought an accordion, boxes of cakes, ice cream and jelly into the common room.

Spread these around, he said. We'll have a tea party later. What do you say, dear?

Splendid.

Mister Farquharson played a selection of Scottish waltzes, then said, Ladies and gentlemen. Take your partners for 'The Gay Gordons'.

Miss MacLaren asked me to dance. When she asked me a question in class I blushed and could not speak.

Do you think I'll be able to birl under your arm? she said.

Half way round the room, I saw Jaymo ask Martha to dance, but she got up with Wilma Anderson. The next dance was a 'St Bernard's Waltz', ladies' choice, and Martha rushed over to me.

What were you dancing with her for? she asked.

I had to; she asked me.

You should've said no. You should've told her you were dancing with me. You don't like her or anything, do you?

She's a teacher.

Doesnae matter. You watch it. She's got her eye on you.

With the dancing finished, we got a cup of tea and a plate with two cakes and a sandwich, then Mister Farquharson played what he called a selection of well-known Scottish songs, which we all joined in: 'I Love a Lassie', 'Loch Lomond' and 'Keep Right On to the End of the Road'. On the reprise, Martha sang me different words to the first song:

> I know a wumman, she awfae fond o' bummin
> And she lives doon the Hokey Pokey Lane.
> She wears a pair o troosers and is never oot the boozers
> Nae wunner she's cairryin a wean.

I danced with next two dances with Martha. When Mister Scott got her up for 'The Valeta Waltz', I asked Wilma Anderson to dance.

Are you goin wi Martha? she asked.

She goes wi you, she said when I didn't answer.

The party ended with Mister Farquharson and Miss Bainbridge leading us all in 'The Quartermaster's Store':

There were bugs, bugs, the size o' collie dugs,
    In the store, in the store.

After dinner Miss Hassan made a speech, thanking Miss Bainbridge. We ate ice cream and jelly and sang 'Auld Lang Syne'.

Miss Bainbridge went round us all, shaking hands and wishing us well, saying she'd come back to see us all soon and perhaps Mister Farquharson would bring his accordion. They left before bedtime, with everyone on the steps in the rain, waving till the tail lights disappeared over the hill.

* * *

Miss Joyce said London was wonderful, noisy and much, much busier than Glasgow or Edinburgh. She brought back souvenirs and pictures, telling us she had been to Madame Tussauds, the Tower of London and had seen Buckingham Palace. She had also seen the preparations for the new Festival of Britain, which would open next summer on the South Bank of the Thames.

Mister Scott told us that driving back to Nerston he caught a rabbit in the headlights. The poor little thing, he said. It was mesmerised by the light. We had to stop the car and turn off the lights. When we started the car again, there were four of them. All the way from Glasgow to the village, we kept finding rabbits in our headlights. I'd never seen so many.

* * *

Twice a week the child psychologists came. The woman always looked tired, as though the strain of seeing us was adding to her problems. One of the men was cheery, asking what team do you support, where would you like to go for your holidays and so on, but the other snapped his questions. No one liked him.

Everyone was seen maybe once every two or three weeks. For the first couple of weeks you were seen every time they came, then once a week, then in turn with the other children. We were sent for in class. Everyone knew what was going on and quizzed you afterwards about who you saw and what was said.

Martha saw the woman three times in a row.

What did she want? I asked.

Nothing.

Then she had a visitor. He arrived just after three and sat in the hall, cap in hand.

I was looking for her and came in the front door as she came downstairs.

Come on, she said to the man and walked out the door.

When I asked, she shook her head and said, Nothing, and walked away.

That's no fair, I said. You get me to tell you things, but you never tell me anything.

That's because I don't want you to know, she said. You've no idea what's going on and neither does anybody else. And you cannae tell, you canne tell anybody. If you do tell, then your ma, or you or somebody'll get intae trouble. Naebody believes you, so you've got to lie. It's the only way to get anything done here and the only way to get out of here, tell them what they want to know. Tell them you're better. How are you today Martha? Fine, thank you. Are you feeling happier about things? Yes, miss. And smile, Carlie. Be sure to smile. I don't want to go home, so I tell them the truth; but if you want to see your ma, tell them you're better. They're sure to believe you and you'll see her in jig time.

So where did you go with your uncle? I asked.

She sighed. He's no an uncle. He's one of my ma's boyfriends and he comes up to see me.

Does he know if your ma's alive?

He says she's getting better. Wait here.

She came back with Wilma Anderson.

Tell him about your uncle, she said.

Wilma looked at her.

Go on. Tell him.

You're lucky you're a boy, she said, and you're lucky you've a ma who wants to see you.

Wilma looked at Martha and ran away.

I didn't understand, but knew I couldn't ask.

We talk about it, Martha said, all the time, at night before bed and when we're in bed. We talk aboot it and we're gonnae run away. It'll no be for a while. He said my ma wants me back cause there's naebody to look after her, naebody to do the messages and I've to hurry up and get hame. But I'm no goin. If they try and make me go, I'll run away.

That afternoon we practised for a concert for the visitors on Saturday afternoon. Miss Joyce taught us 'Dream Angus', asking me to read the words because she did not have time to make copies. I read a line and the class repeated:

> Dreams to sell, fine dreams to sell,
> Angus is here, wi dreams to sell, oh.
> Hush ye, my baby, and sleep without fear.
> Dream Angus has brought you a dream, my dear.

I think you need your eyes tested, she said.

I'd been told I might need glasses. We had lined up outside Classroom Three in Keppochhill Primary, stripped to the waist, with bare feet. Our joints, ears, tongues, chest and eyes were tested.

Glasses, the woman said as I walked away. Check again in six months time.

I hated the prospect, especially here, where I was sure glasses would be another sign of weakness, another thing to be broken.

We'll have to write to your mother. Nothing can happen without her permission. I'll have a word with Miss Hassan. It's nearly your birthday, isn't it?

April 5, miss.

I think that's around Easter. I don't want to raise your hopes, but we'll see what we can do.

* * *

It was in every letter, though I seldom wrote such a thing in my letters home. I thanked my mother for the parcel, said it was good to hear from her, thanked her for the postal order, which I had handed in to the office, and hoped everyone was well.

We wrote home after school, on Wednesday afternoons. Miss Joyce asked us to tell her what we thought would be the week's news from Nerston so we could put it in our letters, usually two or three sentences, preceeded with news of ourselves.

Something nice that has happened to you this week, she said. Something you would like your relations to know. Now who can tell me something nice that's happened? You could tell them about 'Dream Angus' and 'The Wild Rose', she said.

Part of the performance would be three boys and two girls, singing English words to 'Heidenröslein'. She told us about Franz Schubert and the girls made two costumes from crepe paper. Martha would stand in the middle of the room as a rosebud. Tom Bennett would see her, would try to pluck the flower, but the thorn would stick in his finger.

Writing home was always difficult. When the class was finished, the letters written and envelopes sealed, we would wander downstairs and sit in the common room. No one felt like playing; even football was difficult. We waited for dinner, when there was always a pudding, usually with extra helpings. Facts emerged like shooting stars.

I lived in Dennistoun, then we moved down to Ayrshire. Anybody know it?

Whereabouts in Ayrshire? My granny lived in Kilmarnock.

This was Kilbirnie. My da ran away wi Annie McCaskill, so we had to move cause my mammy couldnae pay the rent and the weans in the playground started getting on at us.

Any brothers or sisters?

A big sister and two wee brothers. How about you?

My mammy died. I was in a foster home, but the foster parents' weans didnae like it when I got things. They thought they should be getting everything. They were paid to keep me, paid to look after me, but they never did.

We lived with my granny and my ma started going to the dancin. My granny would tell us stories about when she was wee and then she'd start greeting about an uncle who was killed in the war at Arnhem.

My uncle was at Arnhem.

He wisnae killed but.

I ran away fae the foster home and they sent me here. Miss Hassan says I'll get another foster parent, and that I can say if I don't want to go, but I cannae stay here and I'll need to go some time.

Martha sat on the edge of the group and stared at the floor, sometimes with Wilma Anderson, but mostly on her own. If she caught my eye, she'd glance towards the cloakrooms, then go out the front door. When the time was right, I'd go to the cloakroom, and wait for her to climb in the lavatory window.

We often said nothing, but she liked me to talk about my father. She'd ask about Oban, Fortingall and Kettle, which always made her laugh. I tried to tell her about Francie, but she always interrupted: What happened to The Man Who Said Everything Twice.

Peter Price, he said everything twice.

Everything twice?

Everything twice.

She laughed and put her hand to her mouth, shrugged her shoulders and smiled, suddenly turning towards the door, her left forefinger at her mouth.

Jaymo came in as I stood up. He smiled and closed the door.

That's us for it now, she said.

Next morning, after breakfast, Miss Hassan called me into her office. Her desk was tidy. She indicated I should sit, as the telephone rang. She said she would call back and wrote the number on the back of an envelope with her gold propelling pencil.

Well, Carl. How do you think you are?

Fine, thank you, miss.

For once I'm inclined to agree with you. You've made very good progress, Miss MacLaren speaks very highly of you and your reports are good, much better than when you arrived here. Your work in class has improved and you seem much more sociable than you were, readier to enter into the spirit of things. I see you need new glasses, so we'll maybe arrange for your mother to come down and take you for an eye test. Would you like that?

Yes, miss.

Good. Off you go now. Your class is waiting.

As I turned towards the door, she said: Tell me about you and Martha?

I stared at the floor.

Miss Joyce tells me you and Martha were in the cloakroom last night. Is there anything I should know about?

I don't know, miss.

Well, if you don't know, neither do I.

I felt my face get red, my throat tightened and I knew I would stutter.

Is Martha still your friend?

Yes, miss.

As I've said already, she could be a good friend to you and I think you would be a good friend for her too, but you understand why I'm asking, don't you?

I think so, miss.

I wouldn't like you to get into trouble, Carl. And I imagine Martha could be a bit bossy and maybe lead you into doing things you might not want to do, so you'll keep a look out for that, won't you?

She picked up the telephone and dialled the number on the back of the envelope.

THIRTY-ONE

Francie

A SUDDEN FROST turned the windows pale. We got hot milk with our porridge, walked around in scarves and jumpers with the radiators turned up full. We shivered.

At least it's dry, Mister Scott said every day as we happed ourselves for the afternoon walk.

Frost glistened on the rhododendron leaves, shone along the fence wires, stained the posts and telegraph poles. Puddles in the fields were frozen. Ice covered the sheuchs and tractor tracks, fog moved in drifts and skeletal leaves were stuck in the mud.

For goodness sake, wipe your nose, Scott said when he passed a child.

We slipped up the bank of the burn and ran screaming through the wood, calling on each other to do something about the cold that nipped our brows and made our eyes water.

Have you thought of getting married? Martha asked.

We were on a short walk. Miss MacLaren said it looked like rain and took us through the village. I'd been trying to catch up with her, but she walked on, chatting with the group in front while Martha dawdled.

I said, have you thought of getting married?

To you?

Why not?

Why?

I wish I was big. I wish we were big. I wish we could just be on our own for a while.

What would we do?

I don't know. Whatever we liked.

We could go to the pictures.

I suppose I'd have to make you something to eat.

Ice cream.

Stew.

I'd have to get a job.

But I'd have your tea ready when you came in from work.

Then what would we do?

I don't know. Stay in and talk. Sit in front of the fire and listen to the wireless. What do you want for your birthday?

I don't know.

I'd like to take you to see your mother. We could have tea in your front room, then come back here.

If I went back I'd want to stay.

Would she let me stay?

She always wanted a wee girl.

Instead of you?

No, before my daddy died.

That would be the three of us.

I know.

On an afternoon, when mist lay in patches and the corn stubble would not yield, she stopped on the edge of the wood. The man was walking up the drive. He wore his cap on the side of his head. We could hear his boots on the tarmac.

No, she said.

What is it?

Come on with me, Carlie. Help me. Quick.

We ran round the back of the home, clambered through the cloakroom window and opened the door. We tiptoed through the common room and waited till we heard Miss Hassan's door shut.

She ran upstairs, gathered her stuff, ransacked her locker and took some money from an envelope at the back of the drawer. There was a ten shilling note, a half crown, a sixpence and some coppers.

Keep them away, Carlie. Keep them away, she said, running across the fields towards the woods on the far side of the home. When she got to the gate at the edge of the wood, where the mud was frozen, she stopped. Her breath came in handfuls.

538 Keppochhill Road?

I nodded.

That's your address?

Uh-hu.

Run back. You run back and say you never saw me. Say I ran away. Promise you'll say you never saw me, that I ran off on my own and you got lost.

She threw her bag over the gate and clambered over. What are you waiting for? she asked, then stuck her face through the bars of the gate. Give me a kiss.

We smacked our lips and she ran up the path, on to the road, towards the city.

I ran back, through the woods, down the hill into the village and walked up the drive, as the stragglers were making their way back home. Nothing had changed; the lights were on in some of the houses, and as I turned towards the front door, someone switched on the common room light. My mother was sitting in the hall in her good coat and hat, her handbag on her lap.

My God, you've grown, she said. And burst into tears.

She knelt on the floor, my face in her hands. I put my arms round her neck and tried to wipe her tears from my face.

Goodness me, Miss Hassan said. What a day. Everybody arriving at once. If you'd like to use my office Mrs MacDougall, I'll see if I can track someone down. Have you seen Martha, Carl?

No, miss.

Wasn't she on the walk?

She ran on ahead, miss.

I'll find her. You go with your mother and I'll send in a cup of tea. I suppose you could do with something after your journey.

My mother smiled. Miss Hassan held the door open and the man walked into the hall, his cap in hand.

That man was on the bus, my mother said. Is he related to someone?

I don't know.

Well, how are you? Come and sit here. You're too big now to go on my lap, but God, look at how you've grown.

She told me about Granny and Grandad, Barbara, George and Michael, Toby was well and had brought a mouse home. It was alive and she had to waken my grandad to get it shifted.

Miss MacLaren brought in two cups of tea and a plate with two ginger snaps and a pair of shortbread fingers. There was a milk jug and sugar bowl on the tray, though milk had been put in the tea. She introduced herself to my mother and smiled at me. I blushed. I'll just get Carl's things together, she said.

Am I going home?

Just for a wee while.

Am I getting my eyes tested?

We'll maybe do that tomorrow

She drank the tea and put the cup on the saucer when Miss MacLaren came in with the teapot. I'll just leave that there, she said. There's a bus in half an hour from the top of the road. Carl knows the stop.

My mother poured more tea, took a sip and smiled.

I've something to tell you and I don't know how to say it. It's Francis McDade.

She tried to drink the tea, then tried to smile.

Poor wee soul, she said. He was drowned. In the canal. Two days ago. He was swimming. In this weather. It happened at the generator, where the water's warm. It was after school. The kids were swimming after school. They couldn't have known. They'd let the warm water out and the kids dived in, but they couldn't have let all the water out and when they let the second lot out, he drowned. They couldn't find his body. They got him yesterday morning. He'd been washed down to the Maryhill Basin. Floating in the reeds. The funeral's tomorrow morning at St Theresa's. I found out and phoned Miss Hassan.

I hadn't realised I was crying. The lump was back in my chest, but I wasn't sure if it was for Francie or Martha. Standing with my head against my mother's breast I thought the sobbing would never stop.

She took me into the cloakroom and washed my face, drying it on the roller towel. When we came back in the hall, Miss MacLaren had packed my bag.

I've put a change of clothes in, Mrs MacDougall, and Carl's wash things are there as well. So, we'll see you soon, Carl.

She knelt and kissed my cheek.

Your eyes are all red, she said, smiling at my mother.

The man was smoking.

You'd better come into the office, Miss Hassan said. And would you mind putting your cigarette out, please.

He nipped his fag at the door and walked into the office, while Miss Hassan and my mother whispered. Miss MacLaren held my hand.

We'll miss you when you're not here, she said. And when you're back, it'll soon be your birthday and then, I'm sure, it won't be long till you're back home again with all your friends.

They think that wee girl's ran away, my mother said. And I don't think Miss Hassan's too sure about him. He's a dour bugger. He got off at the same stop as me, walked in front of me and never even looked the road I was on. I had to ask at the shop if this was the right place. Now, we've got chicken for your tea and I've made some jelly. Are you feeling better? I'd get you some chocolate, but you'll be sick on the bus.

* * *

Look at that wean, my granny said. He's lost a lot of weight. She ran her fingers over my face. God, but you've grown. And you're needing glasses.

You'll soon be a man, my grandfather said.

Toby wrapped himself round my legs and sat on my lap while I ate.

Did you hear he caught a mouse, said George. Marvellous. Isn't it marvellous. All the news from Keppochhill Road, the cat caught a mouse.

Barbara played with Michael, who cried when he saw me, but soon said my name. Tal, he said. Tal Madoola.

The front room had been decorated. There was a new three-piece suite, a carpet that covered the centre of the room, with a band of new linoleum round the edge and the doors had been varnished. There was a table with a castor oil plant at the window.

Bloody thing, my granny said. God knows what it's there for. Folk keep bumping into it.

My mother pulled down the divan bed and I slept all night in spite of the tramcars, the light from the street and Toby at my feet.

I wakened with the eight o'clock whistle, the smell of my grandfather's pipe in the lobby. The fire was lit and he was in his chair.

Carl, he said, when I'd had my breakfast. Run down to Fraser's and get me the *Express*.

Get it yoursel, my granny said. That's boy's to get ready.

Shush, Jo. He's old enough to go for the paper.

Is that you? said Ada, as Mrs Fraser came through from the back shop.

Gosh, she said. Look at how you've grown. You soon won't be able to get in the door.

What did you get? my granny asked.

The *Express*.

Did Fraser give you anything?

No.

Not even a sweetie? God Almighty. Miserable bitch.

I think you should polish your shoes, my grandad said. Do you know how to do it?

Of course he knows how to polish a shoe. God Almighty, you'd think the wean was stupid.

Let me show you. I'll do one and you do the other. Put some polish on the toe-cap, like that; rub it well in. Now spit on it. That's right. Spit.

Don't you teach that wean to spit. He'll end up like you, God only knows how that fire stays lit with you spitting at it all the time.

My grandad shook his head and smiled. Now run the spittle into the polish, he said. Little circles'll do. That's right. Now take the brush and put on more polish. Not so much. That's about right. Now, take the polish off with the other brush. And make sure there's no dirt on the heel. That's fine. Lovely. You can see your face in it.

I told him how we polished our shoes to go to the pictures, but hadn't used spittle.

He laughed. Your Uncle Willie taught me how to do it, said he learned it in the army, so I'm not sure if it's right or not, he said.

My clothes were laid out on the brown velveteen cushion of a front room chair: grey trousers, white shirt, black tie.

It's at ten o'clock, my mother said. We've got a few minutes. You can put on your jacket and a raincoat on top. It'll look very smart. And we'll just walk round. Can you tie your tie?

My grandfather stood me in front of the mirror. This bit hangs down, he said. And this bit here crosses over, then goes round the back and in through the loop. Lovely. Very smart. Now, I'm not going to this funeral because I don't know the family, but you know them, so be sure to have a word with the boy's mother. It's an awful death. Terrible. A tragedy.

He kissed me at the door. Your mother has every reason to be proud of you, he said.

Barbara and Michael came up from downstairs. Gosh, she said. You look smart. Look at your shoes.

Once past Vere Street, by the new houses, my mother talked as if I'd never been away.

Your Aunt Cathie's moved, she said. I don't know if she'll be here or not, I don't suppose so; they didn't really know the family. It was you who knew them, wasn't it. Jean Delacourt was saying they'll get a new house. Now, you've to be on your best behaviour here. Be sure to mind your manners and have a word with Mrs McDade.

There was a white coffin on two trestles in the middle of the centre aisle. Francie's mother and sisters were in the front row, staring resolutely ahead, wearing the clothes they always wore. My mother said his relations were in the row behind. Two or three other rows were filled with neighbours and his class had been given time off school. There were strangers at the back of the chapel.

The priest asked if anyone from the press was present. If so, he said, I would ask you to respect this family and their grief. I would ask you to go about your business and leave us to mourn the loss of a loved one. Francis McDade was part of this community and we have come to lay him to rest. We ask anyone who is not here to help us do this duty before God and our neighbours, to thank God for the life of Francis McDade and to grant his soul eternal rest, we ask you to go now and leave us in peace.

I stared at the coffin and could not imagine he was in there. What was left of him, his sandshoes and jumper? I remembered him in the Gospel Hall, praying. O Lord we thank you for all your goodness and mercy unto us, your servants, the priest said.

My mother asked, Do you want to go up for the communion?

I shook my head and couldn't take my eyes off the family, who clung together, sobbing. I wondered if they thought the service had anything to do with Francie, or if I saw him differently from everyone else, if I was the only person who knew him; and when I thought of that I smiled and smiling stopped me crying. I remembered the way he looked when he read a word he didn't know.

Acasial, he said. No that's no right? Occasio, occason, occasIonal. Is that it? Wait. Occasional.

I nodded. And he smiled.

Mrs McDade was by the door, her children round her. The family were on the other side; the women crying, the men nodding as the congregation left. Mrs McDade and the children were crying. Francie's sister tugged her mother's coat.

Shush, not now, said Mrs McDade, touching her daughter's hair.

There's Carl, the girl said.

Mrs McDade looked up, saw me and started to wail. She pushed everyone aside and ran to me.

God Almighty, she said. Carl, son, you came. They let you out.

And she gripped me, held me, stretched me to her arm's length and held me in again.

There was hardly a day, but he spoke about you. He was saving up to see you. He had money put away, son. He'd money put away. He tried to write you a letter and wanted to get the bus to wherever you were but he didnae know where it was. I never thought. You must've thought, God knows what you thought. Wee Francie. If you were there, he wouldnae've gone swimming. I don't mean that, son. I don't mean it was you. God knows, you'll miss him near as much as me.

When she took me in her arms and pressed me again in to the sour smell of her coat, I felt myself fly away, felt it drop. She was on her knees by the chapel door, holding me and hugging me, the children round me, touching me. A girl had her arms round my neck.

This was his pal, she said to no one. This was my boy's best pal.

We stayed that way for a very long time, me and the McDade girls and our mothers crying.

Thank you for coming, said Mrs McDade.

My mother had her glasses in her hand. She wiped her eyes.

We couldn't have stayed away, she said.

God knows, yous've had your crosses to bear. Will yous come roon the hoose, after the burial? Will yous come roon and have a cup of tea?

We can't. I'm sorry. I'd love to come and so would Carl. I've to take him into town and then he's to go straight back.

Of course. We'll see to this. God knows what's going to happen. God knows what we'll do. Promise me you'll come and see me. Will you come and see me, Carl? Promise.

I'm sorry I can't come now.

I know, son, but come when you're out, when you can. Come when they let you come.

And she held me again, ruffled my hair and kissed me.

I don't know how we parted. With the door of the black car open, she opened her arms again, took me inside and held me the way she'd held Francie.

I've messed your hair, she said, fixing it.

My mother and I stood by the white statue of St Theresa with the infant Jesus in her arms. As the cortège pulled away, Mrs McDade turned to see me, her children's faces pressed to the glass.

THIRTY-TWO

Seeing

MCQUILKEN & CO was on Sauchiehall Street, between Buchanan Street and West Nile Street.

The windows' display area was covered with blue velvet, with binoculars, cameras, magnifying glasses and spectacle frames laid at precise angles.

Inside, the shop was lined in wood with glass cases and two globe lamps. A display of Kodak film covered the wall beside the window, with coloured views of the Swiss Alps on the other side of the wall. The spectacle frames were in a glass case on the right; cameras, binoculars and magnifying glasses were in the opposite case. The floor was tiled with green linoleum squares, with two rubber mats beside the counters and Leica written in white in the centre. Assistants covered the counter with yellow dusters to protect the instruments.

Mister McQuilken had short, black, wavy hair, flecked with grey. He wore a dark suit with a patterned silk handkerchief in his top jacket pocket and what looked like a small white ruler.

This way, he said, ushering me through to a small wooden booth at the back of the shop where letters were displayed on an opaque glass frame. He covered my eyes with large metal spectacles, which he adjusted at the sides, asked me to look up, took out the ruler and held it across my eyes.

Fine, he said. Now, tell me, what can you see?

The glasses were empty. I read the letters. He pressed a switch and changed the screen.

Good. Now, how about this? Can you read the letters, starting from the top?

He selected small monocles from a velvet-covered tray, slotting them into the lens over my left eye, covering the other with a black metal disc.

He told me what he was going to do before he did it, even though I wanted to cheat and tried to peer round the disc which covered alternate eyes, adjusting my arc of vision, so that some part of the lettering was always obscure.

He pressed the switch and lines appeared.

Where do they meet? He asked. And what difference does this make? Better? Worse? Or pretty much the same?

Eventually, he sighed and said, Are you ready for this?

When he removed the black disc, it took me a few seconds to adjust to the clarity and the light. For the first time ever, I could see the letters clearly, read the small print along the bottom line, detected the parallel lines and circles. I looked at my mother and smiled.

Can you see me? she asked.

The glasses will take about three weeks. You can come in and collect them.

That might not be possible, my mother said.

We're open after school.

Carl may be away. But I'll come in and send them on if need be.

That should be all right, said Mister McQuilken, holding the door open as we passed into Sauchiehall Street.

He touched my shoulder.

That's you Specky Four-Eyes now, he said. Everything will be different. You'll see the world in a different light.

* * *

God, I'd die for a cup of tea, she said. And you'll have to watch yourself. We don't want you being sick on the bus.

We ate in a cafe at the top of Buchanan Street, fish and chips, tea, bread and butter.

Wait till you hear about that bloody cat, she said. Did I tell you about the mouse? God love it, I think he thought we'd eat the bloody thing. Did you know Maisie McAllister, a waitress I used to work with? Anyway, she told me there was a policeman in the Calton called Eat the Moose, because he told the women in a shop he was a German prisoner o' war and was that hungry he ate a moose. He thinks he's a bloody cat, said Maisie. Anyway, the name stuck, and him a big broser six feet or more with a belly on him like a drum, expecting folk to believe he'd eaten mice. Daft bugger. Did they no have cats in the concentration camp, or did folk eat them an a', asked Maisie. She was a cheeky bitch. That polis lifted her man two nights later for swearing and saying you couldnae get a decent bit of meat in the Calton since he'd telled the women there was good eating in a moose.

Anyway, I was in the Grosvenor and somebody left this wee bit Gorgonzola cheese. Naebody'd eat it for fear of the jaundice, so I said, That'll do me, and I takes it home for your grandad; God help him, he likes his bit cheese. Father, I said. Wait till you see what I've got you; and while I'm putting the kettle on, the bloody cat's in my bag and away with the Gorgonzola. Ate the bloody lot, licked its lips and cried for more.

Two days later it ate the Delacourt's budgie. That daft wee yellow yite they had in a cage in the front room. Jean, of course, was roaring and greeting. Your cat's ate my budgie, she said. Mrs Kaufmann, what'll I do? So we had to get her another bloody budgie, a blue one this time. But I don't think Toby's so fond of the blue budgies; he's no been near the place since.

Auld Delacourt's sleeping, Mrs Delacourt's in the shop with Jean and when she comes in to make her father a cup of tea, he's out like a light and the cat's got yellow feathers all over the place.

Then, just last week, Cameron up the stairs comes down, a week past Friday it was, just about teatime. Mrs Kaufmann, Mrs Kaufmann, you cat's ate my steak. Jesus Christ, I've never seen a bloody beast like it. It would eat the food off your plate, without even a by your leave or a knife and fork. Who in the name of Christ ever heard of the Camerons having steak? A quarter of mince it was, but we'd to buy them pope's eye. That cat's better fed than ourselves. Greedy bugger. Imagine leaving your door wide open with a budgie flying round the place and the steak for your tea lying on the table. What in the name of God is the world coming to.

Then your granny says it's because we'd no been giving it fish. Christ himself couldn't get any fish to give it. And if that cat thinks I'm going round Possil just to get it fish, it's got another think coming. Bloody thing, prowling about the place, stealing folks' food out their mouth. It's a hell of a thief. Of course, cats are bad for that, always were; cats are awful thieves. Terrible, so they are. I swear to God, they'd take the money out your purse.

Your grandad says it smells things. It can tell when there's steak on the table or a budgie flying round the house. It's got good earsight, your granny said. Good eyes, good smell and good hearing. It'll also have a good kick in the arse if it steals any more food. I'd rather keep its bloody picture. Come on, we'll need to get you back.

* * *

I slept on the bus. She wakened me and we walked slowly down the road, holding hands.

Miss Hassan came out her office. You're back, she said. And did you get your eyes tested? Good. Well, Mrs MacDougall, I think you can see Carl this weekend. Now, if you'd like to come into the office, we'll get you a cup of tea and Carl can go into the common room, where, I believe, they're going to have a singsong.

My mother smiled. I'll see you on Saturday, she said.

Jaymo and his group were standing round a radiator at the bottom of the room. The chess club was in the corner and some children were playing draughts. I walked over to join them and Wilma Anderson sat beside me.

Did you see her?

No.

Joycie tellt me she wasnae coming back. See if you asked Miss Hassan, she'd tell you. She asked Martha about you. Martha tellt her yous were getting married. She said she was going to live with you and your mammy, that your mammy had always wanted a wee lassie and that you were taking her to see your mammy, that she'd meet her when she came to visit you. She knew all about your family and told me about the folk that died and the man that said everything twice, everything twice.

Jaymo and his group had been watching and were about to move when Miss Hassan, wearing her coat, hat, gloves and scarf, put her head round the door. She took off her hat, shook it and crooked her finger at me.

That's your mother away, she said in the office. I walked her down to the bus stop and we had a nice chat.

She hung her coat on a hanger behind the door and put her hat, gloves and scarf into a filing cabinet drawer. It's a lovely, fresh evening, she said. Now, how did you get on?

Fine, miss.

Most funerals are very sad, especially a child's funeral. Were you upset?

Yes, miss.

I imagine you would be. I think it's terrible to lose a friend. Did you cry, Carl?

I cried when Francie's mammy hugged me.

Was it unusual for him to be swimming in the canal in this weather?

The water's hot when it comes out the power station. It's good to swim in and great to be in hot water when it's cold.

Have you done it?

No, miss, but I've seen boys do it.

Carl, you don't have a bath at home, do you?

No, miss.

And Francie wouldn't have a bath either?

No miss.

Have you ever had a bath before coming here?

In Oban.

How did you and Francie meet?

I told her about Alec Irvine and Willie Simpson, the drowned kittens and Mrs Jamieson, who made her smile. I told her about going to the library and being barred from the Minors. I did not tell her we were blood brothers, nor about the plank in the park.

I think he was a very important person, she said. Have you ever seen the *Reader's Digest*?

No, miss.

I'll bring some in for you. They have a column where people write about a very important person. The interesting thing is that most people don't write about the sort of folk you and I would think were important, Mister Truman or Mister Attlee, Winston Churchill or anyone like that. They write about ordinary people, like Francis McDade. And I think you could do something similar. I'm sure that if you thought about him really deeply and thought about how you feel you'll be able to come up with something worthwhile.

I was crying.

Miss Hassan sat with her arms on the desk and, when she thought I'd finished crying, took a man's handkerchief from the drawer.

Tell me about your new glasses. Are you worried?

I nodded.

Because you'll be called names?

No. If I get hit the glass could cut me.

And do you expect to get hit?

I blew my nose into the handkerchief.

Miss Hassan wrote into the folder on her desk.

Who do you think might hit you? Has anyone at Nerston hit you?

They might not hit me. It could be an accident. I could fall.

Carl, do you ever tell lies?

No, miss.

Is that a lie?

No, miss.

You may not tell a direct lie, but I've noticed you're very skilled at avoiding the direct truth. I think you're the sort of boy who could easily find himself saying things that weren't true to impress people or to make you feel better, because you think you'll get into trouble, or, more likely, because you think you'll upset someone else or get them into trouble. Does that sound familiar?

I don't know, miss.

I think you do know and I think it's something you'll have to be aware of. Now, how do you feel about moving to Miss MacLaren's class for a while?

Fine, thank you.

She smiled. Good, she said, opening the folder. And tell me about Martha. Did she run away?

She ran on ahead, miss.

Did you ever tell Martha things that weren't true?

No, miss.

I saw you talking with Wilma Anderson and I presume she told you Martha won't be coming back?

Yes, miss.

You were fond of her, weren't you?

Yes, miss.

And she was fond of you. Did you know that?

I wasn't sure, but I believe it now.

Is that because she isn't here? You surely don't believe everyone you love, or even like, leaves you? You love your mother, don't you?

Yes, miss. But she isn't here.

I know you've known some awful losses, but that isn't because of you. These are things that happened to people, often without reason, they just happen.

Does God make them happen?

I don't think he makes them happen, no.

But he could stop them.

I think this is something you could discuss with the chaplain. That's what he's here for.

She reached in her drawer. A letter came this morning, she said. I think it's from Martha.

My name was spelled correctly. There was no address and no date.

Dear Carl: I hope you are fine. I wish you had come with me. If you'd come we could even be going to America to stay with my Auntie Sadie. I will send you a card for your birthday, which I know is April 5 and will let you know my address to write to. Love and kisses.

> *Martha. xxxxxxxxx*
> *PS lots of love. I miss you.*

Is she all right?

I think so.

Good. Well, I think you've had an exciting day and it's time for bed.

THIRTY-THREE

Birthday

WE FILED IN while the organ played and sat in the first couple of pews below the pulpit.

After his sermon, the minister led the congregation in prayer. And as we offer our own silent prayers, he said, let us remember those poor, unfortunate children with us today, and as we remember and pray for them let us also thank God for his tender mercies.

The phrase fascinated me. I didn't know what tender mercies were, but thought I might like them.

My experience suggested something beyond misfortune. If God existed and, as we were taught, held us in the palm of his hand, looked after us, then He obviously didn't like me. It wasn't a matter of faith. It was a simple truth.

Every couple of weeks, the minister came to see us: If anyone has any problems, he said, if things aren't quite working out; if you're lonely, tired or upset; if you feel lost and friendless, come and have a chat.

Then he told jokes and sang 'The Cobbler's Song' from *Chu Chin Chow*. I'll be around, he said.

He came on the walk, chatted and tried to get us to sing what he called hiking songs: If you're in the Scouts you should know these songs, he said. Doesn't your scoutmaster sing them?

He was funny and approachable in his checked shirt and flannels; and when he waited at the foot of the burn while I scrambled down the hill and asked how things were, I wanted to tell him everything.

It's easy for folk to get confused, he said, but I don't think God works the way folk think. Everybody has an idea of God, everybody wants to believe, but somehow they feel the very idea of God doesn't make sense, or something happens that makes them question the very existence of God. And we don't take enough interest in that. We just assume folk will believe because we believe or because they think they have to believe, but we don't look at why folk stop believing. These are important issues and I think you should think about them.

I have thought about them.

And what conclusions did you reach?

I told him.

When things aren't going well, we can ask God to help us rather than blame him. We can ask him to give us strength and show us what to do. That's the first thing. Secondly, don't you think it's a bit silly to suppose that out of all the people in the world God chose you to punish in this particular way and for no reason? There are things we don't understand, like life itself, why we're here and it's a question of faith. We have to believe that things will get better. You have to believe you won't always be here in this school and whatever troubles you have will soon be over, but you also have to do things to make it happen. You have to act. It's up to you. I know you have a birthday coming up soon. You'll be in double figures. That would be a good time to stand up for yourself. Thirdly, and most importantly of all, God loves us, completely and unconditionally. Do you know what that means?

No.

You must know what it means to have someone love you totally.

I shook my head. I'm not sure, I said.

In that case, you need God more than anything. You need to know God loves you.

* * *

Some time in the night, you'd hear children leaving, the slip of sandshoes moving along the corridors or windows being lifted.

And there were the children like Sandy Brown and Cockeye Bell who ran away from home and came back to Nerston. I wondered if Martha would come back.

I lay awake, clutching her letter, thinking of what I could do to stand up for myself, when I heard someone get up. When they did not come back after the lavatory flushed, I dressed and ran downstairs.

A boy I hardly knew, Davie Wilson, was putting on his shoes.

Jaymo's gonnae smother me, he said.

Without thinking, I put on my shoes and raincoat, pulled the door behind me and we ran down the path, through the village, up the brae and on to the road.

Which way's Glesca?

I pointed to the right.

I'm going this way.

He ran towards East Kilbride, while I ran to the end of the lane and climbed the gate where I fell in the mud, where I had last seen Martha. It started to rain. I sat by a tree, then moved to a clearing.

I felt the rain soak into my hair, gather and slide down my face. It tasted of soap, then of nothing. When water ran down my back, rather than have them soaked I piled my clothes beneath the tree and sat naked in the bracken.

Tears mingled with the rainwater. I didn't know why I was crying, but I knew I didn't need a reason, it was everything: Daddy and Nerston, Willie and Eva, Charlie, Francie and Martha, for the fear and isolation, of knowing what to do, but not knowing how to do it.

I knew I was now in serious trouble, but I couldn't go back. It was difficult to move. I tried to build a shelter, then sat in the middle of the wood, in the moonlight, the noise of rain around me.

I felt I was being cleansed, by the shivering rather than the water, that the black crust I knew was inside my skull was being loosened and would gradually chip away, that I'd be able to breathe without the threat of tears and to speak without a stammer, that no matter how anyone saw it and irrespective of what might happen, I had done something, formed an experience that was mine.

I was a witness at my wake, between an old me that was dying and a new me that was sprouting wings. For the first time in a long time I did not feel guilty, did not feel I had done something wrong, was waiting to be caught and reprimanded, did not feel I was an uninvited guest who shouldn't be wherever I was, that I was no longer sleeping with my eyes open.

I asked myself, what would Francie do? Or Martha, what would she do?

There was neither thunder nor lightning, but the steady fall of rain.

* * *

I heard my name as torch beams flared the trees.

Davie Wilson was in bed. He ran away every week and always came back. He asked if they'd found me. Miss MacLaren had wakened Mister Scott.

She wrapped me in her coat and blankets and gathered my clothes. Mister Scott carried me back. Miss MacLaren washed me and bandaged my cuts; then put me in the sick room, with hot water bottles, the heater and light on all night.

There, she said as she kissed my brow. I'm sure you could do with a good night's sleep.

I wakened with Miss Hassan on the chair beside me. She did not speak for a very long time.

Well?

Sorry, miss.

I quite believe it. Not one of your brighter ideas.

No, miss.

Anything you'd like to tell me.

I don't know, miss.

Why did it happen?

I heard Davie Wilson get up and when he didn't come back, I went downstairs and that was how it happened.

Were you looking for Martha?

I don't think so, miss.

Were you going back to Glasgow?

No, miss.

And what about Martha's letter?

I think I left it in the wood.

Well, she said. I don't know what to do. I'll have to discuss this with other colleagues, but I have to say I think it's set you back a bit. It'll soon be your birthday, so once the doctor's seen you and we're sure there's nothing wrong, we can get you back to class and maybe things will return to normal, or as near to normality as they ever are with you.

* * *

On the Thursday morning break, Miss Joyce handed me three cards, from my mother, Aunt Barbara, Uncle George and Michael, Granny and Grandad. I was on my way to class when Jaymo snatched them from me.

Any postal orders? he said. He tore the envelopes and cards and threw them into the waste paper basket.

Are you all right? Miss MacLaren asked.

Yes, miss.

Then why is your lip trembling?

It isn't, miss. It isn't trembling.

Miss Joyce came into the room. Why did you tear up your birthday cards? she asked.

I didn't tear them up.

Leave this with me, said Miss MacLaren.

After lunch, we sat in the hall. Miss MacLaren held my hand. We can go in and see Miss Hassan right now, she said. That is a very serious offence and I think you should tell me the name of the person who did it to you. Please, Carl. Tell me. If I mentioned a boy's name, would you nod your head if it was him?

I shook my head.

Why not? Are you frightened of what he'll do? We know more than you think. We are aware of what's going on. We know who's being bullied and who the bullies are; but what we need is confirmation. Will you tell me, please?

I can't.

Why not?

I don't know.

Will you think about it?

I nodded.

* * *

Jaymo put his hand round my mouth and pulled me into the cloakroom. He shoved me into a corner while three boys watched the door.

What did you tell her?

Nothing.

He slapped my face.

What did you fucken tell her?

Nothing.

He slapped me again.

If you've tellt her about me, I'll fucken choke you.

He punched me on the stomach and when I bent double his fist connected with my cheekbone. I fell to the ground and he kicked me twice in the side. The others kicked me before they left.

I got up, washed my face and when I went into the common room Miss Joyce presented me with a birthday cake with ten candles. Everyone sang 'Happy Birthday' and I blew out the candles.

I went round the room, offering the others a piece of cake.

I did not offer a piece to Jaymo nor the boys who'd been with him. He stood up and walked towards me. I turned to face Miss Joyce. She was talking to some girls.

When Jaymo came near I picked up a piece of cake and in view of the school stuck it into his face.

Everyone laughed and there was a big cheer. Even the boys beside him where laughing. Miss Joyce turned round.

I didn't tell, I said, but I will now.

I carried the plate down to the bottom of the room and handed it to Miss Joyce.

No one else wants a piece, miss.

Then you have what's left.

I sat on the opposite side of the room, beside the piano and ate two pieces of cake, giving Wilma Anderson the other piece.

Did Martha send you a card?

I shook my head.

Maybe she hasnae any money?

That's what I think.

Maybe she sent it to Keppochill Road?

How do you know my address?

She told me you tellt her, but she never said the number. What are you gonnae do about Jaymo?

Wait till he's on his own.

He'll kill you. He's never on his own.

Aye, he is.

Miss MacLaren was on dormitory duty.

Don't you go to sleep the night, said Jaymo.

Please miss, what happens if you're being bullied?

Are you being bullied, Carl?

No, miss, but I just wondered what would happen if I was bullied. Could I report the person who was bullying me?

Miss MacLaren smiled.

They would never know where the complaint came from, she said.

I repeated my multiplication tables to stay awake, got up twice and checked the other dormitories and corridors. When my dormitory was asleep, I picked up my pillow, tiptoed along the corridor and crossed the room to Jaymo's bed. He was on his back. I stared at him till my knees trembled, and was about to turn away, when Sandy Brown wakened.

Jaymo, he shouted.

I put the pillow over Jaymo's face, lying across the pillow and yelling while he kicked his legs and tried to punch the air. Sandy Brown tried to haul me off, but I held onto the iron bed base, then ran back to my own bed when I saw the light go on in the corridor.

Jaymo followed me, punching, screaming and crying. He jumped on my bed and grabbed my pyjamas, banging my head against the wall. I shoved his chin upwards and was trying to punch his neck when the door swung open, the light went on and Mister Scott hauled Jaymo off me.

What's going on? he said.

Please, sir. I said. He tried to smother me and get into my bed.

* * *

Miss Hassan asked what happened. I told her Jaymo had tried to get into my bed before and it had frightened me. I told her he had threatened me and had gone into other boys' beds. I told her he told me he was coming into my bed on my birthday and that I didn't know what to do. I told her he took the stuff my mother left, tried to smother me, tore up my birthday cards and threatened me with a cigarette he probably got from Tommy the scoutmaster. I told her he and the other boys had threatened me continually and that was why I ran away. Davie Wilson told me it was why he tried to run away and I was sure there were others. I did not want to clype and knew what it would mean as far as other children were concerned, but I was frightened and did not know what else to do because it was never going to stop. I knew this because the first thing happened the day I arrived and the only time it stopped was when he and Tom Bennett were in the punishment wing.

You know the importance of telling the truth, don't you?

Yes, miss.

Especially in a matter like this; for I know you haven't always been truthful about how you feel.

I feel better now, miss.

I think you tell us what you think we want to hear and I am sure this started when you came here. It's a survival technique, so I wouldn't like to think you were telling lies, and I especially would not like to think you were telling lies to get someone into trouble, that you were using this as a means of getting rid of someone you didn't get on with, someone who was more popular than you.

It's not fair, I said without thinking.

What isn't fair?

The way you're getting on at me.

I'm trying to find the truth. You attacked him and I want to know why.

I've told you why.

Are you afraid of him?

Not anymore.

Were you afraid of him?

Yes, miss.

Was that why you attacked him?

No, miss. He punched and kicked me in the cloakroom because he thought I'd told Miss MacLaren he tore up my birthday cards. He's caused trouble ever since I arrived here. I told you, he's tried to smother me and he's been saying for weeks he was going to get me.

On you go, she said. Get back to your class. And thank you.

Miss Hassan came into the dining room at lunchtime.

I am going to do something unusual. Today we'll have a lunchtime roll call. She called out our names and we answered, like in class.

I don't think I've missed anyone out, she said, so you may have noticed,

James Donaldson is no longer a pupil at this school.

The place erupted. The girls were cheering and most of the boys, even those who were in his gang the day before, were smiling.

That afternoon Wilma Anderson asked if she could be my girlfriend. Others offered me stuff out the cupboard. Two or three boys walked beside me during the walks and for a week or two they picked me first for their football teams even though I couldn't header a ball because of my glasses.

* * *

I was at the window when she came up the drive, waving at the bend by the rhododendrons.

That bloody bus. Do you know, I've been standing at that Killermont Street bus station since the dawn of creation, and then when I got one that would take me here, it took me everyplace else first.

I'd been packed and ready, standing by the window since before lunch. It was now almost two o'clock. The children had said goodbye before going to the swimming pool in East Kilbride. Wilma Anderson asked for my address. If I hear from Martha, I'll let you know, she said.

Miss Joyce had wished me well the previous evening. Mister Scott, Miss MacLaren and Miss Hassan were in the hall with my mother.

Well, Miss Hassan said. I hope you'll come back and see us.

I nodded.

Promise?

Yes, miss.

Good.

Mister Scott shook my hand and wished me well.

Miss MacLaren carried my case to the bus stop, chatting with my mother.

Well, she said, while my mother climbed up the three steps to the front. I hope you'll come back and see me.

Yes, miss.

She kissed my cheek and as she pulled herself away I flung my arms round her neck.

She giggled and lifted me onto the bus, then stood at the stop till the bus was out of sight, her hair lifting behind her in the breeze.

That's a very nice girl, my mother said before I tried to sleep.

There was too much to think about, the end of something or maybe the start; so much I didn't understand, so much to look forward to, so many changes.

There were things I wanted to store, like the way I felt holding Martha; others I knew I would never need again, playing football with glasses. I was confused by the way things regularised after Jaymo left, then I remembered how pointless everything felt after my scrap in the school playground.

More than anything, I wanted to find Martha. I did not know why, but knew it had to do with the way I felt walking to Jaymo's dormitory, knowing what I was going to do, but not knowing why, anxious and frightened, in the grip of handing so much of myself over to something I did not understand beyond the way the feeling terrified me.

We sat in the cafe by Killermont Street station, my mother having a cup of tea, while I gathered myself for the last stage home.

And I've seen nothing of the McDades, she said. Did you know they've moved?

Somebody said it was Milton, but Big Aggie, who knows all there is to know, reliably informed us they had not gone to Milton, but to a rather superior housing scheme up the back of Petershill Road. She also said it had nothing to do with the wee lad's death. Overcrowding, she said. It was overcrowding.

How the hell did it take the corporation so long to find out they were overcrowded? someone asked.

Same way as they found out that wee woman who used to live there needed a house when she took a rat in a shoe box into see her councillor, said wee Mrs Morrison, who's man's no right in the heid. God love him, he doesnae seem to have too much trouble lifting a pint of heavy beer and can always find his way to the betting shop. And Harry Neil is top of the class, so we'll need to do something about that. Now there's a thing I don't understand. They say your schoolwork's not one bit better, and they've let you out. I thought you went there to get on with your lessons.

My granny was standing on the landing, her hand holding the wall, when I ran up the stairs. Barbara and Michael were in the kitchen with my grandad. My mother took my bag to the room, and we were at our tea when George arrived home from work.

That's you back. Marvellous, he said. Isn't it marvellous? Here we are again, happy as can be.

Are there any letters for me? I asked.

None that I've seen. Are you expecting something?

Uh-hu.

Do you think you'll know the folk around here now? my mother asked. Or will you only have pen pals scattered across the country.

I looked out the window. Alec Irvine and Willie Simpson were kicking a ball in the backcourt.

Can I go out?

Please do, my mother smiled. We're not at all used to you sitting there, quiet and still.

Surely to God you're not letting him out when he's just back, my granny said. Honest to God, Marie. That backcourt is full of bad weekit boys and he's no used to them.

I ran down stairs, past the fruit shop and post office, up the Long Stairs and round the Back Lawn to the ash track up to St Theresa's. Just by the boulder was a pile of stones, then another pile and another and so on, leading to the edge of the path.

The tin had rusted. The lid was stiff and dug into my nails. But everything was as it should be, sealed and water tight. Francie's favourite books *Henryk's Forest Home* and *Beaver Lodge* were at the bottom, my map of the stars and picture of my father were with Francie's pictures of the sea and a wooded glade. The book list, Christmas cards and the blood brother paper had been entered in a jotter. There were four pennies, two ha'pennies, a shilling and a threepenny bit, a Scottish Youth Hostels Association badge, a new pencil, half a map of Inverness and two leaves of calendar.

Two names were written on the first page of the jotter: Francis. Carl.
I wants too write you in the home, was on the second page and the third was a letter:

Deer Carl: How are you? I m fine. I mis you to. Are yu well?
Yours sincerely,
Your pal, Francis.

It was getting dark. I ran home, the biscuit tin rattling beneath my arm.

Afterword

THERE ARE SO many aspects to life at Nerston I haven't mentioned, most obviously the children who came back as visitors. Those who found life at Nerston better than life at home returned with hopes of staying.

We were invited to visit, and I went back, I think, three times, usually on a Saturday or Sunday afternoon.

Why do you want to go back there? my mother asked.

To see my friends.

Folk'll be in and out of your life like a peep of gas, she said.

Adjusting to life after Nerston was difficult. Quite early on, a boy who wasn't especially friendly but had the same name as my Canadian cousin, John Miller, asked me to come home with him at lunchtime. We chatted, he collected his stuff and as we approached the school he told me to wait by the wall at the foot of the brae: I don't want them to see me with you, he said.

It didn't happen often, but it didn't need to. It was more of an undercurrent and I eventually made friends in high school with folk who knew nothing of my family or my past.

Of course, there are always leftovers and nothing resolves itself into a *Nicholas Nickleby* ending. People leave, others stay and there are fresh arrivals, which can confuse children, especially when Christmas cards are used to fill the gap, often with a wee note attached.

In my case, it seems to be about loss, vanishing things, my mysterious grandfather, my hearing and Martha.

When Aunt Cathie left Keppochhill Road, Uncle Charlie's boys were lost to the family. We came together at their youngest son's wedding, but it's almost a lifetime since we met. In the meantime we have also scattered and the generation who made these decisions have gone.

I met John in Toronto and he's in regular touch, which gives us hope that other contacts can be renewed.

We have never confirmed my grandfather's secret, and even Barbara, who spent her later years devising alternative scenarios for herself and others, never quite came up with a solution. My mother apparently arranged it through an MP she had contacted and visited in London, which, to my mind, deepens the mystery.

I find it difficult to believe, but there are folk who never knew I was deaf. I found it most obvious when I could hear a chord but not repeat it, far less tune a guitar. An audiologist told me I had probably taught myself to lip-read, but I have no idea how that happened.

Sometimes, walking alone, but more usually late at night, I think about Martha, wonder where she is, what she's doing. Did she cross the world to stay with her aunt? Is she now an American citizen, is she married, does she have children, did her vigorous accent and glottal stop disappear into a softer, higher register? The image of me shivering and kissing her through the five-barred gate remains. Did she touch my hair or is that imagined, did she leap slightly with one sock loose at her ankle as she turned away and never looked back.

Of course, there are others, but that will do for now and though pieces of flotsam surface occasionally, I have to distinguish between remembering events and constructing the story.

And so on.

There are those who need to be thanked.

Euan MacDougall and Kirsty Chapman, Michael Hewitt and Joanna Andreano.

In Oban, Katie Berry and Margaret Gallacher were invaluable, as were Margaret and John McFadyen.

Thanks are also due to Anica Alvarez Nishio, Catherine Deveney, Heather McCabe and Hugh Hoffman. Without them this would have been a less truthful record; and little would have happened without Iain Campbell.

Finally, readers unfamiliar with Scotland need to know that our mid-day meal is dinner and our evening meal is tea.

Luath Press Limited

committed to publishing well written books worth reading

LUATH PRESS takes its name from Robert Burns, whose little collie Luath
(*Gael.*, swift or nimble) tripped up Jean Armour at a wedding and gave
him the chance to speak to the woman who was to be his wife and the
abiding love of his life. Burns called one of the 'Twa Dogs'
Luath after Cuchullin's hunting dog in Ossian's *Fingal*.
Luath Press was established in 1981 in the heart of
Burns country, and is now based a few steps up
the road from Burns' first lodgings on
Edinburgh's Royal Mile. Luath offers you
distinctive writing with a hint of
unexpected pleasures.

Most bookshops in the UK, the US, Canada,
Australia, New Zealand and parts of Europe,
either carry our books in stock or can order them
for you. To order direct from us, please send a £sterling
cheque, postal order, international money order or your
credit card details (number, address of cardholder and
expiry date) to us at the address below. Please add post
and packing as follows: UK – £1.00 per delivery address;
overseas surface mail – £2.50 per delivery address; overseas airmail – £3.50
for the first book to each delivery address, plus £1.00 for each additional
book by airmail to the same address. If your order is a gift, we will happily
enclose your card or message at no extra charge.

Luath Press Limited
543/2 Castlehill
The Royal Mile
Edinburgh EH1 2ND
Scotland
Telephone: 0131 225 4326 (24 hours)
Email: sales@luath.co.uk
Website: www.luath.co.uk